TROPICAL INLAND FISHERIES

NOTE

THIS volume is one of a series of books on tropical agriculture which are being published with the active encouragement of the Colonial Advisory Council of Agriculture, Animal Health, and Forestry, under the editorship of Mr. D. Rhind, O.B.E., Secretary for Colonial Agricultural Research, formerly Director of Agriculture, Ceylon.

Already published:

Rice, by D. H. Grist
Tea, by T. Eden
Bananas, by N. W. Simmonds
An Introduction to Animal Husbandry in the Tropics,
by G. Williamson and W. J. A. Payne
Beekeeping in the Tropics, by F. G. Smith
Cocoa, by D. H. Urquhart
Termites, by W. Victor Harris

TROPICAL INLAND
FISHERIES

C. F. HICKLING
C.M.G., M.A., SC.D.

Fisheries Adviser to the Secretary of
State for the Colonies

LONGMANS

LONGMANS, GREEN AND CO LTD
48 GROSVENOR STREET, LONDON W1
RAILWAY CRESCENT, CROYDON, VICTORIA, AUSTRALIA
443 LOCKHART ROAD, HONG KONG
PRIVATE MAIL BAG 1036, IKEJA (LAGOS)
44 JALAN AMPANG, KUALA LUMPUR
ACCRA, AUCKLAND, IBADAN, KINGSTON (JAMAICA)
NAIROBI, SALISBURY (RHODESIA)
LONGMANS SOUTHERN AFRICA (PTY) LTD
THIBAULT HOUSE, THIBAULT SQUARE, CAPE TOWN
LONGMANS, GREEN AND CO INC
119 WEST 40TH STREET, NEW YORK 18
LONGMANS, GREEN AND CO
137 BOND STREET, TORONTO 2
ORIENT LONGMANS PRIVATE LTD
CALCUTTA, BOMBAY, MADRAS
DELHI, HYDERABAD, DACCA

Printed in Great Britain by
The Camelot Press Ltd., London and Southampton

CONTENTS

PHOTOGRAPHS

PREFACE

SOME justification for including the Tropical Inland Fisheries in a series of books devoted to tropical agricultural products lies in the fact that fish is a crop. It is a crop, however, which is not improved by husbandry except in fertilised fish ponds; there is no cultivation, no sowing; only gathering. The lack of property rights in the fish is one cause of this. No man will spare, for all to take. But the study here presented to the reader should leave no doubt that the fish crop could almost everywhere be improved by simple and often indirect measures.

If this book has any constant theme, it is the astonishing powers of recuperation of a tropical inland fishery. This is due, I am convinced, not only to the high mean temperatures, which accelerate all life-processes, including the whole chain of events which leads to the growth and reproduction of fishes; but also to the abundance of plant-eating fish with the shortest, swiftest, and least wasteful food-chains. A given body of water, producing a given amount of primary food-material, is therefore able to support a manifold population of fish as compared with temperate climates; and to regenerate this population when it may be decimated by natural catastrophes or by severe and almost total fishing.

This being so, there seems to be an excessive concern, as expressed by the various fishery laws and regulations, to secure an escape-ment of fish. Such rules are based on practice in Europe and America; but the scanty fish-life of temperate freshwaters, and the slow rate of growth of the fish, are of an entirely different order from those prevailing in the tropics. If, by analogy with these temperate fisheries, an unnecessarily large escapement of fish is attempted by a regulation of the fishery, it may well be that the only result is a waste of fish potential.

For example, the construction of an all-weather road, to open up to a reliable and lucrative market new areas of water, will do more to relieve fishing pressure on a non-migrant stock of fish than all the regulations at present applied, even assuming that these regula-tions were in fact enforceable at economic cost. The clearance of a swamp will make a new fishery; so will the stocking of new species or of new waters.

The mechanisation of the fishing boats, the installation of pilot-scale ice plants, the introduction of new fishing gear and modification of the old, will all tend in the same direction. These are the constructive side of fishery work, and these should be the main interests of technical fisheries staffs.

Research in the tropical inland fisheries and their environment has only been started in the last decade or so: that is a very short time. Already, the background is becoming known; the next few decades will see the results of research added to those of technical development. There is already the knowledge that the deeper waters of lakes hold vast stores of nutrient materials; already there has been the suggestion that these may be pumped back into circulation. The results could hardly fail to cover costs many times over. A better knowledge of the fish and their habits will lead to the stocking of species able to use materials in the waters not usable by the existing species, and this has been started—there is the possibility of producing improved fish by cross-breeding.

And so the ideas grow, based on growing experience. What is wanted is faith, by those who hold the public purse, in the value of fisheries research, and full and confident backing through these earlier years.

*　　　　*　　　　*

I have used the Latin names of the fish throughout. This is not pedantry, but because the tropical fish necessarily have no genuine English names. Such names have been invented, but may be understood by few people besides the inventor. Where such names have been introduced, they may be applied to different fish in different territories. The African or Asian names will clearly differ from country to country, and even from tribe to tribe. But, in a book such as this is intended to be, the Latin names avoid all ambiguity. My labourers at Malacca soon learnt to identify fish by their Latin names, and thought nothing of it.

*　　　　*　　　　*

The greatest of the tropical inland fisheries, the fisheries of the floods, will be doomed in the next hundred years. Populations are increasing too fast, and land-hunger with them, for countries to allow any land to be subject to seasonal flooding. The rivers will be trained between embankments, and the land will be settled for intensive cultivation. Much will be lost, as well as gained. This possibility was foreseen by the Jonglei Investigation Team, in their study of the effects of the Equatorial Nile Project in confining the Nile and reducing the area seasonally flooded. There seems to be no doubt that their conclusion was right: that, to compensate for the loss of fish production, there must be intensive fish-culture in a small part of the reclaimed land. Thus, I believe, fish culture arose in China thousands of years ago, when the great rivers were first controlled in the interests of cultivation. A hard-working and observant people will soon have seen the rapid growth of the fish confined in the ox-bows of the river beds, and will have taken steps to foster it and to perpetuate the water and the fish. As the wild flood-fisheries decline, the importance of fish-culture is certain to increase.

ACKNOWLEDGEMENTS

THE views expressed in this book are the writer's personal views, and are in no way the expression of any official policy. He is grateful to the Colonial Office for permission to publish.

I would here express my thanks to Mr. H. Carey Gilson, Director of the Freshwater Biological Association's Laboratory on Windermere, for the facilities he afforded for study in the Association's Library; and to his staff for valuable hints and stimulating discussion.

Dr. G. S. Carter, Fellow of Corpus Christi College, Cambridge, very kindly read through the text of the chapters dealing with general principles of limnology, and made many valuable suggestions. My son, Dr. R. S. Hickling, kindly helped with the proof correcting.

Dr. K. F. Vaas, recently of the Netherlands East Indies and Indonesian Fishery Departments, gave me most valuable help with reference to dam-stocking work in those territories.

Dr. E. Trewavas, of the British Museum of Natural History, helped over the outline drawings of fish in Figures 1 to 3.

The Chief Fishery Officer, Uganda, and the acting Chief Fishery Officer, Messrs. D. H. Rhodes and A. M. Anderson, respectively, gave the author valuable help with the statistics of the Lake George fishery. The author is also very grateful to the Geological Department of the Government of Tanganyika for the analyses of water from lakes and dams in the Central Province (page 252).

Finally, the author thanks his colleague, Mr. D. Rhind, Editor of this series, for his help in the preparation of the book, and for helpful criticism.

Most of the illustrations are the author's own photographs, but he acknowledges with thanks permission to use copyright photographs, as follows:

Mr. K. R. Stacey Morris for 5, 6, and 7.

Mrs. Rosemary McConnell for 26, 27, and 30.

The Central Office of Information for 4.

The Editors of the *Bulletin Agricole du Congo Belge* for 17, 28, 36, 37, 38.

Mr. George Tay, of the Fish Culture Research Station, Malacca, for the hand paintings of planktonic organisms reproduced in Colour Plates III and IV.

The diagram on page 95 is reproduced from the proceedings of the IPFC 4th Session, 1952, Section II, by permission of the Executive Committee of the Indo-Pacific Fisheries Council of the Food and Agricultural Organization of the United Nations.

I thank Mr. M. J. Holden for permission to reproduce on the dust-cover his photograph of a fishing festival with clap-nets in the flood-plain of the River Sokoto in northern Nigeria.

I also thank Mr. D. N. F. Hall for kindly giving me permission to quote from his paper on Indo-West Pacific Penaeidae (reference 106) while still in proof.

Chapter One

GENERAL PRINCIPLES, PHYSICAL AND CHEMICAL

WATER is not only the medium in which fish live but it is also the source of most of their food, whether directly or indirectly. The quantity and kinds of fish which waters will support vary greatly with their physical and chemical condition, and these have their origin in the past history of the water as well as in the present conditions.

In the waters, as on the land, the sun is the source of energy which drives the whole cycle of events. Indeed, apart from the energy derived from the spin of the earth, which may deflect water movements in large masses of water, such as big lakes, and the heat of hot springs, neither of which plays any significant part in freshwaters as a whole, we may agree with Ruttner[1] that heat, derived from the sun, is the cardinal point in all freshwater investigation.

RAINWATER

Water starts each of its cycles as rain, and here also it is the sun's energy which has evaporated the water, and has generated the winds which blow it into the region in which it is condensed and falls. While it is in the atmosphere the water dissolves many substances, and when it falls as rain, it often contains important amounts of material. Eriksson[2] has recently reviewed the composition of atmospheric precipitation. It is well known that substantial quantities of fixed nitrogen, such as nitrates and ammonia, fall in rainwater. These quantities are obviously linked with the amount of rainfall, but they may amount to as much as 30·4 kg. of nitrogen per hectare (Sumatra, with 2045 mm. of rain). Java, with 902 mm. of rain, has 2·06 kg./ha. Mauritius, with 1002 mm. of rain, has a fall of 12·45 kg./ha. and Ceylon 13·04 kg./ha. with 2850 mm. of rainfall.

Schuster[51] writes that a fishpond in Java may obtain, in rainfall,

BTIF

about 12 kg. of nitrogen per acre in the course of a year. Capart and Kufferath[144] estimated that the nitrogen contained in rain falling on the Congo was equivalent to that contained in nearly 25 kg. per hectare and per annum of fish.

It is widely believed that the nitrogen fixed in the atmosphere is the result of lightning discharges, but Eriksson shows that in the tropics, where thunderstorms are most frequent and severe, there is not a proportionately greater amount of fixed nitrogen than in temperate climates. At Melbourne, the content in nitrates and nitrites of the rain is greatest when the rains are due to low-pressure areas of tropical origin. It appears that nitric nitrogen should be fairly evenly distributed throughout the troposphere. Eriksson suggests that much of the nitrogen in rain originates from the soil, from volcanoes and, especially significantly, from forest fires.

Rain may contain many other substances, some of which are acid, and help in the slow disintegration of rocks, and the release of their materials into circulation.

SPATES

Debenham[3] points out that rain, when it falls, may fly away, soak away, or run away. In the tropics generally, one does not often have the gentle rain lasting for hours or even days which is usual in temperate climates. Rainfall tends to be very heavy, of the order of an inch an hour, and much or most of it tends to run away. Anyone who has had to look after an estate in the tropics will know the care necessary to check serious erosion and at the same time to try, by checking the rate of run-off, to get as much of the rain as possible to soak into the soil. That is the reason for contour planting and contour furrowing. Where this cannot be done the water sweeps down into the streams and rivers, carrying with it a load of soil. The rivers themselves run down in spate, and the writer recalls flying over Somaliland, an arid country where the rivers are dry in the dry season, during a spell of heavy rain. The plane was flying through the rain-clouds, but through gaps in the clouds a tawny wave of water could be seen crawling down the bare river beds, laced with white foam and mottled with the branches of dead trees. One night the writer crossed the dry river in Hargeisa by a concrete causeway; at midnight the river came down in spate due to rain in the hills and he had great difficulty in recrossing. All night the unfamiliar roar of the river sounded into the dark and, when morning came, the spate had subsided, leaving no trace except the wet sand, trees and creepers newly torn from the banks, and the concrete causeway cracked and shifted.

Rainfalls like this, so far from doing good, are a curse rather than a blessing. They carry the fertile soil into the river beds, where it smothers the water vegetation and causes sandbanks which bring about further flooding. They upset the balance of life in the water not only in this way, but by altering the bed of the river they fill up old stable lagoons and create raw new ones. Spates, in fact, can make a considerable temporary difference to a river as a habitat for fish.

Ultimately, of course, the soil is swept out to sea, and is to be seen off the deltas of rivers like the Orinoco, Ganges, Niger and Zambezi, as sea discoloured far out by the suspended silt.

EROSION AND CHECK-DAMS

The process of erosion can be hastened by cultivation. It is said that many rivers which are now muddy ran clear at the time of first discovery. This must be so, for when the Niger was first discovered, many of the mouths were navigable. Now only the Bonny Bar is navigable, the rest having more or less silted up. The Malacca River ran clear in the fifteenth century before the hinterland was opened up. Quite large caravels are to be seen lying at wharves in Malacca in pictures made during the early days of the Portuguese occupation. Now, with great areas opened to paddy cultivation owing to the increase of population in more settled conditions, the river runs a chocolate colour and has carried down so much silt that there are only two or three feet of water on the bar in spite of dredging out enough material to reclaim a large area of foreshore for a park. Ships must lie far out to sea and Malacca has become a lighter port. All this has happened in the last four hundred years.

The danger of erosion is well enough known, and efforts are everywhere being made to reduce the loss of soil, to induce heavy rainfall to soak into the ground or into vegetation, or to be checked by reservoirs and stored. Great efforts are made to distribute heavy rainfall or to disperse it in such a way that it flows in the rivers more evenly and steadily over a long period of time, if possible perennially. The impressive anti-erosion campaign in Southern Rhodesia may be quoted as an example. The Minister of Agriculture has pithily remarked that the one export which Rhodesia would not permit was the export of water.

In Rhodesia, with the grass grazed away, the unchecked run-off of the heavy rains has eroded the shallow valleys into rocky gorges, down which the cattle of the Africans have to be driven to find water in the pools. The cattle tracks themselves lead to erosion, and so especially do the heavy wooden sledges dragged by the draught oxen. By cutting deep ridges and furrows along the contours of the land and by the use of subsoilers between the ridges to cut deep clefts into the subsoil, efforts are made to check the flow of water down the slopes and to drive it into the ground. Finally, check-dams are built in the valleys, stepped one above the other, to check the flow of the stream itself and to store the water.

In Plate 1 a tractor is shown operating a ridger, and in Plates 2 and 3 a dam-building team is constructing a water-storage and check-dam at an African village in Southern Rhodesia. The extra-large dam-scoop used is shown in Plate 3.

The result of all this work is plain to see when one flies over the country. In valleys where there are these check-dams the aspect is green, for the water has soaked into the ground and the water-table has risen (compare Plates 5 and 6). There is grass to protect the soil and to give grazing to cattle; there is water for drinking and perhaps for irrigation. Even more important from the fishery point of view, the stream in the valley may be converted from a seasonal torrent to a perennial stream. This also resulted from the dam building on the tributaries of the Volta River in Ghana by the anti-trypanosomiasis campaign. The Kamba River, one of the tributaries of the Volta near the French frontier, formerly dried out between the rains to a series of pools of various sizes. A dam was built across the river, with the result that in the dry season there is now a shallow lake of large area which is not only very productive of fish but which has caused the Kamba to have a small perennial flow in most years. This has greatly affected the movements of fish in the main river.

Plate 4 shows one of the dams across the Kamba tributary of the Volta in Ghana. It is of earth pitched with laterite. Plates 5 and 6 contrast the area of water remaining in the tributary towards the end of the dry season before (Plate 6) and after (Plate 5) the construction of the dam. Plates 5 and 6, which were taken from the same position, show in a vivid way the effect on the vegetation of the raising of the water-table. Plates 6 and 7 compare the yields of fish from the lagoon before and after the construction of the dam. The fish shown in Plate 7 are only a small part of the catch.

Anti-erosion work, designed for other purposes, can have a valuable effect on fisheries in two respects. The check-dams themselves may be used as a source of fish and, by raising the water-table, they may turn seasonal torrents, which, because they dry out in the off-season cannot support fish life at all, into perennial streams able, not only to support fish life but to link the side streams with the main river.

The value of forests as temporary storage for rainwater is well known and all countries are trying to protect their forest cover. The trees, their roots and the carpet of decaying vegetation all soak up the rain and release it in perennial streams. A similar sponge-like capacity is possessed by the swampy valleys, or dambos, of Uganda and the Rhodesias, and governments are wary of the possible ill-effects of draining these valleys and of reclaiming them for agriculture.

STREAMS

Rainwater, whether it is driven into the ground to emerge as springs or soaks through forest or swamp to emerge as streams, becomes much changed. Water that comes out as springs may have dissolved much material. It must have contained some dissolved carbon dioxide when it entered the ground and there it may have become enriched in carbon dioxide dissolved from the humus and often with other acids which may reduce its pH to 4. If it then passes through soil containing lime it will dissolve the lime as calcium bicarbonate. If the solution is sufficiently rich, some of the carbon dioxide may be given off to the atmosphere when the water emerges as a spring, and the lime it held in solution may be deposited. This may take place on a fantastically large scale. Ruttner[4] describes hot springs in the Kuripan area of Java which have formed pure white deposits of lime 15-20 metres in height. Marlier[5] mentions streams in the basin of the Kadubu at the headwaters of the Ulindi, a tributary of the Congo, where the stones and branches are thickly coated with lime.

In soil containing iron, which is very common in the tropics, water containing carbon dioxide can dissolve the iron as ferrous carbonate. When this water emerges as a spring, the carbon dioxide is given up, and in the presence of oxygen the iron is deposited as iron ochre, a common enough sight in the tropics. Most people will have seen the bright red smears or patches of these deposits, usually surrounded by an oily-looking fringe of iron bacteria.

Carter[6] analysed some streams emerging from swamps in Uganda. A few hundred yards from where they emerge from the swamp they may be poor in oxygen (less than half saturated) but rich in free carbon dioxide. They may be slightly acid and have a high content of iron as well as a relatively high content of nitrogen compounds and some phosphate. This is much the same composition as the swamp water itself. Water which has been caught in swamps, when it emerges into the flowing waters, may have a very different composition from spring water.

At Malacca the water which seeps out of the jungle belt has a high sulphur content, as high as 0·1 per cent, and the acidity may be very high, with a *pH* of 3·5 or even less.[7] Such acid water may be toxic to many species of fish. The common carp, for example, and the Chinese grass carp, are killed by acidities of this order.

Marlier,[8] who worked on the headwater streams of the Congo tributaries and on those of the Nile in the central mountain massif of the eastern Congo, points out that the streams that arise in forests are different from those that arise in open savannah country at high altitudes. Streams that arise in forest are cooler than those that arise in the savannah, and they are also much more constant in their rate of flow. That again illustrates the value of forest cover as a conservator and regulator of stream flow.

Marlier also shows how the chemical composition of the soil through which the stream flows affects its contents. In the savannah streams of fluctuating flow, the rocks are exposed to the sun for months on end, and so are rendered more friable and easily leached out when the stream flow increases again. Where a stream dries out entirely in the dry season the first freshets are notably richer in dissolved salts than the later ones.

Blanc, Daget, and d'Aubenton[9] also show that the first floods in the Middle Niger flood-plain are notably richer in dissolved salts than those coming later, because the first floods pick up the leachings of ashes of bush-fires, of dung and other decaying organic debris. The water, which is usually slightly acid, may become slightly alkaline for this reason in June, early in the flood season. But generally speaking, the waters of the Upper Niger are very poor from the chemical point of view because the headwaters of the Niger traverse insoluble granites and schists. If, in spite of this, the Middle Niger produces some 45,000 metric tons of fish annually, far more than the sea fisheries of Senegal, it is because the flood plain is so extensive and not because there is a high rate of production per unit of area.

Marlier[8] contrasts two streams in the Congo and 12 km. apart, the one arising in bamboo forest, the other in more open country. The latter has nearly twice as much salts in solution. The same may hold good for river systems; the Lubero, rising in open savannah, has three times the content in salts of the Lutunguru, which flows through forest.

The conductivity of the water, which is a guide to the salt content, cannot be taken as a direct indication of the potential fertility. Animal life in water, as on land, depends on plant life, and plants depend partly on the presence of adequate amounts of the essential nutrient salts, such as nitrates, ammonia, phosphates, potash, magnesium, calcium, iron, and sulphates. But the annual report for 1954-5 of the East African Fisheries Research Organisation[117] gives comparisons to show that, for example, in the great lakes of East Africa, the total conductivity would give a falsely optimistic estimate if used as an indication of the potential fertility. This is because these lakes have a considerable soda content and soda has no direct value as a plant nutrient. If the soda content is subtracted, "the content of biologically valuable electrolytes is much lower than might at first appear" (loc. cit.).

The streams, then, in flowing from their sources, are further modified in their composition by what they may dissolve from their surroundings. These not only vary according to whether they flow through forest or through open or cultivated country, but with the geological nature of the soil. Marlier shows that the affluents of the River Ruzizi and of northern Lake Tanganyika, which flow through insoluble micaceous schists, quartzes and gneiss, are very low in dissolved substances, while the Rutshuru, which flows north into Lake Edward and so belongs to the Nile system, runs through recent volcanic rocks and is rich in dissolved substances. The great fertility of the water (as of the land) in Java and Sumatra is due to leaching of rich volcanic soil, while in Malaya, so near in distance, volcanic activity ended long ago and both the land and the water are much less fertile. This difference can even be traced in the sea-fisheries; for the best fishing grounds in the Malacca Strait are on the Sumatra side, where the rivers bring down the nutrient salts in far greater abundance than on the Malayan side.

RIVERS

Sioli (quoted by Braun[10]) used the composition of the water of rivers and streams in the Amazon basin to discover the nature of the soil of the unexplored lands through which they had flowed. A simple chemical analysis of such water can give some indication of the likely characteristics of the soils in areas so densely forested as to be well-nigh inaccessible. When backed by biological research they allow conclusions on the chemistry and nature of the soil, since a given association of plants and animals needs a specific environment. For example, streams in tertiary areas have, in the Amazon forests, a striking poverty in dissolved salts, especially lime, and frequently contain large amounts of carbon dioxide. They are generally very acid, and such tertiary soils are not very suitable for rational agriculture. On the other hand, streams in carboniferous areas were found to vary; those flowing through sandstone were nearly as poor as the tertiary streams, while streams derived from marine sediments, partly of lime, with gypsum here and there, were rich in salts and neutral or even alkaline in reaction. Sioli points to past disastrous failures of attempts at the clearing and colonisation of the primitive Amazonian jungle, attempts which failed in three years. These could have been avoided had a simple analysis of the water of the jungle streams been used as a pointer to the likelihood of the presence of fertile land in their drainage basins.

Carter[6] shows that streams flowing into Lake Victoria from swamps and surface drainage in lateritic soil have a high or very high iron content, and he used this characteristic to show that the water in the shoreward parts of papyrus swamp bordering the lake is derived from the swamp and not from the lake. Beauchamp[11] used the varying composition of the water in the Albert Nile (which is partly derived from Lake Victoria via Lake Kyoga and partly from Lakes Albert and Edward via the Semliki River, and to a lesser extent from local torrents) to show which of these sources—they vary in composition and therefore in conductivity—has contributed most water to the Albert Nile and how these proportions may vary.

The salt content of a river may vary during its course. Two examples will be given. According to Marlier[8] the Ruzizi, in the

Congo, when it flows southward out of Lake Kivu, has a high conductivity due to its salt content of 1350×10^{-6}. By the time it flows into Lake Tanganyika the effect of its tributaries has reduced this to 627×10^{-6}. The Musi River, the longest river in Sumatra, was examined by Ruttner[4]. In its upper reaches, where it still has the character of a hill stream, it has a conductivity of only 32×10^{-6} which Ruttner describes as very low. It is joined by tributaries, some of which may come from volcanic springs and have a conductivity as high as 391 with considerable quantities of chloride and phosphate. Yet in its middle course the river has a conductivity of only 71, the chloride vanishes and the phosphate falls to a trace. Finally, at the river mouth, the conductivity dwindles to 27, which is nearly that of rainwater. Clarke[12] writes, "A river is the average of all its tributaries, plus rain and ground water . . . small streams are the most affected by local conditions; large rivers, as a rule, resemble each other more closely." He lists the conductivities of some tropical rivers as follows:

White Nile	174×10^{-6}
Blue Nile	130×10^{-6}
Amazon at Obidos	37×10^{-6}
Courentyne	30×10^{-6}
Mahamuddy (India)	86×10^{-6}
Seragoe (Java)	122×10^{-6}

A river quickly dissolves both gases (oxygen, carbon dioxide, nitrogen) and salts from the atmosphere, the products of decay and photosynthesis as well as salts leached from the country it passes through. It may have a very variable value as a medium for the growth of fish life, both directly and indirectly through the processes of plant and lower animal life.

In small and fast streams turbulence secures a thorough mixing of the water. Welch[13] writes that in a stream the current velocity is not uniform in all parts of a transverse section, "but is reduced at or near the surface because of surface tension, and diminishes as the bottom and sides are approached, because of frictional effects". Obviously, then, turbulence set up by these differences in flow and by irregularities of the bottom will cause the water to be thoroughly mixed and homogeneous with regard both to dissolved gases and dissolved salts. The temperature will be close to that of the air and will be uniform from top to bottom. So much is this assumed to be the case that only rarely do workers think it worth while to make observations at midwater or on the bottom in flowing rivers; one sample is enough to represent the well-mixed water. Blanc and d'Aubenton[9] made a few observations on the Middle Niger, but reported only slight differences in temperature between top and bottom in shallow rivers.

When a river is in its middle and lower course and has become slow and often deep, mixing through turbulence becomes much slighter. Moreover, tropical rivers undergo great seasonal variations in level. In flood, they may be great tawny maelstroms; Plate 8 shows the Zambezi in high flood. In the dry season they may be little more than a chain of lagoons, separated and split by sand and mudbanks linked by a winding stream of no great strength. They then have much of the character of lakes or pools, and may, especially in the backwaters, be practically stagnant. Mixing no longer occurs and important differences may appear between the surface and bottom waters. The surface layers, in contact with the air and exposed to the sun, may be warmer and have a higher oxygen content than the water near the bottom. Braun,[10] for example, found such a layering or stratification in the Rio Tapajoz, a great river and tributary of the Amazon. This river is 30 metres deep but has a rate of flow of only 200 metres per hour. The surface waters were only $1 \cdot 4°$ C. warmer than the bottom, but this is a very significant difference in this context. There was a distinct discontinuity layer between the warmer and cooler water at a depth of 2 to 4 metres below the surface. As Braun remarks, these great and slow rivers compare, in both thermal and biological aspects, with lakes, and the two terms tend to lose their difference. Carter[14] gives data which show that rivers in British Guiana, such as the Mazaruni, may at low water show slightly less oxygen at the bottom than at the surface. Ruttner found that there was slightly less oxygen at the bottom of the Musi River in Sumatra, at a depth of 10 metres and near its mouth, than at the surface. This layering, which is a conspicuous feature of most deep standing waters, will be more fully discussed when lakes are dealt with. It has the greatest significance for fish and fisheries.

DISSOLVED GASES

In those parts of river systems where there is rapid flow and thorough mixing, there may be homogeneity as regards temperature and dissolved gases and salts, but the latter may undergo great changes due to biological activity. Vegetation growing in sunlight uses up the carbon dioxide and releases oxygen; it also uses up some of the dissolved salts such as it requires for growth. The water tends to become less acid. On the other hand, at night the plants give off carbon dioxide and use up oxygen, while the animals do this both by day and night. When the plants and animals decay, their remains contribute to the salt-content of the water, as also do the by-products of animal life.

When the river becomes slow and deep, or where it breaks up into lagoons in the dry season and the water is not well mixed by turbulence, the lower layers may become deoxygenated by the decay of organic matter of all kinds which accumulates at the bottom of standing water, as well as by the absence of light, which prevents photosynthesis. In the absence of turbulence or strong winds, which might force oxygenated water to the bottom, anaerobic conditions prevail, in which the organic matter undergoes a partial oxidation or fermentation. Two typical gases produced by this fermentation are marsh gas (methane), and sulphuretted hydrogen. The latter gives rise to the foul smell associated with anaerobic conditions. At the Malacca Fish Culture Research Station there is a great deal of sulphur in the soil and water, and when the station was newly constructed there was frequently this foul smell wherever there was lack of oxygen, as for instance, where a dense bed of water grass prevented the free access of oxygenated water. With the clearing of the ponds, so that the wind could blow the oxygenated water in free circulation, this phenomenon completely disappeared.

Holden and Green[15] worked on the hydrology of the River Sokoto in Nigeria and on some pools in its flood plain, and found that the main factor affecting oxygen concentration appears to be the wind. The rains are preceded by strong winds and their wave-action causes peaks in the oxygen content of the water both of the river and of the pools. In July and August the oxygen falls to a low level but they put this down to the washing out of stagnant swamp water by the rains. They found no deoxygenation of the bottom water in the river, which had a depth of 2·5 to 7·5 metres; they found little or no differences between the results at different depths. There was also no deoxygenation at the bottom of the Fesafari pool, which had a minimum depth of 0·75 and a maximum of 4·5 metres. Even at the time of minimum oxygen concentration at the beginning of the rains, it rarely fell to levels lethal to fish. But the waters here are not very productive and it may be that there is not the accumulation of organic matter in the bottom mud which could lead to the deoxygenation so commonly found in these conditions. The bottom, both in the river and in the pool, was of soft mud, but in the case of the river, free of vegetation.

A secondary peak in the oxygen concentration was due to an outburst of filamentous algae. The water was poor in nutrient salts, especially sulphates, which here, as elsewhere in Africa, may be a limiting factor on plant production and therefore, indirectly, on fish life. During the flood period the volume of water entering the river is so great that it dilutes the important chemical contents to a considerable degree, while in the dry season, evaporation causes a rise in the concentration of the nutrient salts.

POLLUTION OF RIVERS

In countries where industrial development is taking place, the fouling of rivers by the discharge into them of organic waste matter is likely to become a most serious nuisance and a considerable social and hygienic problem. The conditions for pollution are a deep and slow stream or river into which a large quantity of organic matter or liquor is discharged. Few tropical countries have yet reached the industrial stage but in countries where there is a considerable timber industry there is already a nuisance from the big dumps of sawdust from the sawmills which tend to be placed on river banks. In the West Indian islands the residues from the rum stills, called "dunder", are very putrescible and they are often discharged into rivers. The Caroni River in Trinidad may be completely deoxygenated by the discharge of dunder, leading to the absence of fish, a foul smell and black colour, and to the appearance of ugly flocks of sewage fungus, like dirty grey cotton-wool.

This problem of pollution is bound to become more serious as countries in the tropics, now predominantly agricultural, pursue a policy of industrialisation. Ganapati and Chacko[16] describe what happens in the River Godavari in south India when the effluents of a paper mill are discharged into the river. The Godavari is a big river which runs strongly during the monsoon from July to December. At the height of the flood, waste from the mill cannot be discharged, but when the water subsides, the discharge of the waste begins. During this time the waste is well diluted with the flood-water and even at the outfall of the effluent the oxygen content of the water is still over 50 per cent of saturation, a safe level for most fish. But during the dry season the level of the river gradually goes down because of evaporation and draw-off for irrigation purposes; then there is little flow. The river takes on the character of a chain of lagoons, and there is serious deoxygenation due to the discharge of the effluent. Ganapati and Chacko mention the death of fish but say that a few small fishes and a poor plankton and bottom fauna were able to survive in the polluted water. But in the unpolluted parts of the river there was abundant plant life, and the water supported a commercial fishery. If such an effect is produced in a big river, then a small river may be far worse affected. In the case of the paper mills, Ganapati and Chacko advised that, if the effluents were diluted with water in the ratio of one part of effluent to 500 parts of water, the mixture could be safely discharged into the river even at times of low water.

Sisal factories, canning plants, tanneries and milk-processing plants are all likely to discharge into streams highly putrescible matter. On the peasant scale, it is well known that the death of fish can be caused where many people at once are preparing cassava, though here there may be a direct toxic effect due to the prussic acid present in the raw root.

A polluted river will slowly purify itself as it flows away from the source of pollution, especially if there is mixing of the water by turbulence. The oxydisable matter is slowly rendered harmless by oxidation, and may then even increase the fertility of the river, if nutrient materials are released at the same time.

SEWAGE DISPOSAL

There is also the problem of the disposal of human sewage, which is bound to become more urgent as rising standards of living lead increasingly to the use of waterborne sewage-disposal systems. This problem is aggravated by the fact that, while high tropical temperatures favour the rapid fermentation and oxidation of organic matter, they also mean that there is less dissolved oxygen in the water than in cooler climates. The remedy, in all such cases, is to dilute the sewage, and either secure the admixture with oxygen by discharging through a spray or by turbulence, or to spread the diluted sewage over a large area relative to volume, as in very shallow ponds.

For example, Nair[17] describes how sewage from the Calcutta Corporation sewage canal is, in some part at least, purified in ponds. The sewage effluent is a foul-smelling and darkly coloured liquid with some suspended matter in it. The water becomes clear after about 15-20 days, and loses its foul smell; it also becomes green with a rich growth of algae. The ponds are then stocked with fish, mainly several species of carp such as the very fast-growing *Catla catla* and *Labeo rohita*. These fish flourish on the algae and on the insects which breed freely in such conditions. The ponds continue to be supplied sparingly with more sewage-water at about monthly intervals, the proportion of sewage to pond-water being about 1 to 4. The sewage is admitted slowly, over 4-5 days. If these sewage ponds are stocked in April, marketable fish can be harvested from September onwards. This is a valuable example of how sewage can be purified; while at the same time there is a salvage, for the public benefit, of the nutrient materials released by the oxidation of the waste material.

Another small-scale, but notable, example of the simultaneous purification of polluted water and the recovery of the valuable constituents, is afforded by Javanese experience. In Jogjakarta, Vaas[18] states that a part of the effluent of a large septic tank is mixed with river water in the proportion of one part of effluent to three parts of river water. A dense crop of plankton is developed in the pond, chiefly diatoms near the inlet, and diatoms, other phytoplankton and zooplankton near the outlet. The pond was stocked with the Common Carp, *Puntius javanicus*, *Helostoma temminckii*, and *Trichogaster pectoralis*, and yielded at the very high rate of 4000 kg. of fish per hectare per annum. Moreover, a comparison of the inflow and outflow water showed that all the typhoid bacilli had been eliminated and that the Coli titre had been reduced to 1/100 of its original value. The amount of organic matter and ammonia was so reduced by oxidation as to be quite safe to discharge into the river.

In the great Munich sewerage scheme the purification of the liquid effluent is carried out in fish-ponds on a very large scale.[19] Briefly, the effluent, diluted with river water, is sprayed into large ponds of about four acres each and four feet deep. There, the foul organic matter is oxidised and the nutrients are released. These enrich the ponds so that they can be used to raise substantial crops of fish, at present mainly carp, but formerly both carp and Rainbow Trout. The aggregate increase in weight of the stocked fish is of the order of 500 lb. per acre per annum, and this is the more impressive when it is remembered that the growing period for the fish is only from about April to November in each year. The water, after passage through the ponds, is perfectly safe to discharge into the River Yser.

The Munich scheme has one disadvantage, which would not apply to such schemes in the tropics. In winter the low temperatures make this method of purification very difficult and fish growth is then at an end. The fish which are not yet of marketable size have to be put in wintering ponds. The Munich Corporation do not run the fish side of the business themselves but let this out to contract. The Corporation takes its profit from the difference between the price paid for the three-year-old carp bought at the beginning of the summer, and the price realised for the well-grown four-year-old carp at the end of the summer.

In tropical conditions, where there is no winter check to the rate of oxidation of the sewage nor to the rate of growth of fish, this would seem a particularly suitable method of sewage disposal. The sale of the fish would be a useful contribution towards the cost of any sewerage scheme. This is a possible answer to the vexed question of the safe disposal of such industrial wastes as the "dunder" from rum distilleries, mentioned earlier. Diluted with water and sprayed into fish-ponds, or into ponds stocked with fish, many industrial wastes are known to have enough nutrients to be able to nourish a good plankton, which would be the basis of a rich diet for fish. The sale of the fish would go some way to cover the costs of disposal and the water could be safely discharged into rivers which are now turned into stinking drains.

Another indirect way in which some of the nutrient value of sewage can be salvaged, is to be seen in the fish-cages set in drains in Indonesia. The sewage nourishes a dense population of Tubifex worms and Chironomid larvae, and these are swept along with the current. In the drains, there are placed wicker cages containing carp, which grow at a great rate on the food organisms they are able to catch from the water as it goes by.

Buschkiel[20] points out circumstances in which, in tropical conditions, the accumulation of large amounts of faecal matter can nevertheless allow of fish life. Provided there is some oxygen, there will soon develop a heavy growth of filamentous algae, and a carpet of attached epiphytic algae on stones, sand and other plants, which produce in the presence of sunlight an excess of oxygen. This accumulates as a mass of bubbles trapped in the meshes of the algal filaments. These bubbles dissolve during the night and provide the oxygen necessary to sustain the life of the fish until photosynthesis begins again with daylight.

Chapter Two

GENERAL PRINCIPLES, PHYSICAL AND CHEMICAL, CONTINUED

SWAMPS

SWAMPS are the great natural example of accumulations of organic matter leading to more or less complete deoxygenation. Rivers can give rise to swamps when they are continually changing their course, as when traversing very flat land. There is not only the continuous erosion of the banks; but the great weight of spoil from the banks and from the land settles out where the current slackens, forming sand and mudbanks. These divide the river into a number of branches at low water. Some of these branches may become closed by mudbanks and form lagoons or backwaters at low water, and these are temporary lakes. Other mudbanks may become colonised by plants and grow into islands, gradually rising as they collect more silt. The backwaters may become permanent; they and the old river channels may become choked with vegetation. The Upper Nile Valley shows these backwaters and old channels very clearly from the air.

In the vast Sudd of the southern Sudan the Nile spreads out over thousands of square miles of flat land. There are also those cases, such as Bangweulu and Lukanga in Rhodesia, where subsidence in a plain near a river has led to a big sheet of very shallow water. All such sheets of shallow water become swamps by the growth of vegetation. They shrink in the dry season, exposing grassland at their margins which may make good grazing for game and cattle. Such are the *toiches* of the Sudan. Besides these permanent swamps, there are the temporary swamps formed when rivers overflow their banks in the flood season.

A swamp may be roughly defined as an area of water so shallow that it may be more or less completely overgrown with vegetation. According to Welch,[13] the swamp is destined to become dry land by the gradual accumulation of humus derived from the swamp vegetation. There are all the intermediate stages between a lake fringed with a belt of vegetation, and a true swamp. Lake Kioga, for instance, has almost as much fringing vegetation as open water.

We owe almost all we know about the physical and chemical characters of tropical swamps to Dr. G. S. Carter. In 1926-7, with Dr. Beadle, he spent the greater part of a year in the shallow swamps of the Gran Chaco in Paraguay. Here the land is so flat that no differences of level greater than a few feet occur over wide areas, though the swamps have a very gentle slope towards the Paraguay River. In the rainy season the land is flooded to a depth seldom exceeding three or four feet; in the dry season much of the swamp dries out, except for the central parts, which dry out less frequently and for shorter periods.

Carter found[21] that both the outer and the inner regions of the swamps were poor in animal life. This was associated with a very low oxygen content. The reasons for this low oxygen content are suggested as: (*a*) a lack of mixing of the water, both due to insufficient cooling at night and by protection from wind disturbance by overhanging and surface vegetation; (*b*) the shading of those waterplants, which, by their photosynthetic activity might have oxygenated the water; and (*c*) the large amount of decaying vegetation which used up any oxygen available. Owing to the high temperature this rate of decay would be high.

Carter[14] included some swamps in his investigation of the fresh waters of the rain-forest areas of British Guiana. The water may be a deep brown or almost black colour in many of the streams. Carter found that the depth of colour of the water was related to the amount of free acid, which was frequently great. These swamp waters had a very low mineral content: for example, a conductivity of 23 to 26 reciprocal megohms (Loch Katrine, one of the softest waters in Britain, has twice that amount of dissolved mineral matter) and practically no lime was present. The amount of free carbon dioxide was high, while the oxygen content was very low, being seldom greater than 30 per cent of saturation and sometimes zero. The bottom mud and decaying vegetation were even more strongly deoxygenated; gas escaped in large quantities whenever the bottom was disturbed. In one swamp there was even the escape of sulphuretted hydrogen.

Measurements of light penetration were made, and it was found that in a swamp pool of darkly-stained water red light penetrated farthest, but even so, was reduced to only 40 per cent of its original strength at a depth of only 18 inches.

In 1952-3, Carter worked on the papyrus swamps of Uganda.[6] The swamps he investigated were of two types: those fringing Lake Victoria and those filling the shallow valleys.

In the fringing swamps Carter distinguished several regions. There were: (*a*) the open lake, (*b*) the water-lily zone, (*c*) the fern and sedge zone, (*d*) the papyrus zone, and (*e*) the grass swamp. These regions follow each other in order, from the lake to the land. Zone (*c*) is not always to be distinguished.

In the open lake there was almost complete mixing of the water and so a homogeneous composition except within a very short distance of the bottom. Because the mud there is highly reducing, the water tended to have less oxygen just above the mud. The water-lily zone, where the water may be 7 to 15 feet deep where it passes into the open waters of the lake, and 5 to 10 feet at its inner margin where it merges with the papyrus, has the surface about 50 per cent covered with the floating leaves of the water-lily, water-chestnut and reed. These plants are rooted in the lake-bottom and have long stems reaching to the surface. These leaves and doubtless also the clusters of stems prevent free mixing of the water such as occurs in the open lake under the action of winds and waves. Consequently, while this zone contains plenty of dissolved oxygen, as much as 50 per cent saturation even at its inner margin, incomplete mixing is revealed by a stratification such that, for example, at a depth of 5 feet, there may only be 32 per cent saturation with oxygen, while there is 90 per cent at the surface. Moreover, the effect of the highly reducing mud at the bottom is felt at a much greater distance from the bottom than in the open lake where mixing is free. Nevertheless, this zone has enough oxygen to support a rich fish fauna.

The papyrus zone is, as its name implies, dominated by the papyrus reed.* Papyrus is peculiar in that it may not be rooted in the bottom but may form a floating raft of tangled roots and mud, in which other plants, including climbers, are rooted. The papyrus itself has a large brush-like flowering head which may rise as high as 15 feet above water-level. There are two layers of water in such a mass, one above the mat of roots and a lower layer between the mat and the bottom. At its landward end the papyrus is grounded, while at its lakeward edge it may be afloat in 15 feet of water.

* *Cyperus papyrus* Linn.

Plate 9 shows typical papyrus swamp. The water in the papyrus zone is derived from two sources; firstly, from the lake by way of the lily zone, and secondly, from the land from seepage and streams. The land water is easily distinguished by its yellow colour (due to humic acids and dissolved iron compounds).

Oxygen is usually very low or absent in the water in the papyrus zone. This is due to three causes. First, the bottom mud has a strongly reducing quality which uses up what oxygen is available. Secondly, the lack of light, due to the shade of the papyrus mat, completely prevents photosynthesis and so the release of oxygen by plants. Thirdly, there is no circulation of the water because of the shelter from wind. These are the same factors that Carter found to be dominant in the South American swamps. Nutrient salts, such as ammonium and phosphate, are present in abundance, released from the mud, and if there were access to light, plants would freely develop, increasing the oxygen and reducing the carbon dioxide.

Similar conditions prevail in the valley swamps, namely, more or less complete deoxygenation except where there are open pools large enough to have good access to light and wind. Here, as in open pools in the Gran Chaco, there could be a very good flora and fauna of aquatic organisms.

To sum up the conditions typical of swamps: the key factors are emergent vegetation, which shades the water and prevents stirring by wind action; a bottom mud of strongly reducing properties; a high temperature, and often darkly coloured water which further hampers photosynthesis. These factors give rise to absence of oxygen, abundance of carbon dioxide, an acid reaction, but a high content of nutrient salts.

OTHER FLOATING VEGETATION

In the illustrated newspapers of July 1959, there were photographs showing a very dense growth of the water-hyacinth, *Eichhornia crassipes* Solms, in the Gebel Aulia Dam on the Nile, in Sudanese territory. The floating mat of these plants was said to be three feet thick, so that people could walk over it, and so compact that navigation was impeded or stopped. It is certain that the effect on the fish living in the dam must be serious; for, beneath the mat, as beneath papyrus, oxygen would be low or absent, and carbon dioxide abundant.

For some years the water-hyacinth has been a serious pest in the River Congo and especially in the tributaries and backwaters. Not only has canoe navigation, so essential for the riverside Africans, been brought to a halt, but the passage of powered craft has been seriously hampered. A campaign of eradication on a very large scale has been waged by the Belgian authorities. A full account is given by de Kimpe.[114] The spraying of 2, 4-D from motor launches and canoes has been the main weapon, and considerable success has been achieved. The creation of swamp conditions by this plant is not only harmful to fish, but makes all methods of fishing difficult or impossible.

More recently there has been a report of the aquatic fern, *Salvinia auriculata*, running riot in a dam in the Kitale District of Kenya. It soon multiplied until it completely covered the surface of the water, and the fish in the dam, which had previously supported a useful fishery, died out, or migrated up the feeder stream. The Report for 1958 of the Kenya Fisheries[115] describes how two aerial sprayings with chemical herbicides failed to control the pest, and the dam had to be drained in the dry season. This seemed to cure the infestation; but the costs of the control measures were considerable. It is bad news, therefore, to learn that this plant has appeared in the great Kariba Dam.

Recently, there has been a rapid spread of this weed in Lake Kariba. Plate 51 shows the track swept by a motor-launch in a continuous mat of *Salvinia* estimated to be some miles long and broad. As yet, the floating mats are swept to and fro by the wind; but, in the creeks and backwaters, the *Salvinia* mat is tending to become more permanent, by the growth of grasses and other plants with long roots which bind the masses of *Salvinia* together.

There is a sharp fall, or even a complete absence, of oxygen beneath one of these dense masses of *Salvinia*; so its continued spread would have, in time, a serious effect on the abundance of fish. Already a problem may have arisen, where a *Salvinia* mat obstructs the estuary of a side-stream up which such fish as *Labeo* normally run to spawn. If there were a sufficiently complete deoxygenation beneath the mat, the spawning run would be checked; and unless the fish were able to adapt themselves to spawn in other conditions, the result must be a decline in the population of *Labeo* and other river-spawning fish.

The appearance of *Salvinia* in Lake Kariba has not been

explained; but it has for some years been a serious nuisance in Ceylon, where it was introduced by the University for the purpose of botanical studies (Williams[142]). By 1956 it had so spread as to infest some 22,000 acres of paddy land, and some 2000 acres of waterways.

At first, hand removal was tried, but there was immediate re-infection. The process of hand gathering tends to spread the weed by breaking off the lateral growths by which vegetative reproduction mainly takes place. Moreover, the collected weed has no economic value. It contains some 90 per cent of water and cannot be composted economically. It has been used as a mulch for coconuts, rubber and cocoa; but this use could spread the pest if heavy rains swept the mulch into the nearest stream.

Experiments were made with chemical herbicides. Chow, Thevasagayam, and Wambeek[143] were interested in the eradication of the weed because it may be the breeding place for *Mansonia* mosquitoes, vectors of several diseases. These authors, as well as Williams (loc. cit.) report promising results with P.C.P. (Pentachlorophenol). They give formulae and techniques, and suggest that complete eradication is possible with repeated spraying. Fish are not harmed unless they happen to be in shallow water or near the surface.

So far as Lake Kariba is concerned, the vast size of the lake, and the serious degree of infestation, would need a major campaign, and a costly one. But the weed has serious implications for the lake, not only for its subsidiary function as a source of fish, but for its primary purpose, namely the generation of power.

SWAMP FISHES

Only those fish able to breathe atmospheric air can live in a true swamp habitat. In the African swamps there are only two fishes of commercial importance able to live in this way, but in the South American swamps there are many, and Carter and Beadle have described the ingenious ways in which they use air for breathing (see Chapter III). In the Far East, there is a rich association of swamp fish, which not only includes a close relative of the African Barbel, but the important family of the Anabantids, the Climbing Perch, the Gouramis and the Snake-heads, all important food-fish.

The Bangweulu Swamps also have much papyrus, but these are

among the biggest swamps in the world, covering 1500 to 2000 square miles. They are not continuous swamp, but have open channels and lagoons, often of considerable size. These are rarely if ever stagnant, and there is a slow movement of water in the swamp towards the Luapula River in the south-west, as well as a fairly brisk flow in the open channels. Conditions must be very different from those in the Gran Chaco and the Uganda valley swamps; for the Bangweulu Swamp produces a large quantity of fish, estimated at some 5000 tons in 1957. Moreover, these included a high proportion of ordinary lake and river fish which are not modified to breathe atmospheric air.

It was found that the oxygen concentrations of the Bangweulu Swamps were low, even in rapidly-flowing channels,[22] and that noxious products are secreted into the water by the decaying vegetation. This observation is in line with experience at Malacca. Ponds constructed in former swamp land, which had stood under water for at least two years, tended to be toxic to introduced fish and there was often a poor rate of survival in the first stocking of some of the ponds. But it was found that a second stocking, made after the ponds had been drained and refilled afresh, did not suffer from this factor. So it is possible that these harmful products accumulate slowly, and are quickly flushed out.

However, in general, sufficient oxygen must be present in the Bangweulu Swamp[22] to allow a large fish population to live. The oxygen values fluctuate with the seasons, the amount of water, etc., with consequent fluctuations in the composition of the fish population. For instance, the Tiger-fish, *Hydrocyon*, may occur in a certain channel only when the flow is sufficient to keep the oxygen tension at levels tolerable to this species, while at other times the oxygen values may fall so low that this species is temporarily driven from the area.

Catastrophic changes can occur, as when heavy rain brings a rapid inflow of new water, which may flush out the water which has been lying stagnant in certain areas of the swamp too quickly for the fish to be able to take avoiding action. Mass mortalities of fish may then occur. In general, the picture is one of the fish populations moving about the swamp according to changes in oxygen conditions, as well as to other causes such as breeding and feeding migrations. Clearly, these movements are extremely important in their effect on the fishery.

Another African swamp with an important fishery is the Malagarasi Swamp in Tanganyika. This swamp covers above 700 square miles and drains into Lake Tanganyika by the Malagarasi River. It was studied by a party from the Jinja Research Station in October 1952.[23] They examined an area covered by blue water lilies and containing dense stands of submerged water plants. The water was less than 10 feet deep and the bottom consisted of finely divided vegetable detritus, associated with which was a rich fauna of flagellates and ciliates. The overlying water was crystal clear, so that the movements of fish could be observed as in an aquarium.

The dense fish population of this swamp included most of the species found in lakes and rivers, and this suggests that plenty of oxygen was present. The fact that gill-nets are used by the fishermen shows that there must be large areas of water reasonably free from vegetation, and this probably allows access of oxygen. There was, as the clearness of the water would suggest, an almost complete absence both of phytoplankton and zooplankton. Conductivity was fairly high at 300 reciprocal megohms,[9] which suggests a plenitude of mineral salts. Analysis of the water showed abundance of ammonia and phosphate, both essential plant foods. It could be that the nutrients were being taken up by the submerged vegetation, or that the absence of some essential element, possibly sulphur, prevented the growth of phytoplankton. The considerable fish population must have had some other sources of food, and these will be considered in Chapter VI.

SWAMP CLEARANCE

Carter's work points clearly to the fact that the denser the swamp the greater the lack of oxygen and the lethal excess of carbon dioxide. There may also be present the very poisonous gas, sulphuretted hydrogen, in these conditions and there may be other toxic substances released into the water. Therefore, as Carter says, the obvious way of increasing the productivity of swamps and indeed of making them habitable at all to most kinds of fish, is to clear the vegetation, and especially the emergent plants. Then there can be a free flow of water in swamps draining into a river, and in any case the possibility of mixing of the water by wind action and night overturn. By allowing light to penetrate, there would be a vigorous growth of plant life, both algal and planktonic, which

1. A ridger at work in Rhodesia.

Constructing a T-dam Rhodesia.

3. A large dam-scoop.

4. A check-dam across the Kamba River at Lyssa, Ghana.

5. Fishing the lagoon formed upstream of the check-dam.

6. The very small catch of fish made in the Kamba River in the dry season pools before the check-dam was built. Note the effect on the vegetation of the raised water-table after the building of the dam, in Plate 5, as compared with Plate 6.

7. A part of the big catch made in the lagoon held back by the check-dam shown in Plate 4.

8. The River Zambezi at high flood.

9. A papyrus swamp, Lake Naivasha, Kenya.

would further oxygenate the water and use up the carbon dioxide. This would again result in the water becoming less acid and, in the presence of the nutrient salts known to be plentiful in many swamps, to a high rate of production of material directly or indirectly useful as food for fish. It has been one of the points raised by the work of the Jinja Research Station that the clearing of the fringing swamps in Lake Victoria would increase the breeding areas for fish. The fact that vegetation cover is also the refuge for the young stages of fish is made less important when it is remembered that the lack of oxygen in much of the fringing swamps makes it uninhabitable for most fish. Moreover, even where young fish find a part of the fringing swamp where they can live, they are liable to be driven out when there is a flushing out of the deoxygenated water into the outer belt of vegetation by an inflow, under the papyrus, of rain or land-drainage water.

It might be less difficult and costly to clear such emergent vegetation than would at first appear. So far as reeds are concerned, there are on the market reed-cutting punts, self-propelled, which will cut reed-beds close to the bottom. At Malacca a very successful machine was improvised by mounting a grass-cutting machine on a raft, and making an extension piece to carry the cutters well below the surface and near the bottom. This machine, operated by a 4 h.p. petrol engine, had to be pushed by two men wading in the water; but it cut some 36 acres of reed-filled ponds quickly and thoroughly, and with a great saving in time and man-power. It would not be possible to have men wading in Lake Victoria, and in any case these swamps are in many feet of water. But the reed-cutting punts mentioned above will cut at a rate of one or two miles per hour and could clear a large area of reeds in a short time. The clearance of papyrus, which is not rooted but floating, would be a different problem. But it is certain that it would not be difficult to invent a cutter, mounted on a self-propelled punt, which could be revolved about its bearing, so that it could make a series of deep vertical cuts into the papyrus mat, and then tear out the segments so cut.

The Rawa Pening in Java was cleared of a dense mat of water-hyacinth, *Eichhornia crassipes*, by the use of hand-labour and saws. There was a dramatic increase in the production of fish in the lake; and the benefits went far beyond this. A fuller description is given in Chapter XV.

At all events, it seems certain that, as the population of such territories as Uganda and Rhodesia increase, more use will have to be made of the swamps (some 30 per cent of the countryside in Uganda may be papyrus swamp) as sources of fish, always bearing in mind the importance of these swamps as water-conservers. As that day may not be far ahead, by even short-term historical standards, it would seem a good investment to try out the mechanical clearance of swamps and their stocking where necessary with fish (and as reservoirs for irrigation, for example) on an adequate scale. Probably the line of such development would follow the idea of the mixed small-holding so common in the Far East; each small-holding consisting of some irrigated land both for cash crops and for vegetables, poultry, pigsties, and a fishpond, or a share in the proceeds of a communal cleared swamp-area stocked with fish and subject to some simple measures of management to increase the yield.

As the reeds grow from root-stocks in the mud, they will regenerate after cutting. But experience shows that these root-stocks are soon exhausted of their reserves. If the reeds are cut again as soon as they reach the surface regeneration will be very slow, or indeed not occur at all.

Passage through swamps may greatly affect the composition of river water, though only temporarily. Carter (loc. cit.) found that streams emerging from a swamp soon picked up oxygen, sometimes within a mile or two of emerging. It is the same process of self-purification mentioned under Pollution earlier in Chapter I. The Nile, when it has flowed through the swamps of the southern Sudan, becomes deoxygenated and enriched in free carbon dioxide; yet there are fine fisheries in the Nile at and above Malakal, not many miles downstream.

Chapter Three

GENERAL PRINCIPLES, PHYSICAL AND CHEMICAL, CONTINUED

DAMS

WHERE a river overflows into backwaters and creeks temporary lake and swamp conditions are set up. Similarly, when a river is dammed the current is checked and lake-like conditions appear. The Gebel Aulia Dam on the White Nile above Khartoum stores the waters of the White Nile, and causes the flow of the river to slow down and its level to rise in such a way that the lake extends back some 250 km. above the dam. The depth of the lake so formed naturally increases to the maximum of the dam itself.

This check in the flow of the river, and the creation of almost stable conditions (for the rate of flow of the river is reduced by the dam to less than 200 metres per hour) have a great effect upon the flora and fauna of the river, and this in turn affects the composition of the water.

According to Brook and Rzoska,[24] the first effect of the check in the rate of flow of the river is the settling out of the silt and detritus, leading to an increased transparency of the water. Then the phytoplankton develops, from a sparse community in the river to a very dense one in the dam, and the zooplankton follows suit. True planktonic organisms are shown in Colour Plates III and IV. Phosphate is depleted as it is used up and stratification appears in the distribution of the dissolved gases. At the surface, the carbon dioxide is used up, and oxygen is produced. But the dense phytoplankton absorbs all the light, so that the deeper waters of the dam have no light and no photosynthesis can take place. So the deeper waters have less oxygen than the surface waters, though this tends to be temporary, as there is still a good deal of mixing of the water.

LAKES

In true lakes, even when they occur in the course of rivers, the phenomenon of stratification may be very marked and may have a big effect on the productivity of the lake and so on its value as a fishery. The content of dissolved solids will depend on what the streams and rivers bring to the lake and on what it dissolves from its own basin. The content of gases, of which oxygen and carbon dioxide are the most important, likewise depends partly on the inflows, but chiefly on the exchange between the water and the atmosphere. Both the content of solids and the content of gases are very much changed by the activities of the plants and animals which live in the lake.

Clarke[25] states that the infra-red or heat component of sunlight is almost entirely absorbed in the uppermost metre from the surface, so the heating effect is confined to the surface only. Since warm water is lighter than cold water, at tropical temperatures it might be thought that the result would be a fairly thin heated layer with cooler water below, but this is seldom the case. The heated water is driven deep by the wind, because the wind sets up a surface drift, with a compensating return drift at some depth below; this also sets up eddies which again help to distribute the heat far below the surface. The energy of the wind overcomes the resistance, by inertia, of the cooler and heavier water. Conversely, cooler water sinks because it is heavier. Consequently, the deeper parts of a lake will have a temperature of about that of the air at the coolest time of the year. Since, in the tropics there is not usually a great annual variation in temperature, the difference between the surface water and the bottom water may be slight, of the order of 2° to 3° C. or even less. Yet the differences in density may be considerable; because, at tropical temperatures which are of the order of 20° to 30° C., a small rise in temperature leads to a big fall in density. It is possible, then, to have a stable stratification in a tropical lake, where the surface layers are only a couple of degrees warmer than the deeper layers, because the centre of gravity of a given column of such water will be well below midwater.

STRATIFICATION

There is a limit to the depth to which the wind can drive the warmed surface water. It has to do work against the greater density of the cooler, deeper water, and a point is usually reached beyond which the warmer water cannot be driven. There is then a more or less well-defined discontinuity layer, or thermocline, with a layer of warm water lying above it and a layer of cool water lying below it. There may be an abrupt change of temperature occurring over a few metres in depth. This is very well illustrated by the work of Ruttner[4] in Java, Sumatra and Bali in 1931. He worked out the distribution of temperature in a large number of lakes of sizes ranging from very small ones with a surface area of less than a square kilometre, to the Toba Lake with a surface area of over 1000 square kilometres. They were situated at altitudes ranging from practically sea-level to 1500 metres above sea-level. First, he shows that there is a relation between the temperature of the bottom layers and the altitude of the lake. This is illustrated in the table below, abstracted from Ruttner's monograph:

Table I

Lake	Altitude above sea-level	Bottom temperature,°C.
Ranau Klindungen	10 m.	25·9
Ranau Lamongan	240 m.	25·9
Danu Ranau	540 m.	25·4
Telaga Ngebel	730 m.	24·6
Danu Batur	1031 m.	22·4
Telaga Pasir	1290 m.	20·1
Danau di-Atas	1531 m.	20·2

The greater the altitude of the lake, the cooler the climate, and so the cooler the temperature of the bottom water. Ruttner also found that the larger the lake, the deeper the situation of the thermocline. Thus, in a series of lakes with an area of less than 2 square kilometres, the thermocline lies at a depth of 4 to 8 metres; in a group of lakes of intermediate size, of about 100 square kilometres, it was about 12 to 15 metres; and finally, in the Toba Lake of more than 1000 square kilometres, it lies at about 30 metres. To this series may be added the great African deep lakes, where the thermocline lies between 50 and 150 metres according to the season.[26, 27]

The reason for this connection between the area of a lake and the depth of the thermocline, that is, the depth to which the warmer surface water is driven by the wind, is that over a large unbroken surface of water the wind speed is greater than over a small area, the volume of water transported is much greater, and its kinetic energy is greater. Hence it can be driven deeper into the underlying cooler water than in a small lake.

The action of the wind, therefore, transports the heat from the thin surface layer which receives it, to a varying depth, and this transport is aided by the eddies set up between the surface wind-driven current and the deeper counter-current, until a balance is reached between the energy of the wind and the resistance of the deeper, denser water. There is then a more or less temporary condition of stability, with warm water overlying cooler water.

SEICHES

The wind has a further indirect effect which helps to mix the waters of a lake. This is the setting up of internal waves or seiches. When a wind blows hard and steadily over a lake, the water is blown with it and becomes heaped up on the lee shore, so as to give a small but important head of water. When the wind drops, the water tends to swing back again, and currents may be set up. But when the stratification has set in, with a well-marked lighter warmer layer over a heavier cooler layer, the heaping up of the surface layer on the lee shore forces the cooler layer downward. When the wind drops, this deeper layer swings back and sets up a wave in the discontinuity layer. This wave is, of course, invisible at the surface but travels back and forth across the lake, and is manifested by a rhythmic rise and fall of the boundary between the two layers. Beauchamp[28] shows how these internal waves in Lake Nyasa set up a turbulence which transfers heat still farther into the depths. He concluded that warming of the deeper water in a tropical lake may be continuous over a period of years, until a temperature is reached which approaches very close to that reached by the surface waters during the cooler time of the year. When the whole lake thus becomes of uniform temperature, stratification breaks down and there is no longer resistance to the complete mixing of the lake waters. Beauchamp continued "the indications are that the temperature of the water at the bottom of a deep tropical lake is a function of the last unusually cold season, and the time that has elapsed since".

These water-movements not only carry heat but also oxygen dissolved from the atmosphere into the deeper waters of the lake. In the upper warmer and lighter water there is constant circulation and therefore good oxygenation. There is also available abundant carbon dioxide. As these are also the illuminated layers, plants can develop freely there and use up the carbon dioxide and enrich the water with oxygen.

On the other hand, the deeper layers are stagnant, for they are below the region stirred by the wind and eddy-currents. By the growth of plants, which shade off the light in the upper illuminated layers, there is little or no light in these deeper layers so that plants, or at least those plants which can perform photosynthesis, cannot grow, as they can in the upper illuminated layers. They are thus doubly deprived of oxygen; for at the same time such oxygen as there might be present is being used up by the respiration of living plants and animals, and by the decay of dead organisms and the oxygen demand of the organic bottom deposits. The lower layer, below the thermocline, the *hypolimnion*, may thus become temporarily or permanently deoxygenated in this way. In deep lakes such as Tanganyika, Nyasa, and Kivu, the deeper waters may be permanently deoxygenated. For example, in Lake Nyasa there is no dissolved oxygen below 250 metres,[28] and in Lake Tanganyika none below 100 to 225 metres, according to the season.[27] In the case of Lake Tanganyika, it has been proved that about three-quarters of the entire volume of the lake is thus a mortal desert for animal life, and can certainly contain no fish. In Lake Kivu, no less than 99 per cent of the volume of the lake is uninhabitable by fish.[29] Ruttner, derived the same lesson from his work on the lakes in Java, namely, that the volume of a lake which is suitable for the life of fish might only be a small proportion of the whole. The great expanse of Lake Tanganyika, a veritable inland sea, blue and sparkling with whitecaps like the sea itself, can nevertheless produce fish for the people only in its uppermost layers. Lake Nyasa may be exceptional to some extent, since there is evidence that one catfish is able to live at or even below the thermocline, and is caught in "deep-sea" fish traps; and there are "rises" of insects, Chaoborids, which suggest that, by some special mechanism, these are able to find some oxygen, or can do without it for short periods. But it seems certain that these exceptions do not disprove the fact that the deep water of the great tropical lakes is barren of fish life and offers no scope for development.

Braun[10] in his research on a group of lakes in the Amazon basin in Brazil found that, though these lakes are very shallow (from 6 to 10 metres deep in the rainy season and 2 to 5 metres deep in the dry season), they show well-marked physical and chemical stratification. The stratified layers may be very thin; for example, the *epilimnion* and thermocline together may be only one to two metres thick. Lake Jurucù, for example, which is $5\frac{1}{2}$ metres deep, had a thermocline at 2-3 metres. These lakes are very poor in dissolved salts. Braun's work confirmed earlier analyses suggesting that these were among the purest natural waters in the world, with contents of dissolved substances of the order of distilled water.

INVERSION

A peculiar case of layering in a lake may occur when one of the sources of the water-supply has a high mineral content. Such lakes are not uncommon and a good example is Lake Kivu, in the Rift Valley of Africa, in Congo territory. Water which has a load of dissolved salts is naturally denser and heavier than purer water, and this greater density may outweigh the differences of density due to temperature differences. Lake Kivu was studied by Damas.[30] It is situated among high mountains, close to a region of volcanic activity. In fact, the Virunga volcanoes have recently been in eruption. Damas describes the lake as being rather grimly picturesque and very stormy. One must admire his hardihood in tackling deep soundings in this lake with the boats he had, especially when he describes how the wind could rise from a calm to a gale in a very short time.

Damas's soundings showed that Lake Kivu was less deep than had been supposed, the maximum being about 700 metres (2100 feet). The distribution of heat in the lake was striking. To a depth of 70 metres from the surface, the temperature decreases with depth. Below that, it increases again, until, at the bottom, the temperature may even be higher than it is at the surface. In the upper layers, one can make the usual distinction into an epilimnion, which is warm and homogeneous, a thermocline at about 20-25 metres, and a cooler hypolimnion. Below 70 metres, on the contrary, the reverse occurs. Damas suggested that this reversal was due to inflow, probably below the surface, of warm and heavily mineralised water from volcanic springs. He supported this suggestion with data on the conductivity of the water. Below about 70 metres, the electrical conductivity of the water shows a sharp rise, pointing to an increase in the quantity of dissolved salts, which rendered this water heavy enough to keep it at the bottom in spite of its higher temperature.

The gas content of this lake was equally strange. Down to a depth of 20 metres, the water was well oxygenated, but below the thermocline, to a depth of about 60 metres, the oxygen diminished by two-thirds. From 65 metres to the bottom there was no oxygen at all. Indeed, when Damas lowered his sampling bottle into the oxygen-free zone, it came up with the metal blackened, and the water not only had a strong smell of sulphuretted hydrogen, but also sparkled and bubbled like mineral water. Damas did not identifiy the gas, and though there was a very great increase in the content of carbon dioxide, from 33 mg./l. at 75 metres to no less than 1008 mg./l. at 375 metres, this is not enough to cause the effervescence even under reduced pressure. Damas thought it might be due to methane (marsh gas) or nitrogen. Subsequent research has shown that it is methane.

Lake Kivu is absolutely devoid of oxygen below about 70 metres, has a high content of carbon dioxide and a lethal amount of sulphuretted hydrogen. It is yet another lake, though an extreme case, where only a small proportion (about one per cent) of the whole water volume is habitable by animals, such as fish, which require oxygen. As Damas writes, the scarcity of fishing villages on the shores of the lake reveals the principal characteristic.

Lake Victoria differs from Lakes Tanganyika, Nyasa, and Kivu, and from most of those investigated by Ruttner in Indonesia, in having a very great area in relation to its depth. At its deepest, it is but 94 metres (306 feet) deep, and the wind blows freely over its surface, which is as great as that of Ireland. Hence there is seldom a marked thermocline in the lake water, though Fish[31] has found that a thermocline does exist at certain times of the year. In fact, Fish found a seiche movement in this thermocline, which led to the very important effect, from the fishery point of view, of carrying cool and deoxygenated water into the shallow arms of the northern part of the lake. The unseen wave, surging across the whole lake, not at the surface, where it could be seen, but below the surface where only the thermometer can detect it, breaks over the sills of these shallow bays and bights and leaves in the shallows a bottom layer of cool water which sets up a brief stratification there, and may indeed cause some fish mortality. Damas ascribes the great fertility of Lake Edward, which has a maximum depth of 70 metres, to its shallowness and the frequency of winds, which prevent layering, and keep the whole lake uniform in temperature and so well oxygenated.

OVERTURNS

Though temperature differences between epilimnion and hypolimnion may be very small, of the order of one degree Centigrade, the layering is stable because of the greater density which even so small a difference gives to the cooler water at the temperatures (of the order of 25° C.), which prevail in tropical lakes. Yet there is an external element of instability, for the temperature of the air over the lake may fall by this amount or more at night, especially when there is strong radiation, to a point where the surface waters become as heavy as the deeper layers. This may cause considerable convection currents and mixing to be set up, and the longer the cooling the greater the mixing. On Lake Kivu, the epilimnion is thus mixed nightly during the rainy season. In the dry season, much stronger nightly cooling results in mixing to the point where the whole of the upper 70 metres becomes homogeneous. It becomes homogeneous, not only as regards temperature, but as regards oxygen. The well-oxygenated surface waters mix with the poorly oxygenated deeper waters, giving a mixture which is little better than half-saturated. Braun found that the shallow lakes of the Amazon basin had very frequent overturns of this kind. A temperature stratification of the order of only one or two degrees set up in a shallow lake is easily upset by local weather conditions and mixing then takes place. Ruttner was able actually to see the overturn of the water in three small lakes on Bali. The surface of these lakes was losing heat due to strong radiation in the monsoon conditions and, the temperature of the whole lake having become uniform, all stability was lost and complete mixing took place. In Danau Brantan, for instance, the temperature at 2 metres was 21·9 and at 20 metres was 21·8; oxygen was 93 per cent saturation throughout. Van Meel[32] states that the upper waters of Lake Tanganyika undergo a seasonal turnover in about October, at the end of the dry season, with some signs of a lesser turnover in the season of the "small rains". Beauchamp[26] who worked on both Lakes Tanganyika and Nyasa, found both lakes stratified, Nyasa more strongly than Tanganyika; yet there was considerably more mixing of the layers in Nyasa than in Tanganyika. He explained this by the shape and geographical position of the two lakes. Nyasa lies farther south than Tanganyika and nearer to the coast. Therefore, during the southern winter (April to September) Lake Nyasa feels the full force of the S.E. trade winds, which may blow with great violence for days on end and which have caused tragic loss of life on the lake. Quite aside from the surface mixing due to turbulent waves, strong surface currents are set up with equally strong counter currents at deeper levels. These cause a high degree of mixing which penetrates deeper as the temperature of the surface water is lowered towards that of the deeper water. In the summer on the other hand, Nyasa experiences variable winds whose frequent changes of direction cause a considerable amount of mixing. In Lake Tanganyika such strong mixing does not take place because this lake is less under the influence of strong winds in the winter, and in the summer the winds are lighter and less variable than on Nyasa. Even so, the mixing affects only the upper two hundred metres. Van Meel points out that it is fortunate that the deepest parts of these great lakes remain undisturbed; for if the whole lake, and not only the upper couple of hundred metres, became well mixed, the resulting mixture of water would not only contain too little oxygen to support life but would also contain lethal amounts of sulphuretted hydrogen. It will be recalled that all three lakes, Nyasa, Tanganyika and Kivu, contain great quantities of this very poisonous gas in their deeper water. A total turnover in these lakes would cause a holocaust of fish and other aquatic organisms of such magnitude that it would have been recorded or remembered if it had happened in historical times, and would also undoubtedly have left its mark on the character of the fauna.

Even in small lakes, where the volume of the deoxygenated water is relatively small, there can be mortalities of fish. Ruttner found in Java, that a single cold night might, in certain conditions, set up a deep circulation in a lake with an oxygen-free bottom layer, which, by mixing with the oxygenated surface layers, might so lower the oxygen content that the entire fish stock could be destroyed. Ruttner had, in fact, information that a number of the lakes he examined had had repeated fish mortalities, and had manifested a smell of sulphuretted hydrogen. As Java is a region of volcanic activity, these fish mortalities and noxious gases had been put down to vulcanism; but they could be fully explained by overturns of the whole of the water, caused by exceptional cooling and mixing.

Damas[30] reports on a small lake on the eastern Congo, Lake

Ndagala, which has periodic overturns. These result in the partial disappearance of the fish fauna. But a few fish are able to survive by living in the estuaries of the small streams which enter the lake, and these survivors partially repopulate the lake during its periods of stability. But the absence of fishing villages on the shores of this lake speaks, as on Lake Kivu, for the paucity and unreliability of fish production in such conditions.

SMALL DAMS

The same effects may be seen in even very small bodies of water. Fish[33] worked out the distribution of oxygen in small artificial dams in Uganda. He found that the quantity and distribution of oxygen depended on the degree of exposure to the wind, on the presence or absence of the floating leaves of the water-lily, which prevent access of light and restrict wind-action, and also on the newness of the dam. He found that the most effective factor in disturbing the balance between oxygen production and exhaustion in small dams, is the surface cover. He remarks: "The leaves of the water-lilies prevent the penetration of light, so oxygen production of sub-surface plants is severely limited; thus the replenishment of the oxygen used by the various aquatic organisms is prevented. Further, the lilies prevent entry of oxygen from the surface, and its distribution, by free wind-action."

Moreover, in old ponds, where the bottom had a considerable amount of decaying vegetable matter and where there was a lack of oxygen, decomposition continued in the absence of oxygen, with the result that reducing substances accumulated and constituted an "oxygen debt" which had to be paid off before oxygen could be again available. Dams which are narrow and deep, and so less exposed to wind action, also tended to become deoxygenated in their deeper parts. Fish found considerable temperature differences between surface and bottom even in these small dams, differences greater than those between surface and bottom in large lakes. These differences, as in lakes, were associated with a lack of oxygen in the deeper layers. Attempts had been made to stock these dams with fish, but it was found that stocking was unsuccessful in dams in which shading by lilies, absence of wind action or the presence of oxygen-robbing deposits, or all these together, had led to oxygen depletion in the lower layers. It is true that many of these dams were constructed primarily for water storage, but their potential for fish production was realised, so that these results by Fish are of very practical value. Where a pond is constructed with a primary view to fish production, then obviously it must not be too deep in relation to its surface, it must not be shaded by trees which keep off the wind and it must be kept clear of emergent or floating vegetation. It seems certain that fishponds should not be more than six feet deep and that less would be better. The ponds at Malacca are three feet deep, which can in special cases, as for example when very big fish are being cultivated, be increased to four feet. There has never been any lack of oxygen in the water so long as the vegetation was cleared out. A dam put up chiefly for water-storage purposes must necessarily be a makeshift so far as fish-production goes. The control of emergent and floating vegetation, however, is important, not only as tending to a great increase in fish productivity, but also as diminishing or stopping the breeding of mosquitoes. Weed-cover diminishes the rate of evaporation, which is important where a dam is chiefly for water-storage; but the moral of G. R. Fish's work is that a trial of the oxygen conditions in a pond before undertaking stocking with fish will save not only time and money, but avoid disappointment and discouragement.

Chapter Four

GENERAL PRINCIPLES, PHYSICAL AND CHEMICAL, CONTINUED

PHOTOSYNTHESIS

THUS far, the effects of sunlight have been followed in lakes only with regard to its heating effect; but sunlight is also the source of energy by which green plants can reduce carbon dioxide to sugars and starches with the release of oxygen. This is one of the fundamental activities of green plants and the starting-point in the synthesis of all living matter. It has long been familiar in land plants, but it is no less active in water. In small and shallow lakes, vegetation, belonging both to the algae and to the higher plants, is the chief agent in this process. The chlorophyll, the green pigment which is able to intercept and absorb the energy of sunlight, is similar to that of land plants. In larger and deeper lakes the chlorophyll may be masked or modified in various ways to take the fullest advantage of the weaker, more diffuse and selectively coloured light, for the green and yellow part of the light penetrates deepest.

Even so, plants are inefficient converters of solar energy. Clarke[25] shows that the efficiency with which aquatic algae manufacture carbohydrate is only a small fraction of 1 per cent of the optimum. At the least it is only 0·04 per cent; at the most only 0·38 per cent. Kalle[34] estimated that for the North Sea it was also of the order of 0·04 per cent. Not all this production would be found in the tissues of the plant, because a part of it would be consumed by the plant in respiration and in other life-processes. Clarke says "it appears that most of the light incident on the surface of a lake or oceanic areas is absorbed by the water itself or by detritus, and that only a very small part can be utilised by plants or animals. We conclude that aquatic organisms are existing under very unfavourable circumstances in regard to the utilisation of solar energy."

Transparency is obviously of the greatest importance, and here there are very great variations. Blanc, Daget, and d'Aubenton[9] found that in the Middle Niger, penetration of light, as judged by the visibility of a white disc, might be as little as 3 cm. In Lake Tanganyika over most of the year transparency is very great, and may reach or exceed 22 metres (van Meel). Holden and Green[15] found that the River Sokoto varied in transparency, but was generally less so than an associated pool. The water was clearest after the cessation of the rains, when no further silt was being carried down the river. They found that a factor affecting transparency was the concentration of the zooplankton. Turbidity is the principal cause of the lack of transparency and it is chiefly due, in rivers, to suspended silt, plant-detritus, or to living plankton. In lakes it is almost wholly due to plankton. Another cause of loss of transparency may be colouring matter in the water. Swamp waters, which are more or less strongly brown, are not very transparent even when they have not much suspended matter in them.

As green plants cannot carry out the photosynthesis of new organic matter except in daylight, a lake or pond can be divided into a lighted or photic zone, and a dark or aphotic zone. In the former, material is formed by photosynthesis; in the latter, material is broken down by respiration. Somewhere between the two is the region of the "compensation point", where the strength of the light has been so reduced that photosynthesis just balances respiration and there is no net gain or loss of material. Clearly, the depth of the photic zone must vary with the hours of daylight and with the transparency of the water, and so we may have the paradox that the net amount of material produced by photosynthesis may be as great where the plankton is sparse, and therefore where the light-penetration is great, as where the plankton is so dense that the photic layer is thin. Some typical members of the phytoplankton are shown in Colour Plate IV.

Moreover, there is an element of antagonism in shallower lakes, pools and ponds, between the free-living plankton and the rooted or fixed water vegetation. Where fixed or rooted plants have the upper hand in the photic zone, they may so consume the available nutrients that plankton cannot develop. This was found to be the case in the Malacca fishponds. Most of the ponds responded to fertiliser by growing rich plankton which, by shading out the light, effectively prevented the growth of the bottom-living vegetation. But in some of the ponds the response to fertiliser treatment was a great stimulation of the bottom-living algae and plants, and there was little development of plankton, the water remaining clear. It was not possible to determine any factor which favoured the rooted vegetation rather than the plankton; it appeared to be a matter of chance which would be the first to go ahead. Yet once the plankton or the bottom vegetation got a start, this was maintained and the pond remained turbid with plankton or clear with a dense carpet of bottom-plants, in this case especially the algae *Chara flexilis*, or the Composite aquatic *Enhydrias angustipetala*. The difference which this made to the growth of the fish appeared to be considerable, for although the *Chara* and the *Enhydrias* were well covered with epiphytic diatoms and other algae on which the fish could, in the clear water, be seen browsing, they were at an obvious disadvantage as compared with fish in neighbouring ponds in which plankton was dominant.

Smith and Swingle[36] claim to be able to overcome the growth of the bottom-vegetation by the selective use of fertiliser. By scattering the fertiliser in the ponds during the winter or in early spring, the growth of filamentous algae was stimulated and these smothered the rooted vegetation. Malacca knows no winter. The fertiliser was applied in baskets at the surface in an attempt to favour the growth of the plankton. The result was, in most cases, the growth of a rich plankton, but in a very few of the ponds, a rich growth of bottom-living plants and virtually no plankton developed. In a few of these cases, there followed a growth of filamentous algae which smothered the bottom-living plants. The same pond which, in one fertiliser run, grew bottom-plants, in the next run might give a dense plankton. It is still one of the unpredictables and as the same thing happens in nature, the type of plant response to the available nutrients must affect the production of fish.

WATER-BLOOMS

The phenomenon known as "water-bloom" is the sudden development of algae or flagellates in so dense a mass that the photic zone is restricted to the upper few inches of the water. Very often the phenomenon is associated with almost complete deoxygenation of the water beneath the bloom probably due to the shading effect of the dense plankton. Often, too, the organisms concerned, usually blue-green unicellular algae or flagellates, secrete toxic or noxious substances into the water. For example, the flagellate, *Prymnesium parvum*, may secrete a powerful fish toxin, which on occasion has killed off a large proportion of the carp in the fishponds of Israel. It was found possible to control this flagellate by the application of ammonium sulphate.[37] But quite apart from toxic effects, the result of a dense water-bloom is to deoxygenise the water to the extent that fish may be suffocated. The effect may survive the bloom itself, for when it dies down, the rotting mass may again use up all the oxygen and cause the death of fish. This is one of the dangers in the management of fishponds in hot climates. Blooms are also a nuisance in drinking-water undertakings, for they may give an earthy taste and smell to the water.

COLOUR OF THE WATER

According to Ruttner,[1] the colour of a lake may give some guidance to its productivity: "Inland waters are the bluer, the smaller the amount of free-floating organisms they contain. On the other hand, waters with a high plankton content are always from yellow-green to yellow in colour. Observations of the colour of the water thus offer a certain criterion for estimating its productivity, provided that the influence of humic material (which would give a yellow or brown colour due to pigments) can be excluded."

On this basis Lakes Tanganyika and Nyasa, which are usually blue except in the shallow bays and bights, are not very productive. The shallow coastal waters of Lake Victoria are green, though the deeper water may be blue. The very productive Lakes Edward, Albert and George are green; Lake Rukwa is a grey-green. But it will be noticed that the deeper lakes tend to be blue, while the smaller and shallower ones tend to be green; these latter are the ones in which there can be complete circulation and even complete turn-overs. Lake Tanganyika and Nyasa can be very marine in aspect, with whitecaps rolling in over deep blue water.

In the photic zone, then, the phytoplankton and the bottom vegetation reduce carbon dioxide to sugars and starches, and set free oxygen. But this is only the first stage in the building up of new living matter. The reduction of carbon dioxide is carried out by trapping and using the energy of sunlight, and much of this energy is stored up as potential energy in the sugars and starches. It can be released again by oxidation through the agency of enzymes; and a part of this energy is used to reduce inorganic compounds such as nitrates, phosphates and sulphates, and to build up the reduction products into the very complex mixture of colloidal proteins which constitutes living matter. In this way living plants affect not only the gaseous content but also the content of dissolved minerals. Not all dissolved minerals are affected, for sodium and chlorine are not required directly by plants and their composition in the solution is not affected. Carbonates, which are so abundant in Lakes Albert and George, are important indirectly, in that they form reserves of available carbon dioxide which ensure that a lack of carbon dioxide shall not be a factor limiting photosynthesis. But plants cannot grow without nitrates (and in some cases, nitrites and ammonium compounds), phosphates, sulphates, iron, magnesium, potash and calcium. In addition to these major requirements there are a number of trace elements, whose function is mostly unknown but which plants, or at least some plants, need for their full growth. These include manganese, zinc, iodine, molybdenum, copper, boron, and others.

Plants have the ability to concentrate these substances in their tissues from the minutest traces in the water. Sea-weeds, for example, accumulate enough iodine from the sea, in which it is only detectable at all by the most refined analytical methods, for the dried and burnt kelp to have been the main source of the iodine of commerce until comparatively recent times. Plants can use phosphate even in concentrations as low as one-thousandth of a milligram per litre.

LAKE INFLOWS

It has been explained how the chemical composition of the water of the rivers and of lakes will be influenced by their inflows to the extent that these bring in the major part of the water present at any time. In some very large lakes, such as Tanganyika, Nyasa and Victoria, there are no large rivers entering the lakes. Beauchamp[26] states that the annual inflow into Lake Tanganyika from rivers is only about one two-thousandth of the lake's volume, and in Lake Nyasa only one six-hundredth. In Lake Victoria the inflows from rivers are negligible, this lake being replenished by rainfall. Though rain can contain substantial quantities of nitrogen and other material, in Lake Victoria rain makes only a negligible contribution to the salts present in it. In smaller lakes inflows from rivers and land-drainage may be the chief source of dissolved salts. Braun shows that in the case of the Amazon basin the chemical composition of the water was affected by the inflows, and Ruttner found the same in smaller lakes of the Indonesian islands. The river flows themselves may vary in salt content, as has been shown for the Niger, the Amazon, the rivers of Indonesia and the Congo.

When a lake is replenished to an important degree by inflows, these may not benefit the lake. For example, Lake Kivu has a considerable inflow of warm and very highly mineralised water, but it never mixes with the upper, lighted, region of the lake, and so the contained salts cannot be used by green plants. Reference will be made (page 181) to Beauchamp's useful suggestion as to how the inflows of rivers might be warmed up, so that they might stream out over the lake surface, where plants could use the nutrient salts. But an inflowing river unless modified by treatment tends to be cooler than the surface waters of the lake it enters, so that the water sinks to the level of the thermocline and spreads about the lake at that level. No doubt it thereby causes or adds to turbulence in that layer, and so to the mixing of the water above and immediately below the thermocline. Provided there is enough penetration of light to the region of the thermocline so as to allow photosynthesis, some, at least, of the useful salts can be taken up and so add to the productivity of the lake.

Apart from the salts brought into the lake by the inflows and by surface drainage, important amounts of material are blown in by wind, especially in regions with an arid season. Most of the salts present form parts of a closed cycle in which they may become incorporated in the living tissue of a plant or animal, then be deposited in the bottom-deposits by the death of the organism and then be again released by the decay of the organism in the bottom-deposits. In the last case, they will be available to rejoin the cycle of life only when they are brought to the lighted layers of the surface waters by convection or overturn. In the case of the deep lakes there is a continuous loss of material from circulation because the deep water of these lakes knows no complete overturn and no circulation, or only a very slow one.

ORGANIC MATTER

In addition to the inorganic salts, natural waters, even those free from pollution, may have large quantities of dissolved organic matter. The nature of this organic matter is little known; it may be either incompletely broken down organic material or organic by-products of living creatures. Such substances may play a very important part in nature; they may be, or may contain, substances without which there cannot be a complete development of cultures of diatoms, or they may have slightly antiseptic or even toxic properties with an inhibiting effect on the growth of phytoplankton. They contain carbon, hydrogen and oxygen as well as nitrogen and phosphorus, and because they contain carbon they have potential chemical energy. Though they appear to be resistant chemically, they probably support the growth of bacteria and saprophytic flagellates which can get energy by breaking down the carbon constituent and so may bring this organic material back into circulation.

In the photic zone the growth of plants may use up the inorganic salts and this may at times put a check on production. Below the photic zone there may be ample supplies of these materials, not only those brought newly into the lake but those released by the decay of dead organisms. But the thermocline, where there is an abrupt change of density of the water, acts as a barrier to the diffusion of nutrient-rich water which could replace that used up in the photic zone.

DECAY AND REGENERATION

At the high temperatures of tropical lakes life is lived at a fast rate. Short-lived organisms, such as the constituents of the phyto- and zooplankton, grow, reproduce and die. Then their remains sink towards the bottom. Their rate of sinking depends on their size, shape and specific gravity. Most planktonic organisms have devices either to keep them from sinking or at least to cause them to sink very slowly. They may secrete oil globules, or they may have spines or other outgrowths for giving them a large area in relation to volume. Finally, a minute size is itself a cause of slow sinking, since it is well known that the smaller the body, the larger the ratio of surface to volume. Welch[13] gives a table which shows that a body 1/10 mm. in diameter will sink at a rate of one foot in 38 seconds, where, under the same conditions, one of 1/1000 mm. in diameter will take 55 hours to sink one foot. Moreover, the rate of sinking may be delayed by turbulence in the water.

At high tropical temperatures, decay and breakdown of a dead organism must begin at once, and the slow rate of sinking, which may well become even slower as disintegration sets in, can mean that in a lake of even moderate depth dead organisms will have been broken down and their constituents returned to circulation in the water before they have time to reach the bottom. In this process of decay, which is partly due to bacteria and partly to autolysis, oxygen is used up and carbon dioxide released. The nitrogen is set free as ammonia, which may later be oxidised to nitrite and nitrate and the phosphorus is finally released as phosphate.

In confirmation of this, Hummel[38] found that the bottom sediments of the Indonesian lakes investigated by Ruttner lacked the strong accumulation of combustible matter which could have been expected. Evidently, the greater part of the organic matter present in the dead plankton had been broken down before sedimentation, under the influence of the high water temperatures.

Bacteria play a most important part in these processes. It is a pity in many ways, that the importance of bacteria in disease, in public health and in industry has led to so great an effort and emphasis on such bacteria to the neglect of those which may play no part in disease nor in technology, but which are of the greatest importance in the disposal of dead organic matter, especially in fresh waters. Heinrici[39] says, "one cannot imagine any sort of lake environment that would not provide a habitat for some sort of bacteria". He distinguishes chemosynthetic species, which obtain their energy by oxidising hydrogen, sulphur, iron, ammonia and carbon monoxide, from the photosynthetic species, which are chiefly the red and green sulphur bacteria, which use their pigments to trap the energy of sunlight, and with this energy transform carbon dioxide and sulphuretted hydrogen into organic matter. Such bacteria must live where there is oxygen and light. Then there are the anaerobic bacteria, which must obtain their energy and their oxygen from the breakdown of organic matter, since they can live, and often must live, where there is no oxygen. These are the bacteria which break down the substance of dead plants and animals, reducing the nitrogen compounds to amino-acid and thence to ammonia, and the phosphorus compounds, through a number of complex substances, to phosphate. Anaerobic bacteria reduce sulphate to sulphide and so obtain oxygen. Another interesting reaction made possible by bacteria is the reduction of organic matter, which contains some oxygen, to methane, or marsh-gas.

NOXIOUS GASES

Sulphuretted hydrogen is poisonous, so the bacteria which produce or reduce it must be tolerant of high concentrations, and so must many other anaerobic bacteria. Otherwise the presence, together with sulphuretted hydrogen, of reduction products such as ammonia, could not be accounted for. As these processes take place only in the absence of oxygen it is a nice point whether, where there is death of fish associated with sulphuretted hydrogen (as in pollution), such death is caused by the poisonous gas or by the absence of oxygen which made possible the evolution of the sulphuretted hydrogen.

Methane gas may form in very large quantities where there is a lot of organic material and no oxygen. In the anaerobic breakdown of sewage sufficient methane is formed to provide a supplement to town gas for domestic and industrial use. The Munich sewerage works, for example, derives a useful income from the sale of methane to the municipal gasworks. Debenham[40] describes how, in the Bangweulu Swamps, his launch, passing along the channels, caused the release of so much methane that when it was ignited by an incautious match flames three feet high followed the launch along the channel. It may well be that the dissolved or colloidal organic matter, which may be present in greater quantity than the organic matter embodied in living creatures, is in some degree a by-product of this reduction by bacteria of organic matter to methane. Lake Kivu is estimated to contain, in its deeper water, 50 milliard cubic metres of methane.[41]

STORED-UP NUTRIENT SALTS

Ruttner has pointed out the very large quantities of reduced breakdown products, especially ammonia and phosphate, which accumulate in this way in the bottom layers of lakes in the absence of a turnover. He quotes the case of a small lake in Indonesia, Ranau Lamongan, which is only 750 metres in diameter and 28 metres in depth. Nevertheless, the hypolimnion of this lake was estimated to contain 1433 kg. of phosphorus and 12,171 kg. of ammonia. Such figures become gigantic for larger lakes. Ruttner again estimates that Danau Manindjau, another lake in Indonesia with an area of 98 square kilometres, and a depth of 170 metres, contained in its hypolimnion about 1500 metric tons of phosphorus and 7000 tons of ammonium nitrogen. He suggests that these nutrient-rich deeper waters, especially in impoundment dams, should be used for irrigation, for example of ricefields. He rightly says that no great modification would be needed to draw off water from the bottom rather than from the surface, as is more usual. No one appears to have attempted to work out the weights of nutrients locked up in the deeper waters of the great African lakes, but it must surely be a quantity equal to many years' imports of fertilisers. Will some future year see these great and renewable stores of nutrients pumped to irrigation schemes or fishponds? Ruttner anticipates the difficulty which might be caused by the presence of the sulphuretted hydrogen, by pointing out that unless the irrigation channel were very short, this harmful gas would be lost by evaporation.

Capart and Kufferath[41] have made the bold suggestion that the fish production of Lake Kivu could be raised from its present estimated potential of some 800 metric tons per annum to some 35,000 metric tons, if the deep nutrient-rich water were to be pumped up and spread out over the surface of the lake in the photic zone. The prodigious outburst of plankton which could be expected to result from this would support a fish fauna capable, in their view, of providing the great annual crop estimated above. There is, however, the proviso, that there should be introduced into the lake one or more species of fish able to make full use of the plankton.

However, it is clear that even small lakes and dams, if they are of such a nature that stratification takes place, may have in their lower layers valuable quantities of nutrients, and Ruttner's suggestion remains a challenge to the agriculturalist.

LIMITING FACTORS

Not only do growing plants need certain quantities of nutrients such as nitrates, phosphates and sulphates, as well as other materials, but if any one of these is present in insufficient quantity, it will limit growth even if the remainder are present to excess. There is ample evidence that phosphate is frequently a limiting factor, and to a lesser extent, potash. At Malacca, the response of the nutrient-poor water to the administration of phosphate was very striking. The case for potash has not yet been proved there, but German work in Bavaria suggests that potash may limit production at times.

In many East African waters, sulphur may be a limiting factor.

"Sulphur, nitrogen, and phosphorus are not present in Lake Victoria water in sufficient quantities to permit more than a slight growth of test algae. Among these elements, lack of sulphur is in certain samples the first to halt growth. In those cultures with no added sulphate, typical signs of deficiency appear; lack of chlorophyll and very poor growth. The sulphate content of the lake is low, approximately 0·5 to 1·8 parts per million, but it is not generally appreciated that a volume of approximately 0·5 parts per million could be limiting."[23] Holden and Green[15] had reason to believe that in the Niger also, sulphur may be a limiting factor.

In the sulphur cycle water-snails may play a curiously important and unexpected function. Fish[42] has shown that they harbour in their gut bacteria which assist in the breakdown of plant material and that the snails themselves may secrete sulphuric acid. A large population of snails must thus help to keep this limiting factor, sulphur, in circulation and so increase the productivity of a lake. Because some kinds of snails are the intermediate hosts of troublesome or dangerous parasites of human beings and livestock, there are snail-eradication campaigns under way. Who knows but that the eradication of the snails may adversely affect the productivity of the waters where the eradication is taking place? This seems to be yet another case where one evil must be balanced against another in the interests of human welfare.

Chapter Five

GENERAL PRINCIPLES, PHYSICAL AND CHEMICAL, CONCLUDED

LAKE MUDS

ALTHOUGH in the deeper lakes there may be a more or less complete disintegration of organic debris derived from the plankton during its slow descent through the water, in shallow lakes this cannot take place and there must therefore be a strong accumulation of organic matter in the mud. The East African Fisheries Research Organisation has made a considerable study of these muds and a thesis has been elaborated there, which, after the Director might well be called "Beauchamp's Hypothesis".

"BEAUCHAMP'S HYPOTHESIS"

This hypothesis is that animal matter decays quickly, whereas plant matter, or at all events the higher vegetation, decays slowly. At the same time a lake which has few inflows in relation to its volume is a closed system in which the rate of production will depend on the speed with which nutrient materials are brought back, by decay, into the nutrient cycle. Therefore if one could imagine a lake in which there are only higher plants and no animals, such a lake would have only a low productivity, for nutrient materials locked in the bottom deposits would be released slowly. If herbivorous animals are present the cycle is much faster and so the productivity is greater. This is because the waste products of the herbivorous animals are readily used by plants again after their passage through the gut of the herbivores and partial decomposition. The excretions of the herbivorous animals, such as the urine and bile, are also quickly rendered available for re-use by plants. Finally, when the animals die, their bodies are quickly decomposed. Therefore the greater the animal population, whether crocodiles, hippopotamus, fish, birds, snails or zooplankton, the more rapid

ETIF

the turnover of material, and the more productive the lake. On this reckoning the removal of any plant-eating animal is a matter for caution; and the removal, by a fishery, of plant-eating or phytoplankton-eating fish, may be a strong factor in reducing still further the productivity of the lake. There seems little doubt that this is a valid hypothesis. One remedy is the introduction of a plant-eating fish. In Lake Victoria, the *Tilapia zillii*, which is a prolific breeder and which will eat very large quantities of the softer aquatic vegetation, has been introduced. In the course of time, when this introduced fish becomes one of the principal inhabitants of Lake Victoria, its plant-eating characteristic should have a great effect in bringing back quickly into circulation the nutrients locked up in the tissues of water-plants. It will then be considered a fortunate thing that so much study was carried out on the lake before this introduction, for conditions are likely to be considerably changed thereafter.

LAKE VICTORIA MUDS

The muds at the bottom of Lake Victoria contain a great deal of very slowly decaying organic matter. It is derived partly from precipitated plankton and partly from the detritus of higher plants and faecal remains from all the higher animals in the lake. Analyses have shown that these deposits constitute a vast store of valuable organic matter. The dried mud has been shown to be edible, and has been proved to be a useful supplement to the food of cattle, pigs and chickens.

Samples of this bottom mud are almost odourless, and contain few bacteria, though living diatoms may be found in it, curiously enough, as far as 5 cm. below the surface. It shows little tendency to decompose under either aerobic or anaerobic conditions. If boiled, however, it subsequently decomposes rapidly, and if dried and returned to the water it produces a solution which supports a dense growth of bacteria and later, of protozoa and algae. A tentative explanation is that some antibiotic substance, possibly associated with freshly precipitated phytoplankton and destroyed by heat, may inhibit the growth of bacteria. Sea-water is known to contain antibiotic substances but little is yet known about their properties.

THE MUD-WATER INTERFACE

The mud-water interface may not be sharply defined but may be rather a dense suspension of organic matter than a definite layer. This can be observed on the trace of an echo-sounder. Mud cores taken from a depth of 10 cm. below the mud-water interface, when added to cultures of diatoms growing in lake waters, caused an acceleration of growth, but mud from 30 cm. below the mud-water interface caused a much more rapid rate of growth than that from 10 cm. Evidently nutrients are released from the mud under certain conditions.

When the chemical exchanges between the bottom deposits of Lake Victoria and the overlying water were studied it was found that when the water contained plenty of oxygen no phosphate could be detected, whereas under anaerobic conditions considerable quantities of phosphates were released from the mud into the water. The phosphate remained in solution even when the water was again oxygenated. A very low oxygen content of the water also accelerated the appearance of ammonia and it was found that it reached a high value when small quantities of penicillin were added. There was, however, no production of nitrite or nitrate in the presence of penicillin, which indicates that penicillin-sensitive bacteria are responsible for the oxidation of ammonia to nitrite and nitrate. This was confirmed by the presence of nitrite and nitrate in controls without penicillin.

It seems that in spite of the inhibiting effect of some possibly antibiotic substance, the rich bottom muds of Lake Victoria will yield up their nutrients under certain conditions. For example, lake mud, when spread over the land, acts as an effective fertiliser, supplying significant amounts of nitrogen, phosphorus, and sulphur. It has long been known in the Far East that bottom muds, for example from fishponds, are a valuable fertiliser, and in the smallholdings of which fishponds are a part the mud from the ponds, scraped out periodically, is spread over the market garden. Moreover, when such muds are dried and exposed to the wind and sun mineralisation of the organic matter takes place so that on refilling the pond there is a notable increase in fertility. In fact, deliberate exposure of the pond bottom to the atmosphere is standard practice where the pond is drainable. Where it is not, then the mud may be scraped out periodically.

This same factor applies naturally where a pond or lake partially dries out in the dry season. When the lake refills and covers these shallow parts there is a rich growth of soft plants which are good food for fish, either directly or indirectly.

Mortimer[43] demonstrated the release and adsorption of nutrients in lake mud and described the conditions under which it takes place. It is the result of a see-saw of oxidising and reducing conditions; when oxidising conditions prevail the ions become adsorbed on the fine floc of colloids in the mud and they are released when reducing conditions prevail. On release those ions of nutrient value are utilised by plants as soon as they are carried up to the photic zone.

This was confirmed in Lake Victoria by the East African Fisheries Research Organisation. An undisturbed sample from the lake bottom at a depth of 20 metres in the Buvuma Channel, where the water was deoxygenated, was compared with one from a depth of 10 metres in the Napoleon Gulf, where the water is always oxygenated. Measurements showed that the mud from deoxygenated water had a higher redox potential than that from oxygenated water, and this is consistent with the release of reducing substances. Earlier experiments had shown that whereas no phosphate can be detected in water overlying mud where plenty of oxygen was present, under anaerobic conditions or very low oxygen tensions, both phosphate and ammonia can be detected in the water in notable quantities.

Fish[31] showed how this phenomenon may lead to the release of nutrient materials from the bottom mud to the overlying water and thence to the surface layers where, in the presence of light, they can be used by green plants. Usually certain inshore stations in shallow water on Lake Victoria have their water fully mixed, with abundant oxygen in the bottom layers and a temperature about equal from surface to bottom. The mud may be as cool or cooler than the water overlying it. But at intervals a seiche movement, already mentioned earlier in Chapter Three may bring about a sub-surface surge of cool water into these shallows where at once a thermal stratification may be set up with a temporary thermocline. Owing to the presence of reducing substances in the mud, and in the absence of mixing throughout the water-column due to the thermocline, this lower, cooler layer quickly becomes deoxygenated. Under conditions of low or no oxygen the implication is that nutrients are released from the mud. Since the mud may then be warmer than the overlying cooler water, convection currents are set up which distribute the nutrients throughout the hypolimnion. When stratification breaks down again and the water becomes mixed, there follows a dense growth of phytoplankton. Both the temporary deoxygenation and the growth of the plankton have important effects on the fish. The former may drive the fish away to levels or to areas where there is still oxygen, while the latter increases their food supply.

The penetration of oxygen, where present, into the mud is facilitated by the burrowing activities of the larvae of the Chironomids, the midges or "Lake Flies". These may occur in hundreds or even thousands per square metre, and they may perform a similar function on the lake floor to that of earthworms on the land. These midge larvae eat their way through the mud, digesting the organic matter and contributing to its breakdown. Their burrows, which may penetrate more than 12 inches deep, cause the deeper layers of mud to respond more rapidly to the presence or absence of oxygen than can diffusion alone.

SUMMARY

To sum up the first five chapters of this book: an attempt has been made to show the physical and chemical background to tropical inland fisheries. Water has been followed from its beginning as rain or springs, to streams, to rivers, swamps and finally lakes. The changes in the dissolved gases caused by the activities of plants and animals have been mentioned, and it has been shown that deoxygenation is not rare as a natural phenomenon, especially in standing water, and that this may render large parts of lakes unsuitable for fish life, and in swamps may only permit the life of fish which have an adaptation to breathe atmospheric air.

These chapters have also shown how the streams dissolve salts, their nature and quantity depending on the geology of their basins. Some of these salts are of no direct interest to life processes, while others are necessary or vital. Carried into lakes, these salts support plant life on which the animals, including the fish, depend. Within the lakes these salts may undergo a continuous cycle of incorporation into the tissues of living plants, release by the death of the plant or its consumption by animals, and decay or digestion of the plant or animal by bacterial action or by autolysis. Since dead organisms tend to sink, the released salts tend to accumulate in the hypolimnion and in the mud of shallow lakes. The vitally important phenomenon of the overturn, in which these salts are once more brought within reach of green plants and in which oxygen is carried down into the depths, has been described, and attention has been drawn to the large and deep lakes in which no overturn has yet been known and which remain permanent cellars well stocked with nutrient materials which plants cannot use and where fish cannot live.

Chapter Six

BIOLOGICAL FACTORS: THE FOOD–SUPPLY

EXTERNAL FOOD SUPPLIES

A N important part of the food of fish may not be derived from the water at all, but from the land. This is especially the case in the flood fisheries. When the rivers rise in flood and overspread the valleys or flood-plains, the fish have access to a vast store of food of all kinds, so that a river fishery may be very productive although the river itself may have only a poor supply of fish food. Vaas[44] for example, shows that the lakes in West Borneo on the Kapuas River have a very poor production of plankton and rooted vegetation. The water is dark-coloured, acid and has a low content of lime and other minerals; all these spell a very poor productivity. Yet the area produces a great quantity of fish. This is because these lakes have a great seasonal change of level. They may rise in the wet season by as much as 10 metres or more, and inundate big areas of forest, and of land overgrown with a dense vegetation of quickly growing flowering grasses. The decay and mineralisation of this vegetation after inundation creates an enormous mass of fish food. Not only this, but the grasses themselves, and their seeds, are eaten. In the forest, the fallen fruits and leaves are food for certain species of fish, and in the flood, the leaves of trees and shrubs may be eaten off the trees. In the list Vaas gives of the fishes of the area, he names no fewer than thirteen species of fish which are periphyton or vegetable feeders, including submerged higher vegetation, plants and seeds. They include four species each of the valuable *Osteochilus*, *Puntius* and Gourami. *Puntius javanicus* was grown in the ponds at Malacca, and it was found that while they could not tackle tough or fibrous vegetation, they could eat soft grass, and even tougher grasses once these had been softened by decay. The grass carp *Ctenopharyngodon idellus* will clip the grass growing on the margins of their ponds as neatly as a pair of shears, and this fish is regularly fed on cut grass thrown into the ponds. The author has published an account of the growth of two cultures of this fish at Malacca,[45] and showed that some 150 fish of about 8 lb. weight consumed 19,000 lb. of Napier grass in two months, increasing by some 400 lb. in weight, giving a crude conversion ratio of 48 lb. of Napier grass to 1 lb. of fish weight gained. The giant Gourami, *Osphronemus olfax*, is also known to eat great quantities of soft-leaved vegetation.

Three or four species of fish in the Amazon and the Essequibo rivers are known to feed on seeds of land plants which fall into the water. Blanc, Daget and d'Aubenton[9] show how the fisheries of the delta of the Middle Niger are rich in spite of the unfertile nature of the water, because the fish find a very great feeding area in the flood plain when the river is high. They feed on insects and seeds, and at least one species, *Tilapia zillii*, is able to feed directly on vegetation. Even in rivers and lakes, land insects, such as swarming termites, are known to be important sources of food for fish, and cases are recorded where fish have been found feeding heavily on such land insects blown into the water. The 1958 report of the East African Fisheries Research Organisation[137] states that terrestrial insects form a significant part of the food of the fish *Schilbe mystus*, both in Lake Victoria and in two of the rivers flowing into it. However, this source of food from the land is to a great extent balanced by loss to the land, in the form of the adults of insects which have spent their larval life in the water at the expense of material produced there.

Blache[46] states that the Grand Lac of Cambodia floods annually to such an extent that it increases from a dry-season area of 3000 square kilometres to one of 10,000 square kilometres at high water, and in depth from 70 cm. to 11·5 metres. Much forest land is included in the area flooded, and several species of fish feed on leaf debris in the forest. Another rich source of food is the rotting tree trunks and branches, which harbour abundant insects and insect larvae. Three species of fish feed on wild rice and rice grains.

These may serve as examples of food sources unconnected with the aquatic régime, and external to it. The importance of this source of food must not be overlooked, especially when it is recalled that the greatest freshwater fisheries of the world, some of which indeed may fairly rival some of the great sea-fisheries, are the direct result of the feeding of river fishes in the flooded plains.

FEEDERS ON BACTERIA

Next we can consider the cases where the fish feed, directly or in-directly, on detritus or broken-down organic matter. Bacteria are chiefly concerned in this process of breaking-down, and it is not always certain whether the bacteria themselves do not contribute most of the nutriment in the material. Heinrici[39] holds that the bacteria are nutritious. The *Tilapia nilotica* of Lake Kivu may feed directly on bacteria free-living in the lake, notably on a large plank-tonic species of *Spirillum*. As this is not an autotrophic bacterium, it probably feeds at the expense of dissolved organic matter. In Lake Tanganyika, van Meel[32] concluded that the *Dagaa*, small anchovy-like fish, very valuable commercially, fed to some extent on bacteria. As bacteria are difficult to recognise in stomach contents, since they may be rapidly digested, it may well be that they are more important as food for fish than has been suspected. Heinrici considers that in lakes bacteria are relatively unimportant as producers of food com-pared with the higher phytoplankton; on the other hand, they are able to multiply so rapidly that they can more quickly replace the numbers thinned out by feeding organisms than the larger phyto-plankton. Their potential as food organisms may therefore be greater than is suggested by their actual abundance at any time.

Tilapia nilotica grows to a large size, and the mechanism by which it is able to capture such minute organisms as bacteria for food is of great interest. This has recently been revealed by Gosse.[47] He shows that, in addition to the well-known gill-rakers, which in this fish are too coarse to act as filters except for very large particles, each gill-arch, except the first, carries on its anterior face a band which, under high magnification, is seen to consist of very fine processes which Gosse has named "microbranchiospines". These in turn carry very fine spines, 36-40 microns in length, and the space between the spines of two adjacent microbranchiospines is only 16 microns, or 16/1000 mm., and between the spines on the same microbranchiospine, 10 microns. When this band of microbranchiospines, the filtering band, is applied against the posterior side of the gill-arch in front, it forms a sieve with meshes of only 1/100 mm. or even less. If a part of the water taken into the gill-cavity for respiration is strained through this sieve, very fine particles, even so small as large bacteria, will be retained. Gosse's discovery raises a number of problems. For example, filtration through so fine a sieve can only be slow; yet the fish must have a good flow of water over the gills in order to breathe. The gills, and the gill-chamber, must have a more complex action than has been suspected. Light has been thrown on this by some experiments reported by Hughes and Shelton.[48]

Using trout for the experiments, but confirming their general conclusions from experiments on the roach and tench, they measured the pressure changes in the buccal and opercular cavities during breathing, in relation to the movements of the mouth and opercular valves.

Since the microbranchiospines can only function when the gill-arches are pressed together, straining of food would take place, not during Hughes and Shelton's phase 3, when "water is forced through the gills by a buccal pump", but during phase 1 when water "is drawn through by the action of an opercular suction pump". But it seems that a strong flow of water would then be taking place, perhaps too strong for the effective action of the minute micro-branchiospines. However, Hughes and Shelton write that they "have invariably observed a brief period (phase 4) during which the opercular pressure is positive with respect to the pressure in the buccal cavity. This will tend to cause a reversal in the direction of the flow of water across the gills". It seems possible that the micro-branchiospines may have a chance to filter effectively during the first stages of this brief reversal when the water current is slow, and before the gill-arches have yet separated. Gosse found a similar fine filtering band on the gill-arches of *Citharinus*, so-called "moon-fish" of Lake Albert and other waters of Africa.

DETRITUS FEEDERS

In Lake George, *Tilapia nilotica* and *T. leucosticta* feed upon the soft bottom deposits. These are rich in crude protein; in fact they contain as much protein as in the plankton itself. Analysis of the gut contents of these fish showed that the crude protein in the stomach is reduced by 40 per cent by the time it reaches the rectum, thus proving that the bottom deposits have been utilised as food. But Fish [49] was uncertain whether the food was not mainly in the form of bacteria and protozoa in the decomposing debris, and whether this decomposition makes material previously indigestible available as food. *Catla catla* may also feed on bottom debris as well as on plankton, and has a phenomenal rate of growth. At Malacca, *Catla*

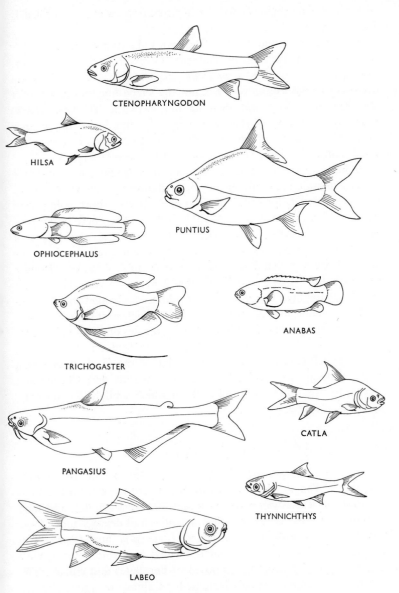

CTENOPHARYNGODON

HILSA

PUNTIUS

OPHIOCEPHALUS

TRICHOGASTER

ANABAS

PANGASIUS

CATLA

THYNNICHTHYS

LABEO

Figure 1. Fishes of the Far East. (Not to scale)

catla reached a weight of 24 lb. in $2\frac{1}{2}$ years, or grew at a rate of nearly 1 lb. per month.

Swynnerton[50] found that the Tilapia of Lake Rukwa, *T. rukwaensis* likewise fed on the bottom deposits. Gosse, referring to the fine filter band on the gills of *Citharinus*, suggested that this fish feeds on detritus in suspension, as it has not the shape nor the mouth of a true bottom feeder. But then neither have the Tilapias. Blache found that 14 out of the 56 species of commercial importance in the Grand Lac of Cambodia were detritus feeders, including the Labeos and Cirrhinas, both members of the carp family.

In the cases given so far, the fish have been feeding, not on newly formed organic material, but on the breakdown products of organic matter previously formed. The food chain is very short, going from debris to fish in one step, or possibly in two steps where bacteria or protozoa are involved. Buschkiel[20] also gives a good example of the feeding of fish in Java on the decomposition products of organic material. He says that faecal matter may be applied in extraordinary quantities in certain fishponds, so that it may lie a metre deep. This matter, at the high temperature prevailing, accelerated the development of an enormous number of bacteria, which start the breakdown of the organic material. Within 24 hours, masses of plant and animal unicellulars appear, of which the protozoa feed on the bacteria. These unicellulars are the starting point of the food chain which leads, through such animals as Tubifex worms and Chironomid larvae, to fish. Here is a food cycle in which sunlight has no part, except as a source of heat.

PLANT FEEDERS

A very interesting food chain was revealed in the Malagarasi Swamps in Tanganyika, by an expedition sent there from the Jinja Laboratory. This swamp covers about 700 square miles, and may contain vast areas covered with water-lilies and dense stands of the aquatic water-weeds *Ceratophyllum*, *Utricularia* and *Chara*. The bottom deposits consisted of finely divided vegetable detritus, with a rich fauna of protozoa, composed of flagellates and ciliates. The overlying water was crystal-clear, with an almost complete absence of phytoplankton or zooplankton. In fact, the water was so clear that the fish, of which there was a dense population, could be observed as in an aquarium.

The explanation of the great productivity of these swamps, in spite of the poverty of plankton, seems to be that two species of fish, *Alestes macrophthalmus* and *Distichodus* sp., were feeding on, and partially digesting, the leaves, buds and seeds of the water-lilies. It seems that the partially digested remains of the water-lilies, after passage through the gut of these two fishes, form a digestible food for the other fishes, including Tilapias. These again may either use it as food, or get nourishment from the associated protozoa and rotifers.

Partially digested plants, whether by bacteria, protozoa or fish, seem a not uncommon food for fishes. The Grass Carp has already been mentioned for its extraordinary ability to ingest great quantities of grass and other vegetation. The faeces of this fish contain the plant material unused by the fish, in a soft and partially broken-down condition. Where other species of fish are stocked in the same pond, as is usually the case, these other fishes may either eat the faecal masses, or live on the plankton which arises from the decay of the faeces. So the grass fed to the Grass Carp plays a multiple role in the pond. This fish may also be used to keep a pond clear of unwanted submerged soft vegetation, and for making the nutrient material available for the plankton. A pond in which there was no plankton but an abundant growth of such submerged plant as *Enhydrias*, *Utricularia* and *Chara*, was stocked with four or five Grass Carp of about 1 lb. weight. The submerged vegetation was soon thinned out, the carp browsing around the sides of each underwater clump, and the water became turbid with plankton. This, by shading out the submerged vegetation, completed the clearance of the pond.

Tilapia zillii will do much the same. A culture of these fish cleared a pond at Malacca of a thick growth of *Enhydrias* in two months. They seem first to eat the leaves, then to sever or uproot the stems, for the final result was the appearance, on the leeward banks of the pond, of a mass of stripped stems. At the same time, the previously clear water became opaque and green with plankton. The closely allied *T. melanopleura* will also eat and clear vegetation in this way. The ability of *T. zillii* to bring back into circulation in the plankton the nutrients locked up in the tissues of water plants has led to the successful introduction of the fish into Lake Victoria, the fertility of which is adversely affected by the absence of organisms able to use vegetable matter. By introducing this plant-eater, the rate of turnover of nutrients in the lake will be speeded up, and that is the equivalent of a greater productivity.

The blue-green algae cannot normally be digested by many fish, including the Tilapias. Yet when these algae begin to die down, they may become digestible by fish. In much the same way, Schuster[51] shows that the Milk-fish, *Chanos chanos*, cannot digest green algae when these are living, but is able to digest them when they begin to decay. Probably decay breaks down some resistant material in the cell-wall, and so exposes the contents to the digestive enzymes of the fish.

FOOD CHAINS

Fish which feed on plants have the shortest possible food chain, and must therefore be the most economical converters into fish flesh of the new material formed in photosynthesis.

Juday[52] estimates that there may be a loss of 90 per cent of the calories in the original newly formed organic material for each successive step in a food chain. Clearly, a fish which feeds directly on green plants will have available far higher quantities of the potential energy originally fixed by the plants in the presence of sunlight, than a fish which feeds on organisms which have in turn fed on plants. Predatory fish, which may feed on fish which have fed on small invertebrates, which have fed on plankton—a food chain with four successive steps—will have a very low net conversion rate of original organic matter into flesh. If we imagine a lake or lagoon which produces a given quantity of plant matter, that body of water will obviously support a much larger weight of herbivorous fish than predatory fish. For herbivorous fish can hypothetically use 10 per cent of the available potential energy, whereas predators can use only 1 per cent if they take their food, say, as insect larvae which have fed on vegetation; or only 0·1 per cent if they feed, say, on small fish which have fed on insects or zooplankton which have in turn fed on plants or phytoplankton. A fishery based on a high proportion of herbivorous fish will therefore be more productive than one based mainly on predators and one of the reasons for the high rate of fish production in tropical waters, even when conditions seem unsuitable, is that there are a large number of plant-eating fish in the tropics.

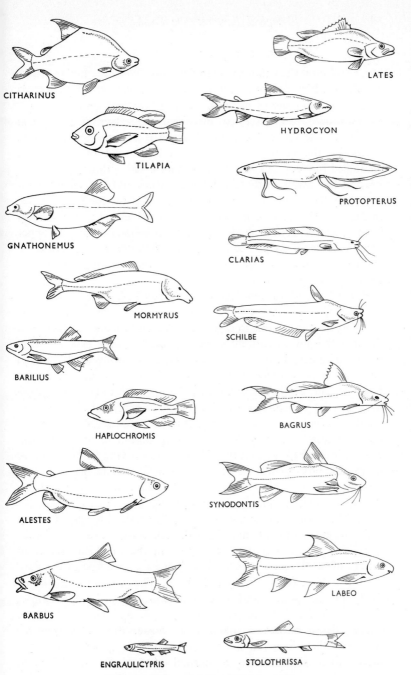

CITHARINUS

LATES

TILAPIA

HYDROCYON

GNATHONEMUS

PROTOPTERUS

MORMYRUS

CLARIAS

BARILIUS

SCHILBE

HAPLOCHROMIS

BAGRUS

ALESTES

SYNODONTIS

BARBUS

LABEO

ENGRAULICYPRIS

STOLOTHRISSA

Figure 2. Fishes of Africa. (Not to scale)

PHYTOPLANKTON FEEDERS

More common than those able to feed directly on the higher plants are those which feed on phytoplankton (Colour Plate IV). As has been said, a number of the Tilapias are phytoplankton feeders, and Greenwood[53] has described the feeding mechanism in *Tilapia esculenta*. The suspended phytoplankton is drawn into the buccal cavity by the normal breathing movement, and there becomes entangled in a copious secretion of mucus. The ordinary gill-rakers prevent the escape of these boluses of mucus and entangled phytoplankton. The collection and concentration of the food takes place in the posterior part of the pharynx, where they become entangled in the anterior teeth of the lower pharyngeal bone. When the upper pharyngeal teeth are moved backwards, the hooked crowns of these teeth pass between the teeth of the lower bone, and rake the mucus towards the oesophagus.

Fish[49] has shown that, although *T. esculenta* and *T. variabilis* in Lake Victoria ingest green and blue-green algae as well as diatoms, they are unable to digest these blue-green algae, which pass through the gut so entirely unharmed that cultures may be made from blue-greens in the faeces. Only where the cell-walls have been damaged may there be any digestion of the cell-contents. But in Lake Rudolf, *T. nilotica* can digest the blue-green algae and grows to a very large size. Diatoms, including epiphytic species growing on the algae, are freely digested. As blue-green algae are among the commonest members of the phytoplankton in many tropical waters, it can happen that the Tilapias are starving in the presence of a dense phytoplankton. Vaas and Hofstede[54] find that the same applies to *Tilapia mossambica* in Indonesia. Schuster[51] found, on the other hand, that, in the brackish water ponds of Indonesia, the Milk-fish, *Chanos chanos*, can easily digest the blue-green algae, while the green algae are not digested. *T. mossambica* eats prodigious quantities of green filamentous algae in the brackish and fresh waters of Java, and has proved its value as an agent in the control of malaria (Hofstede and Botke[55]). The mosquito can breed freely in the ponds and ditches overgrown with these algae, since larvicidal fish cannot reach the eggs and larvae sheltered among dense masses of filamentous algae. But *T. mossambica* will clear these in a few weeks from such waters, and the digested faeces then give rise to a normal phytoplankton. Evidently, this fish can make use of green algae, but not blue-green algae.

Observations were made on the feeding of *T. mossambica* in the fishponds at Malacca, where it was confirmed that the diatoms are easily digested, but the blue-greens not. There was some digestion of green algae, especially *Oedogonium*, if the cell-wall was ruptured. But it was remarkable that Tilapia, whose guts were full of blue-green and green algae, all apparently undigested, were growing well. It seems difficult to believe that the few diatoms present could supply the nutriment necessary for such good growth, unless un-reasonably large quantities of food were to be continually taken. It is possible that there are epiphytic bacteria or protozoa present on the algae which play an important part in the food, and this interesting point is being investigated.

In the Grand Lac of Cambodia the blue-green alga *Microcystis* is produced in enormous quantities as the dominant member of the phytoplankton. The fish *Pangasius sutchii*, which may grow to a length of one metre, feeds exclusively on this and other planktonic algae, and many other fish which comprise this great fishery feed partly or wholly on phytoplankton. Vaas gives the names of five plankton feeders in Borneo, of which *Helostoma temminckii* is the most important.

Besides these adult fish, the young stages of all fish feed on phytoplankton at an early stage, though little seems to be known about their digestion.

EPIPHYTIC ALGAE

Epiphytic algae are food for many fishes. These grow attached to other plants, even very small plants such as diatoms and algae, and on stones or dead twigs and branches. Where fish are found to be feeding on plant material, it may often be that the epiphytic algae and diatoms are the real source of nourishment. Blache[46] again shows how important these are in the Grand Lac: 19 species of fish have these as their principal food. The *Pangasiodon gigas*, which reaches a length of over two metres, and is probably the heaviest known freshwater fish (for the *Arapaima* of the Amazon does not attain so great a weight), has no teeth, and feeds exclusively on algae growing on the bottom of rivers and lakes. *Cirrhinus auratus* and *C. jullieni*, of which 17 tons have been caught in five days in one fish trap, feed on planktonic and benthic algae, and so do *Thynnichthys thynnichthys*, which is so rich in fat that it can be used for

oil extraction, and is so important that it comprises 15-20 per cent
of the whole tonnage of fish caught. *Catlacarpio siamensis*, which
may grow to a length of $2\frac{1}{2}$ metres, feeds on diatoms, the most
important of which is *Melosira*, grazed off sandbanks.

In ricefields, such fish as the small Gourami *Trichogaster pectoralis*,
browse on the encrusting algae and diatoms and on the filamentous
algae growing on and between the rice plants. *Tilapia mossambica*
is very commonly seen browsing on the epiphytic growths on submerged reeds, lying over sideways to do so, so that a shoal of them
look like a handful of small silver coins tossed into the water.
They slowly work their way up, in this sideways position, nibbling
the epiphytes as they go. In tanks, they do the same, leaving little
tracks cleared of the green scum on the sides. Brown and van
Someren[56] deliberately encouraged the growth of epiphytes in their
ponds by planting hurdles; and the author has done the same by
throwing in bundles of bamboo twigs. Van Someren claimed that
his *Tilapia nigra* showed increased growth as a result of this management. There can be no doubt that this is a sensible measure.

Saanin[57] states that filamentous algae, as well as periphytic diatoms, are the food for the fish which are the basis of a fishery which
produces some 17,000 tons of fish annually in Indonesian West
Borneo. In the Grand Lac region of Cambodia, the flooded bush
becomes festooned with algae, especially *Spirogyra*, and the population of floating higher plants such as *Eichhornia*, *Pistia* and *Azolla*,
support a rich flora of epiphytes. The fact that so large a proportion
of the fish feed directly on plants, thus using to the maximum the
new material produced by photosynthesis, must be a main factor
in the vast fish production of these freshwaters. In the sea, and in
the freshwaters of temperate climates, plant-feeding fish are in the
minority; most of the fish have longer food chains, in which, therefore, a far larger proportion of the original energy fixed by photosynthesis is lost in passage through successive stages.

"AUFWUCHS"

The mat of algae and associated organisms which forms on stones
and rocks in running water is named *Aufwuchs* by German
authors. It is another important source of primary food, especially
in streams and fast rivers, and can be very productive. The fast
current ensures plenty of oxygen, carbon dioxide and nutrient salts;

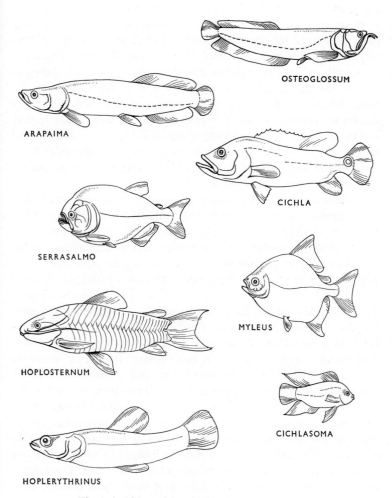

OSTEOGLOSSUM

ARAPAIMA

CICHLA

SERRASALMO

MYLEUS

HOPLOSTERNUM

CICHLASOMA

HOPLERYTHRINUS

Figure 3. Fishes of South America. (Not to scale)

and growth is the faster because the water is shallow, giving access to the maximum light and because the current does not allow the formation of an area round the plants temporarily denuded of nutrients. Marlier[58] describes the *Aufwuchs* in the headwater streams of the Congo, on stones and rocks in rapids and cascades. The basis must obviously be algae with strong holdfasts. A variety of epiphytic plants grows on these and the algal mat shelters a rich fauna, principally of insects. Marlier describes the growth of *Aufwuchs* in the Kawezi, a tributary of the Ruzizi in the Congo. In the rainy season the Kawezi is a fairly large stream, but in the dry season it becomes so much shrunken that in some years it may fail to reach the Ruzizi. As the waters fall the stones are covered with a thick carpet of filamentous algae which become more luxuriant as the water-level falls. No fish feed directly on this, but the *Aufwuchs* is an indirect food for fish.

In these swift streams, certain insects spin nets with which they catch floating debris and especially other insects detached from their supports. Fryer[59] found two species of the larva of flies of the family Hydropsychidae spinning similar nets on the stones on the shores of Lake Nyasa. On the rocky shores of that lake, and especially in the northern parts, the upper surface of the rocks are covered with an *Aufwuchs* similar to that found in rocky turbulent streams. This *Aufwuchs* consists chiefly of two species of the blue-green alga, *Calothrix*, whose filaments are firmly attached to the rocks. With these as a base there forms a thick flocculent layer of algae and diatoms of numerous species. It is significant that Fryer notes the exceptional clearness of the water over and among the rocks. A white disc can be seen to a depth of more than 16 metres below the surface even though at some time of the day, on almost any day of the year, the water among the rocks is in a state of turbulence due to wave action and swell. It is interesting and significant that there is so close an analogy between the conditions in a turbulent, rocky stream and on the turbulent shores of a rocky lake. Fryer gives four factors which favour so dense a growth of algae, namely, great transparency of the water, high light intensity, a high temperature (22-28° C.), and the absence of a winter check. In fact, since the phytoplankton is not well developed in the deeper northern part of Lake Nyasa, the *Aufwuchs*, which occurs in such quantities over such a large part of the lake shores, may well be the chief primary source of fish food.

The *Aufwuchs* on Lake Nyasa harbours a very dense microfauna. There are countless thousands of small Chironomid larvae, Ostracods, and Harpacticoid Copepods. An area of rock, of 510 square centimetres, was carefully scraped clean of the *Aufwuchs*, and the animals contained in the scrapings counted. In this small area, there were 3,500 Chironomid larvae, over 10,000 Ostracods, and over 1,000 Copepods, besides a number of other organisms, such as mites, mayfly, stonefly and caddis larvae.

A large number of fish species in Lake Nyasa, chiefly Cichlids, browse directly on the *Aufwuchs*. Many of them have special adaptations to enable them to scrape or snatch off this material. Some of these fish are large enough to be edible, but most are small. They are, however, of indirect value as food since they are the prey of important predatory fishes.

PREDATORY FISH

There are a great number of fish not adapted to take primary sources of food and although they are much less efficient converters of primary material into fish flesh, since they get this food at second or third hand, they are a most important source of fish production. These are the predators, and they may feed on molluscs, crustacea, and especially insects or other fish.

In Lake Victoria, the lung-fish *Protopterus* feeds on molluscs, the Gastropods being more important than the Pelecypods. Three species of *Haplochromis* also feed on molluscs. In view of the importance of snail-eating fish in the control of the disease bilharzia, there has been an attempt to cultivate these *Haplochromis* species for pond-stocking. *Clarias* and *Synodontis* are also to a limited extent feeders on molluscs, as many as 24 per cent of the stomachs examined in fish from soft bottoms having gastropod remains. In the Far East, one of the Chinese carps, *Mylopharyngodon aethiops*, the Black Carp, is a snail feeder, and is stocked in ponds in small numbers to make use of the snails which may appear.

In Ghana, where bilharzia is a serious problem, it has been found that the Cichlid fish *Hemichromis bimaculatus* is an effective agent for the control of snails and it is being widely stocked for this purpose. In Lake Victoria there is another Cichlid, *Astatereochromis alluaudi*, which has also been found to be a mollusc feeder and is also of interest from the point of view of sanitation.

Unfortunately these are both small fish of little economic value.

Many predatory fish, especially *Barbus* and *Barilius* in Africa, feed on freshwater shrimps. But the crustacea seem to be less important to freshwater fish than to marine fish. In the sea, few fish feed directly on the phytoplankton, which, on the contrary, is conveyed to them indirectly through the medium of invertebrates, and among these the Copepods are especially important. On Lake Tanganyika Copepods are important as food for the *Dagaa*, small freshwater Clupeoids; and on Lake Nyasa the midwater community of small freshwater Cichlid fish called *Utaka*, a mixture of species of *Haplochromis*, feeds to a large extent on Copepods. But these are both deep lakes which not a little resemble the sea in their biological relations.

Vaas and Sachlan[60] found that the Common Carp in the artificial Lake Tjiburuj in West Java were feeding on zooplankton (Colour Plate III), including copepods, and in the ponds at Malacca the Tilapia and other fishes were occasionally found feeding more or less heavily on zooplankton such as Rotifers, Copepods and Ostracods. But it seems that in the freshwaters, the essential role played by the zooplankton in the sea, as purveyors of vegetable material to fish unable to feed on it directly, is largely taken over by insects which occur in great variety and abundance. They may also have an indirect importance, since the work of the Jinja Research Station has shown that even fish which are predominantly vegetable feeders must have some animal food, especially in the young stages.

The 1958 report of the East African Fisheries Research Organisation[137] summing up the first ten years of the work of the Jinja Laboratory on Lake Victoria, states that, from the fishery aspect, insects are without doubt very important. Insect larvae are the main food of certain species of fish throughout their lives and are a very significant element in the diet of young fish belonging to many species that eat entirely different food when adult. Further, even fish which when adult appear to be almost exclusively herbivorous, require animal protein if they are to grow well in the early phases of their life. Possibly the most important insects are the larvae of the Chironomid midges, which occur to the extent of hundreds or even thousands per square metre in muddy bottoms. They are feeders on the decaying vegetable remains, and can live under conditions of very low oxygen concentration.

There is not the space to go further into the importance of the

Chironomids and of insects generally in fisheries. Nor is there the need to describe the predation of one fish on another except to point out the peculiar position in Lake Victoria where there is a complex of species of the Cichlid fish genus *Haplochromis*, which are so abundant in parts of the lake that trawling can produce an average weight of 400 lb. per hour's fishing, with a record catch of half a ton per hour. The commercial utilisation of these small fish is an unsolved problem and the suggestion has been made that the powerful predator *Lates*, the Nile or Niger Perch, a fish which will grow to a weight of several hundred pounds, should be introduced into Lake Victoria to crop the *Haplochromis* down and turn them into more valuable fish flesh. It would be a reintroduction, for this fish inhabited the basin where Lake Victoria now stands in earlier geological times. What makes for hesitation in the reintroduction is whether the introduced Nile Perch would in fact feed on the *Haplochromis* and not on the young of the valuable Tilapia species. The unfortunate results of such introductions as the mongoose into the West Indies or the rabbit and fox into Australia come to mind.

PREDATORS ON FISH

Fish have many predators including birds, reptiles and mammals. The predation of fish-eagles and cormorants is a nuisance to fish culture, while kingfishers may be troublesome in the fry ponds, but at least one of the kingfishers is a friend rather than a foe. Six specimens of the White-breasted Kingfisher were shot on the Malacca fishponds and fish remains were found in only one of them. The rest had been feeding on lizards, frogs and on the larvae of dragon-flies and aquatic beetles. As the last two are predators of young fish and the stomach contents contained many of these, the bird earns the few fish it may take.

Cott[61] worked on the food and habits of the more important fish-eating birds on Lake Victoria, namely, two species of Cormorant, *Phalacrocorax lucidus*, and *P. africanus*, and a Darter, *Anhinga rufa*. Cormorants are numerous and widely distributed, and so are the Darters. The Cormorant *P. lucidus*, tends to fish in the more open waters, sometimes out of sight of land. The birds make a daily migration to their fishing grounds and back to their roosting places, especially at dawn and dusk, and they are gregarious in flight. The other species of Cormorant, *P. africanus*, and the Darter feed close inshore, generally within easy range of the roost. These differences in habits are reflected in the nature of the fish eaten. Most of the fish eaten are members of the commercially not very valuable *Haplochromis* group; and, among 612 stomachs of *P. lucidus*, only one Tilapia was found. This Cormorant would not seem to be harmful to the fisheries, and might perhaps even be beneficial. The other Cormorant, *P. africanus*, is also harmless to the fisheries, since only 1·4 per cent of the recognisable fish remains in the stomachs were Tilapias.

Cott[62] found that fish were a part of the food of crocodiles of all sizes but insects and crustacea were the most important food of small crocodiles less than two metres in length. Fish are the chief diet of crocodiles of a size from two to four metres in length, and among the fish eaten, a large proportion are either predators or fish of little economic value. This study has led to the curious result that the crocodile is now seen to play a useful part in the fishery economy of a lake. When young, they exercise a measure of control on many insect groups; at a later stage they eat crabs, frogs and toads; when they take to a fish diet they destroy many predatory fish, and when very large, they eat otters, turtles and snakes. The vogue of the crocodile-skin handbag and briefcase, which has led to the decimation of the crocodile in so many African lakes, may lead to an increase in the number of otters.

Chapter Seven

BIOLOGICAL FACTORS: THE CONDITION OF THE WATER

OXYGEN LACK

THE condition of the water has a great effect on the distribution of fish, and therefore on the fisheries. Examples have been quoted to show that the deeper parts of lakes, or even stagnant reaches of deep rivers, may not be inhabitable by fish because of a lack of oxygen. Swamps may also be uninhabitable, except for fish adapted to breathe atmospheric air, and even this can only be done where the water is shallow enough for the fish to reach the surface easily. In Africa there seem to be only a few species having this adaptation, of which the most important are the Lung-fish *Protopterus*, *Polypterus* and the Barbel *Clarias*. The two former have lungs, but *Clarias* is a true fish in which a part of the gill-cavity has been modified into a lung-like organ in which the fish can secure the exchange of oxygen and carbon dioxide with atmospheric air. As there may be no other fish in the swamps on which these fish can feed, they subsist mainly on insects and molluscs. There is a much richer swamp fish fauna in the Far East, including the whole family of the Anabantids. These were common in the ponds at Malacca before clearance and stocking, so there was a chance to observe them. They will still come to the surface to take atmospheric air even when the pond is clear enough for the free entry of dissolved oxygen; and each of the species makes a characteristic break at the surface by which they may be recognised. There are vegetable feeders such as the Gouramis, the smaller members of which, such as the Trichogasters, feed on epiphytic growth, and on small insects, while the giant Gourami feeds on the soft leaves of the higher plants. Then there are the predators, including the so-called Climbing Perch, *Anabas*. This fish may never grow larger than about 10 cm., but it has a firm, round body, and is much in demand for curries. The air-breathing snake-head or Aruan of Malaya, the Murrel of India, *Ophiocephalus*, is very popular as a food fish. It is predatory on other fish such as the smaller Gouramis, but will flourish in water without other fish, as it can also do well on frogs and tadpoles, and on insect larvae. A relative of the Barbel of Africa, in this case *Clarias batrachus*, is also very abundant in swampy waters in the tropical Far East. The presence of all these specialised swamp fish makes fishing in such waters a profitable matter for the subsistence fisherman.

ADAPTATIONS TO BREATHE AIR

The swamps of South America have an even wider range of fish equipped to live in a medium of low oxygen concentration. Carter and Beadle[63] show that, while many of the smaller swamp fishes are able to live by coming frequently to the surface to draw over their gills the very thin layer of well-oxygenated surface water, there are four types of genuine aerial respiration among these swamp fishes, apart from the Lung-fish *Lepidosiren* and the eel *Symbranchus*.

The first adaptation is typified by the Characinid fish *Erythrinus unitaeniatus* Spix., the air-bladder of which has a lung-like structure. It is a very big organ, occupying one half the space in the body cavity. There is a very wide air duct, down which it is easy for the fish to force air when swallowed into the pharynx. In the air-bladder, a slightly higher air pressure than the atmospheric is maintained, and the composition of the gas in the bladder is very different from that of the air. There is only 7 per cent of oxygen and there is 0·7 per cent of carbon dioxide, as compared with 21 per cent of oxygen and 0·03 per cent of carbon dioxide in the atmosphere. This indicates a very considerable absorption of oxygen and some excretion of carbon dioxide. But this fish does not depend entirely on this modified air-bladder for all its respiration because when it is placed in well-oxygenated water it will respire through the gills and skin in the way usual among fish.

The second type is represented by *Hypopomus brevirostris* Steidnacher. At first sight this fish shows no marked adaptation to the habit of breathing air. It always comes to the surface when allowed to do so and swallows air, whatever the nature of the water. The greater part of the air is passed to the gill-chamber, which is very large, and becomes swollen after the taking in of air. If the operculum is then pierced, air bubbles will come out of the puncture. There is no special organ in the gill cavity, but the gills themselves have an abnormal development of secondary folds which must increase the efficiency of the respiratory epithelium. It seems, in this as in other cases, that a greater broadening than usual of these secondary folds is necessary if the gills are to be used as organs of aerial respiration.

The third type is represented by *Hoplosternum litorale* Hancock. The accessory breathing organ is the wall of the intestine, from a point a very short distance from the stomach to the rectum. The whole of this part of the intestine is normally full of air and empty of food. Air is taken in at the mouth, and passed to the intestine and an analysis of the air in the intestine shows that, while its composition is much closer to that of the atmosphere than that in the air-bladder of *Erythrinus*, there is a significant reduction in the percentage of oxygen. If the fish are prevented from breathing air they will die of asphyxiation, and an analysis of the gas in the intestine then shows practically no oxygen, and over 3 per cent of carbon dioxide. These results confirm that there is considerable absorption of oxygen in the intestine and some excretion of carbon dioxide. Normally, the spent air is bubbled out of the mouth again but one wonders how the fish is able to feed if its intestine is used as a respiratory organ. The food, which is of a soft vegetable nature, must be rapidly passed through. The gills, though reduced, are not functionless, for the movements of the gill-chamber becomes more rapid when the fish is prevented from taking air and is becoming stifled.

The final type is represented by the Loricariid fish *Ancistrus anisitsi* Eigenmann and Kennedy. The large U-shaped stomach is always full of gas during life, and was found on investigation to be used as an accessory breathing organ. There was no trace of an air-bladder. The wall of the stomach is very thin and transparent and vascular in all parts. The fish breaks surface and swallows air at irregular intervals, and the expelled air is given out at the mouth.

There seem to be no data on the abundance of fish in the swamps of the Chaco, but the same fishes are caught in British Guiana, in the swampy creeks and in the flood-fallowed sugar-cane fields, in considerable quantity and are offered for sale in the markets. The *Erythrinus unitaeniatus* is well known and sold as the Houri, a predator on the *Hoplosternum litorale* or Hassar, another popular fish. Presumably, without these respiratory adaptations, these waters could not support a large enough population of fish to supply these valuable quantities of food.

FISH MORTALITIES

Fish which have no such means of surviving where the oxygen content of the water is low may be killed if they are unable to move to where conditions are better. In Lake Bangweulu, for example, according to a report on the work of the Joint Fisheries Research Organisation, published in the Annual Report for 1956 of the Game and Tsetse Control Department of the Northern Rhodesia Government,[116] oxygen conditions in the Bangweulu Swamp may change so suddenly as to be catastrophic. When water levels rise rapidly as a result of prolonged heavy rain, the rapid inflow of new water may suddenly flush out the water that has been lying stagnant in certain areas of the swamp too quickly for some fishes to take avoiding action, and mass mortalities of fish frequently occur. Fish[64] worked out the tolerance of a number of species living in Lake Victoria and Uganda of oxygen and carbon dioxide tension. He found, as might be expected from its auxiliary air-breathing organ, that the Barbel, *Clarias*, had a high tolerance, but that the Nile Perch, *Lates*, had a low tolerance. Mass mortalities of *Lates* have been frequently reported, for example, in the Nile and in Lake Albert

In the Gold Coast Report of the Fisheries Department for 1950-1,[139] there is an account of such a mass mortality of Nile Perch. A short but very heavy rainfall in the Lawra district caused a sharp though temporary spate in the Kamba tributary of the Volta. On the following day a large number of Nile Perch were seen floating helplessly downstream, apparently dying. At the shallow rapids, a dozen fine fish were taken by hand in a few minutes. They may, suggests the report, have been suffering from oxygen starvation induced by the temporary fall in the dissolved oxygen content of the water, this being caused by the disturbance of organic matter in the river bed by the sudden flood. Enquiries showed that such mortalities were not unknown, though other fish did not seem to be affected.

On page 192 a sudden heavy mortality of fish in Lake George was ascribed to a disturbance of the bottom deposits. There may also be heavy mortalities of fish due to an overturn of the water (page 35).

Tilapias which brood their young in the shelter of reed beds, where the young fish may take refuge, may be flushed out of their cover by rainwater from the land driving deoxygenated water out of the fringing swamps into the reed-beds.

FERTILITY OF THE WATER

While the gas content of the water directly affects the fish and their distribution, the general productivity of the water, that is, the quantity of fish a given body of water will support, is closely related to the mineral content of the water, as many of these minerals will be plant-nutrients. Braun[10] shows that in the Amazon Basin the lakes in the tertiary soils were uniformly poor in dissolved salts. Those in the carboniferous showed varying values; they were poor in electrolytes and acid, as in the tertiary region, if they were in sandstone areas, but rich in electrolytes and neutral or even alkaline when they were in areas where there are calcareous or other soils. The number of organisms living in the bottom muds and the amount of plankton reflect these differences very clearly, and though Braun gives no data as to the abundance of fish, these could hardly be plentiful where there is so little food for them.

Marlier[8] shows how great may be the difference in composition of the streams arising in the Congo-Nile watersheds in the Congo. The streams flowing northwards to the Nile may traverse volcanic soil and be much richer in dissolved substances than those flowing to the Congo. Inasmuch as some of these will be plant-nutrients, one would expect the northward-flowing streams and the rivers and lakes into which they flow to be richer in plant life, and therefore ultimately in fish, than the others. It is difficult to show this, for the various lakes are not only exploited to very different degrees but the deeper lakes have only a small proportion of their areas suitable for fish at all. The statistics published by the Uganda Game and Fisheries Department are very interesting and significant.[118] Below are data abstracted from the Report for the year 1956-7:

Table II

Lake	Area in sq. miles	Production per acre per annum, lb.
Edward and the Kazinga Channel	235	54·9
George	104	104·3
Nakivali	10	168·0
Kachira	14	122·5
Kijanebolola	27	114·1
Kyoga	880	19·8
Victoria (Uganda waters)	10,961	7·2

The table shows that remarkable yields are obtained from Lakes George, Nakivali, Kachira and Kijanebolola, all in the region of drainage of volcanic soils. Lake Edward has a lower, but still notable, yield. On the other hand Lake Kyoga, which is in the same basin as Lake Victoria, is not on volcanic soil, and both give much lower yields. The comparison must be taken with caution, for Lake Victoria is one of the world's greatest lakes and the fishing effort per acre is probably much less than in the smaller lakes, while Lake Kyoga is much choked with vegetation, which must hinder fishing.

The Kavirondo Gulf of Lake Victoria, which is heavily fished, gives a much higher average rate of production, namely, about 42 pounds per acre per annum (page 211).

Depasse[65] shows the influence of the soil on the fertility of water. In the Kibali-Ituri region of the Province Oriental of the Congo, there are areas of granite and gneiss, and areas of metamorphic rocks, composed of dolerites, schists, mica-schists, phyllades, diabases, quartzites, etc., and sedimentary rocks. Some thirty samples from streams in the granite and gneiss areas had weakly acid water, normally little buffered, with a biogenic capacity slight or nil. On the other hand, waters running through neutral or basic rocks, such as schists, basic dykes, mica-schists, dolerites, albitite, old Kibalian lavas and schistoids are much richer. Their pH values are higher, and above all stable, thanks to a strong buffering capacity due to alkaline metals. Aquatic life which develops in this type of water is more varied and abundant.

Samples collected in waters grown with papyrus have abnormal powers of buffering, even though they are feebly acid from granitic soil. This anomaly, at a pH below 7, seems to be due to the presence of abundant humates and tannates from cellulosic muds accumulating under the mat of papyrus and playing the buffering role of weak acid salts.

Finally, says Depasse, it appears that the best fish-producing waters of the district of Kibali-Ituri are to be found in neutral or basic soils. The Kibalian massif of Kilo Mongbwalu especially deserves the attention of fish culturists.

The natural production of waters in granite, on the other hand, is slight to nil, and these waters should be avoided.

Though the nature of the soil has great influence on the fish-producing value of the water, a geological map could not be used for demarcating the best areas. This is because a stream passing from one geological formation to another is affected only after a time-lag depending on the volume of the stream as well as the solubility and depth of the rocks. Thus a stream passing over basic rocks may still show the papyrus vegetation of poor granitic soils.

Lake Mweru, in Rhodesia, is estimated to have a production rate of about 66 lb. per acre per annum. It is fed by the Luapula River, which is not very rich in dissolved salts. As the River Zambezi flows through rather insoluble soils and has a low content of dissolved salts, it seems likely that the Kariba Lake which has been formed as a result of the Kariba Dam, will be only moderately productive. The author has estimated it at about 40 lb. per acre per annum for that part of the lake which will be less than 100 feet in depth.

Blanc, Daget and d'Aubenton[9] show that the waters of the Middle Niger are very poor from the chemical point of view and that the production of fish per acre is low. They estimate it at about 22 lb. per acre per annum and contrast this with the flood fishery of the Mekong, in Cambodia, where the yield may be calculated at about 45 lb. per acre per annum on the high-water area, and at about 132 lb. per acre per annum on the low-water area. Subject always to the proviso that not all the electrolytes represent useful plant nutrients (for example, the soda which gives a high conductivity in many of the Uganda waters), it seems likely that the chemical composition of the water may give a guide to the production of fish which may reasonably be expected from any piece of tropical freshwater. This was in fact the basis of Kufferath's assessment of the productivity of Lakes Tanganyika and Kivu.

Chapter Eight

BIOLOGICAL FACTORS: MIGRATIONS

FISH may be said to migrate when they move in a non-random manner. They often appear to move in a purposeful manner though it is not always possible to discern what their purpose is. Migrations are important for at least two reasons. First, when fish are migrating they are usually concentrated so that any fishing method used will give a high return; and secondly, their purposeful urge may make them easy victims of obstacles placed in their way. The commonest case of such migration is the upstream movement of ripe fish to spawn.

UPSTREAM SPAWNING MIGRATIONS

The impulse is usually the downrush of freshly fallen rain. This will change the conductivity of the water and at one time it was thought that this was the signal for the fish to ascend. More recently there has been some doubt about this. One obvious factor is the sheer physical effect of a larger volume of water in the river, giving more moving space. Another is the fact that the new water, especially as it may come down in a very turbulent way, is well oxygenated. This may be an important factor, for where the migration is obviously a spawning one it is linked to the instinct to place the spawn where it will have the best chance to develop, and well-oxygenated water will give it that chance. The run of *Labeo altivelis* up the Luapula River is one case.

On the other hand, some fish, such as *Labeo mesops*, the Nchila of Lake Nyasa, will ascend very small temporary streams where the spawn, and even the fish themselves, may be stranded high and dry.

The commonest way of catching the fish which migrate upstream is to use that urge to surmount all obstacles. Barriers are put across the rivers or streams, and when the fish find gaps through

10. Lake Bangweulu, a shallow lake.

11. Lake Nyasa, a deep lake, at Nkata Bay, Nyasaland.

12. A fish-fence in the Bahi Swamp, Tanganyika.

13. A basket used in conjunction with a fish-fence.

which they can pass, these gaps are furnished with traps into which the fish can enter, but from which they cannot escape. Nevertheless, so strong is the urge, that some of the fish will get past or over barrier after barrier on the same river.

THE SPAWNING STIMULUS

This desire to run up streams when new water comes down appears to be an extension of the spawning habits of very many tropical fish. It is well known that the fish which are in the rivers or lagoons at the end of the dry season will move out into the shallower water as the level rises, and spawn in these shallows. In the Rupununi Savannahs of British Guiana towards the end of the dry season, when the pools and lagoons left by the previous flood season are drying out, the surviving fish have ripening roes. They would no doubt spawn as soon as new water caused the filling of the pools and their overflow and union with the other pools to form the great flood-plain of the wet season.

As there may be few survivors of these dry spells, while the supply of fish never seems to fail, it follows that the reproductive capacity of these fish must be very great.

This sequence is also seen in artificial waters such as the "tanks" in India. A number of valuable fish, such as the *Labeos* and *Catla*, which are in the reduced volume of water in the tank at the end of the dry season, will move out into the shallow water of the tank as new water flows in at the beginning of the rainy season, and there spawn. In fish culture, this may be artificially brought about. Schuster[51] describes how he obtained the spawning of the valuable pond-cultured Cyprinid, *Puntius javanicus*, by keeping the mature fish in a deeper pit dug in the spawning pond. When fry were needed, he would cause a sudden rise in the level of water in the pond by turning in water from a rainwater drain at a time of rainfall. The fish would then leave the deeper pit and spawn in the shallow water in the pond outside the pit. The young would quickly hatch and grow to the size when they could be taken out with scoop nets. The pond can then be drained, so that the parent fish return to their pit. As each spawning may produce 100,000 fry, and as the process may be repeated frequently, the capacity of a *Puntius* hatchery, as Schuster remarks, is great.

AVOIDING POOR CONDITIONS

While many such migrations are clearly associated with spawning, there are others which are associated with the effort to escape adverse living conditions. Welman[66] describes the mass migration over the dry land of a shoal of *Clarias*. The shoal appeared to be on its way from water which was drying out to more permanent water. He gives an amusing description of the behaviour of the fish on the move.

In the Bangweulu swamps there may be important movements of the fish caused by the presence and displacement of bodies of de-oxygenated water. The fish population of the swamp move about, due to changes in oxygen conditions as well as to other causes, and this affects the fisheries. In Indonesia, the Cyprinid fish *Thynnichthys vaillanti* of the Lake District of West Borneo, lives in the lakes but when the dry season comes and the water-level falls, acid and turbid water from surrounding inundated areas enters the lakes. As this water is deficient in oxygen, the fish move from the lakes to the rivers, and up the rivers in search of cooler and better-aerated water. The migration of the fish usually takes place at night in shoals, which may be dense enough for three tons of fish to be gathered in a single haul of a net. The eggs ripen during the migration, and when the rainy season comes, the fish move downstream to the lakes and spawning takes place along the inundated shores.

That fast-flowing water may be a stimulus to migration, and a concentration of fish, is also shown by observations below dams and weirs (pages 86, 88, and 110). In most cases, these movements are not related to spawning, nor to any other obvious biological factor. The efficiency of fish barriers (Figures 14 and 15) may be due, in some part, to their production of a local increase in the speed of flow of the water.

TILAPIAS

The Tilapias which live in the lakes of Africa may make migrations into the shallower waters for the purpose of spawning, but these are not mass movements, and may merely be reflected as a seasonal variation in the catches in shallow water. This applies especially to those Tilapias which normally live in or over the deeper water offshore. Indeed, marking experiments which have been made with Tilapias in Lakes Rukwa and Victoria show that they normally show little movement. This is entirely consonant with their known habits of taking up and defending territory while in the spawning condition. As there are at least some fish in this condition throughout the year, this is sufficient explanation of the non-migratory habits of the Tilapias.

Yet these marking experiments showed that an occasional fish would make long journeys. For example, on Lake Rukwa Swynnerton[50] found that although most of the marked *Tilapia rukwaensis* were recaptured within a mile of the position of marking, a few were recaptured on the other side of the lake. In the case of the marked Tilapia in Lake Victoria, again most of the fish showed little movement, yet there were marked fish which were recaptured very far from the place of marking. Fish marked in the Kavirondo Gulf have not only moved right out of the Gulf, but have been recaptured far south along the coast of the lake and even as far as Mwanza.

These exceptional movements, in a fish which normally tends to be non-migratory, are biologically very important, for they ensure the introduction of new blood from other stocks in the lake. This will tend to maintain the vigour of the stocks and prevent the appearance of local sub-species.

SMALL-SCALE MIGRATIONS

Johnels[67] describes the fisheries of the Gambia River in West Africa. One of the principal fishing methods in use there is the barrier or fish fence, and observations on the fish coming to the fences allowed Johnels to learn something of the movements of the fish between the river and the temporary or permanent swamps which border it over so much of its length. These swamps fill in the rainy season from two sources, namely direct rainfall and drainage from the land and the overflow of the river. The entrances to the swamps from the river are dammed up by the African fishermen during the rainy season with substantial weirs which are made of a frame of strong tree-trunks, on the swamp side of which are fastened hurdles of split and wattled bamboo on which are fixed mats of densely woven grass. The weirs, according to Johnels' observations, are remarkably tight and permit only a very small amount of water to pass.

It was plain that the fish were showing migratory instincts such that they wished to move with the current. For instance, when the main river began to fall, great quantities of fish appeared on the swamp side of the barriers; when, however, a marked rise of the water in the river caused a temporary current into the swamp, practically no fish were observed on the swamp side, while a considerable number were observed on the river side. Later, when the river water had definitely begun to fall, there was a constant accumulation of fish on the swamp side. Johnels says that this inclination to follow the current must be a definite non-random movement and not a passive transportation with the current, for the accumulation of fish on the up-current side of the weirs still occurred when, owing to the efficiency of the weirs, only a very small amount of water was actually passing through. In the normal way this instinct to follow the current would first take the fish out of the river into the swamps to breed and grow, and then bring them safely back to the river when the water starts to fall.

But Johnels goes on to say that there must be other and more complicated reasons for the migration out of the swamps, besides this sensibility for currents, because the composition of the fish varies on different occasions. Thus, early in the period of observation, the Tilapia species dominated among the cichlid fish at all weirs. Later, their place was taken by *Hemichromis*. The appearance at the weirs of the valuable *Paradistichodus* was sudden, great quantities where previously there had been only isolated examples.

In this fishery the fish are caught by making holes in the dams and causing the water to flow through a basket trap in which the fish are filtered off. Johnels remarks that from a practical point of view no objection should be raised against this method. It can only be effectively used at the end of the rainy season, and at this time the quality of the fish is at its best after the nourishment obtained in the swamps. Secondly, the natural mortality of the fish is extremely great during the dry season, so that all fish which can be captured before this time must be a clear saving. Thirdly, the method can only be applied where local conditions are favourable. The natural propagation of the fish in the numerous swamp areas where weirs cannot be arranged must already be much greater than is really needed for maintaining the population of fish in the river. Johnels' final point is that the damming-up of the water of the swamps permits the fishing to go on for a prolonged period. The fish may, in fact, be regarded as being temporarily stored for capture in the swamps.

RIVER TO TRIBUTARY

Buxton (in the Gold Coast Fisheries Report for 1950-1[139]) studied the movements of the fish passing over the check-dam constructed in the Kamba River. The primary purpose of this and other such dams was to provide water supplies for the new villages of the Kamba Valley, large areas of which have been cleared of tsetse and are now being resettled. The Kamba is one of the larger tributaries of the Black Volta. It flows from May, or whenever the first substantial rains fall, until October.

A number of observations were made on the movements of fish in the Kamba River, which is probably typical of many streams in the Volta system. They covered the nine weeks from April 21, when the first spate of the season occurred, until June 30, and three phases were seen.

First, there was a major downriver movement of the adult fish in the dam as soon as the connection with the river had been re-established. Trial fishing in the dam then showed that few adult fish were left after this downstream movement. At Turi Dam, on a stream which enters the Volta some miles below the Kamba mouth, large numbers of fish, including *Clarias, Labeo, Schilbe, Alestes* and *Tilapia* were actually seen descending the spillway.

Secondly, there was an upriver movement of fry and small fish. This began on April 24, with species of *Barbus* in the lead. The run of *Barbus* reached its peak five days later, when they were seen ascending a small natural fall at a rate of 50 per minute. *Barilius, Chelaethiops* spp. and *Kneria* spp. had become dominant in the run by April 26; by May 22 *Tilapia* young, with *T. nilotica* predominating, *Alestes, Barbus, Heterobranchus, Barilius* and *Chelaethiops* young were all on the move in large numbers. This upward run continued until the end of the observations.

Thirdly, there was an upriver movement of adult fish. No large fish were taken or seen until the period June 7 to 16, when *Bagrus, Synodontis, Auchenoglanis, Alestes dentex, Labeo* and *Polypterus* were met with in small numbers. A major movement was seen after June 24, with the ascent into the dam of *Gymnarchus, Bagrus, Clarias, Polypterus, Mormyrus, Hydrocyon,* and *Alestes macrolepidoterus.*

These migrations appeared to be induced more by rises in the main Volta River than by the spate in the Kamba itself, so it may have been that they continued, after the period of observations, until the flood reached its height in September.

The effect of these movements is that the dams and the pools in those tributaries which do not have check-dams are re-stocked from the main river in the annual flood.

Daget[68] describes the migrations of the small but important Characinid fish *Alestes leuciscus* in the waters of the Middle Niger. The fish quit the river as the water rises and this is a definite migration. When the water starts to fall the *Alestes* gather to start the migration back to the river, being then well-grown and with a high fat-content. They are heavily fished with weirs and traps; but those fish which succeed in regaining the minor bed of the Niger form shoals which ascend the river at monthly intervals, and give rise to an intensive fishery in the river itself.

THE FISH-PASS AT MARKKALA

The great barrage across the Middle Niger at Markkala has enabled some very valuable observations to be made on the movements of fish. This barrage was constructed to provide water for the irrigation schemes which have brought fertility to what was semi-desert. The barrage is 813 metres long and is provided with a fish-pass in the centre. This pass is fairly effective, but cannot allow the passage of all the enormous quantities of fish which present themselves at the pass. The head of water is only $6\frac{1}{2}$ metres, so the pass is short.

The appearance of the fish at the pass is described by Daget.[69] Fishing is forbidden all the year round in a zone one kilometre on each side of the barrage, except for the floating long-line. The object of this prohibition is to protect the fish when massed to ascend the pass. One of the unexpected results of the measure has been to favour the concentration of predatory fish around the fish-pass and principally below it, and fisheries have had to be organised to thin out these predators.

The fish-pass functions and allows plenty of fish to ascend. Big Cyprinids such as *Labeo senegalensis*, *Labeo coubie*, *Barbus occidentalis*, the *Hydrocyon* or Tiger-fish pass very easily, generally following the side where there is the greatest depth of water. Certain Siluroids, such as *Chrysichthys* and *Eutropius*, pass equally well but preferably at night.

The most spectacular period is at the middle falling water, when the *Alestes leuciscus,* mentioned above as migrating in banks in the minor bed of the river, appear at the foot of the fish-pass. They come in successive banks and the pass is confronted by concentrations of fish such as are never seen in temperate climates. Not all these fish are able to pass. The shoals disperse later.

Daget criticises the position of the pass, placed as it is in the middle of the dam. He thinks it would have been more effective had it been placed at one side.

Since the construction of the dam the fishery has become very difficult for the natives above the dam. Instead of a seasonal flooding, the level of the river is maintained at all seasons above the level of normal low-water mark. Besides, it has become less productive in all the area above and as far as Bamako. Unfortunately, there are no data to test this loss of fish-potential. The African fishermen naturally tend to exaggerate the loss, and if the supply of fish has remained constantly below demand on the markets, it must not be forgotten that the number of consumers has notably increased.

In spite of this, the waters of the Niger are very productive of fish above the barrage. The same species of fish are found on each side and reproduce very well. The barrage has, in addition, not harmed the spawning areas which existed before its construction and the spawning fish go there as easily as before. There appear to have been no harmful consequences to the stock.

The diminution of fish above the dam, of which there has been complaint, is due only to a different distribution of the fish at the period of low water. The fishing methods which are appropriate to a régime of flood-plain are not appropriate to a régime of fixed water-level. It would seem that methods more appropriate to a lake will have to be introduced. In any case there are two mitigating factors. First, there is now a regular migration of the fishermen downstream to below the dam, and secondly, there is a new fishery in the irrigation canals.

FISH-PASSES AND LADDERS

The question of the necessity of fish-ladders or passes has been often debated when dams for irrigation or hydro-electric power are to be put across rivers. The question is whether there are migratory fish of such importance that they must be helped over the obstruction. A fish-ladder was constructed at the Gebel Aulia Dam on the White

Nile but it appears that fish species of economic value do not make use of the ladder. Fish-ladders were maintained at the Owen Falls and the Ripon Falls on the Nile at the outlet of Lake Victoria. Only two species of Barbus ever succeeded in ascending the falls and neither of these is of great economic value. It is true that fish, sometimes in considerable numbers, may be seen milling about in the broken water at the foot of waterfalls, and the big Barbus has been seen in the tail races of the turbines at the Owen Falls Dam. But it is more likely that they may be attracted by the rush of well-oxygenated water and by the presence of smaller fish which may make easy prey.

Chacko[70] investigated nine important river fisheries in the Madras State of India which are affected by dams or natural obstructions. There the rivers are usually in flood from June to December when they have a great velocity, a fluctuating depth and muddy discoloration. During this season the migratory fish begin to ascend the rivers. Chacko found that six out of sixteen dams form barriers to the free movements of fish and that all the dams facilitate indiscriminate capture of both adult and young fish which congregate below the barriers in the attempt to move upstream. The chief or only fish which was definitely migrating upstream to spawn was the *Hilsa ilisha*, which is a really important fish. Though it passes most of its life in the sea, it will ascend as far as 175 miles from the sea in its spawning migration, and probably barrages which prevent their migration are harmful to the fishery. But most of the other fishes apparently trying to ascend the barriers were not on a spawning migration, and gonadial and intestinal examinations showed no definite reason for this behaviour. These cases seem analogous to the dam at Markkala on the Niger and to the many other cases where fish congregate below an obstruction. In these Indian dams, as also at Markkala, fishing is prohibited for some distance below the dams with a view to protecting the fish. It seems doubtful whether this is useful. Most fishing methods are designed, in any case, to concentrate the fish for capture, and these fish are not migrating for any obvious purpose, but may be attracted by the turbulent and well-oxygenated water. Since, as was shown in the case of the Markkala Dam, the predatory fish take full advantage of the congregations of fish, there should be allowed at least a fishery for the predators.

Fish-passes are expensive, and there is only a need for them where fish of economic value are known to make regular and necessary migrations upstream to spawn, and where interruption of this migration will seriously affect the fisheries. In practice, the salmon alone seems to warrant the expense of fish-passes, and this is a fish of temperate rivers. Probably the Hilsa will also need passes in the Indian rivers.

It appears that turbines in dams put up for the generation of hydro-electric power can sometimes act as fish-passes. Certainly, two fish, previously known to be present in the Victoria Nile below the Owen Falls Dam, but not hitherto recorded in Lake Victoria, have now appeared in the lake above the dam. These are the *Mormyrus macrocephalus*[146] and the Nile Perch.

It seems that, at certain stages in the working of the turbines, there may be a current of only about six miles an hour in the machinery; so that a fish, having entered the turbine chamber, would have a chance to swim past the turbine and up the shaft to the lake above. This can happen only rarely, for the slaughter of fish in the turbines is a problem in salmon rivers; and, in the case of the Owen Falls Dam itself, there is usually a drift downstream of big Barbus which have been killed by the turbines.

Chapter Nine

FISHING METHODS; PRESERVATION AND MARKETING

THERE have been a number of classifications of fishing gear and methods, and of these that of Burdon[71] is perhaps the most helpful. It is adopted here as the basis of a discussion of the methods of catching fish in tropical inland fisheries.

A distinction has to be made between fishing in rivers and in lakes which have an outlet. In the latter, there cannot be great seasonal variations of level, and strong currents occur only rarely. Fishing methods in lakes therefore tend to be similar to those used in marine inshore fisheries. In rivers, there is the great seasonal change in level, which produces the very important flood-fisheries; and there is the current, which likewise varies with the state of the river. At the time of low water, in the dry season, there are stretches of rivers which are practically stagnant, and which can be fished like lakes. On the other hand, in the wet season the same river may be a fast-flowing stream in which quite different methods are used.

Following Burdon, a description will first be given of fishing methods in which individual fish are the subject of fishing operations.

INDIVIDUAL FISH CAPTURE

Manual Collection

This, the simplest possible fishing, is found where lagoons dry out with the fall of the river after flooding. The water in the lagoons evaporates to a point where the surviving fish may be seen swimming with their backs half out of the water; they can then at times be caught by hand, though it is more usual to use some simple aid such as a strip of cloth, a basket or plunge-basket made specially for this work. The plunge-basket is usually circular, with a hole at both ends. The basket is plunged into the shallow water so as to catch the fish, which is then removed through the hole at the top. The plunge-basket may also be used blindly, in water known to have plenty of fish; it is especially effective used blindly where there are a large number of operators working together. Plunge-baskets are often used in paddy fields, the fish sought being the *Clarias* and Snake-heads.

In this category come the simple Catfish traps of Nigeria, designed to catch one fish at a time. These are just hollow bamboos closed at one end. A Catfish entering for shelter, or out of curiosity, cannot turn to get out, and is in any case liable to be held by its spines. In Nigeria and in British Guiana fish-traps made on the principle of rat-traps are found. A cage is closed by a door which is held open by a suitable spring or weight, in such a way that a fish entering will trip the spring and close the door. Obviously, this trap will take only one fish at a time.

To faciliate manual capture, a piece of water may be sealed off with earth dykes, and the enclosed water baled out (Colour Plate V, and pages 141 and 273).

Nooses

This division includes all devices whereby fish are secured in a simple or complex noose. It is said to be used in West Africa, but the author has never seen it.

Bait Holders

Gorges made of sharp thorns, or thin twigs of a hard wood sharpened at both ends, are attached to twine and threaded with a suitable bait. When bait and gorge are swallowed by a fish, the gorge, jams in the gullet of the fish. This device is used in South America but is being displaced by hooks.

Sharp Projectiles

Fish spears and harpoons are among the commonest implements for the capture of fish. They may be aimed or plunged blindly. Arrows are used by the Amerindians, and with these every shot must be aimed.

Hooks

Hook and line are too familiar to need further description. They may be used singly, from boat or shore, from hand or rod, with bait or with lure. They may be used in connection with a spring so as to fish automatically; a springy sapling or bamboo may be bent over and the hook and line attached to it in such a way that a bite trips a catch and causes the sapling to spring up, heaving the fish out of the water. A fisherman may work a large number of these. The method has the great merit that the fish is held out of the water clear of predators and scavengers.

Then there is the trot or longline, on which many baited hooks may be set. It may be laid on the bottom but in the inland fisheries is more usually laid in midwater between poles. Lining in all its forms is very valuable, as this method is plainly most effective against predatory fish which may not be very easily taken with nets.

Foul-hooking is found in many countries. A line furnished with many sharp hooks is laid unbaited across the mouth of a creek or lagoon. Fish on the move are liable to impale themselves.

Digging

A final example of the capture of individual fish is when fish stranded by the drying-out of the water may be taken; and it is, to my know-ledge, the only "fishery" which is done on dry land. The Lung-fish *Protopterus* will, when its habitat dries up, burrow into the mud and encyst itself in a cocoon. In this cocoon it can survive long periods of desiccation. But this habit is well known and in the Nile swamps, at least, the tribesmen will sound the ground with sticks and where a hollow echo marks the presence of a *Protopterus* in its burrow, the fish will be dug out with spears. They are said to be in prime condition.

In other places, such as the Bangweulu swamps, fish, chiefly the *Clarias*, may similarly be dug out of the dry and caked mud with hoes.

INDISCRIMINATE OR DIFFUSE METHODS

These methods affect all fish within the area of operation.

Poisons

These are universally used, though illegal in most countries. Their use would seem to be unexceptionable in cases where the fish will die in any case, as when trapped in a drying lagoon.

Suffocation

This is often used, and is also a consequence of communal battues or fish drives by large numbers of people. By trampling up the mud, and possibly releasing noxious gases such as sulphuretted hydrogen from the mud, those partaking in the drive are helped to collect the fish by the stupefaction and suffocation caused. There are cases of waters protected by superstition, where this may be the only way of getting the fish, since all forms of fishing gear may be prohibited.

Explosives

These also are illegal but are widely used, unfortunately.

The third class of fishing methods are those in which generally a group or association of fish are the subject of the fishing operation.

MULTIPLE OR COLLECTIVE METHODS

Entrapping Structures

These, in their many variations, are the principal fishing methods used in the flood fisheries, which are the most productive of all the freshwater fisheries. There are, first, the barriers set up across the channels through which fish which have left the main river at the flood try to return to the river when the water falls. They may be of earth, or of brushwood, or they may be substantial dams of planks stuffed with clay. They may be fixed, or they may be movable screens which can be advanced so as to compress the trapped fish into a smaller and smaller space for ease of capture. In essence, these barriers are an extension of the natural barriers which occur where the sill of a side lagoon off a river is higher than the bottom of the lagoon itself. In the latter case, the fish are trapped naturally when the level of the water dries out to the point where the sill is exposed. The setting up of barriers is an improvement on Nature, in that it raises the height of the sill, or puts one where there was not a natural one, thus entrapping fish which would have escaped back to the river in the natural way. The fish so trapped are gathered in a variety of ways, as by spears, plunge-baskets, small drag-nets, or even with the hands, sometimes in conjunction with the use of poison.

More often, however, the barrier is not complete, but has gaps
in which baskets or traps are put, so that there may be a regular
catch of fish trying to pass the barrier. This seems to be an advantage, inasmuch as it is easier to dispose of small quantities of fish
over a long period, than of great quantities in a short period,
especially where methods of preservation are rudimentary, and
temperatures are high. Plate 12 shows a fish fence with a
gap into which a basket-trap is set; and Plate 13 shows the
basket-trap.

Where fish are trapped like this, those fish which have accessory
air-breathing organs, and are thus able to crawl across at least
short distances of bare ground, may try to crawl around the barrier.
According to Burdon, in Burma a pit may be dug at each end of a
complete barrier, so that fish trying to crawl round, such as the
Snake-heads and Catfishes, will fall into the pits.

Another accessory to the enclosure may be the shelter of brushwood or branches, which attract the fish either for the sake of the
cover, or because of the development of epiphytic plants and their
associated fauna which provide food. At fishing, these shelters may
be surrounded by netting or screens, and the fish made accessible
to ancillary fishing gear by the removal of the brushwood.

Filtering Devices

The next method still depends for its action on water movements,
but in this case on a fast-running current. As a simple example,
there are the trumpet-shaped baskets, without any valve, which
are set in cataracts and under small waterfalls. Fish which are swept
down the rapids or over the fall may drop into these baskets, and
are unable to jump out because of the narrowness of the basket.
In place of a basket, a screen of rotan or similar hammock-like
platform may be placed where fish, being carried down a fast and
turbulent piece of water, presumably not under full control, may
be filtered off.

A more elaborate version, the *Ngola*, is described from the
Congo. In this case, there are palisades of boughs placed in the
rapids to guide the fish over an inclined screen which filters them off,
and from which they are gathered by a watchman (Plate 28).

Lowe[73] describes how box-traps may be set facing upstream in
the rivers flowing into Lake Nyasa, to catch the fish, presumably

spent fish, returning to the lake after the upstream run. Again, the presumption is that this is a passive movement.

Another example of a screening device set in moving water, which screens or filters out the catch which appears to be swept more or less passively by the current, and is retained by the force of the current, is the *day* of the Mekong in Cambodia. This is a big

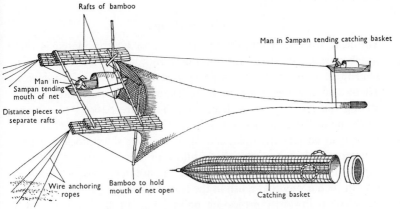

Figure 4. The *day* of the Mekong River

net anchored to the river bottom, and with a mouth deep enough to filter fish from most of the water column. It seems to be one of the costliest and best-constructed of all river-fishing nets, and is fully described and illustrated by Sao Leang and Dom Saveun.[74] It seems to fish in one direction only (Figure 4).

A final example is found in Johnels' description of the capture of fish in the Gambia River (page 84).

Barriers

Screening devices also work in an entirely different manner, in which the fish are not more or less passively swept down but actively swim up into the barriers. These barriers are exceedingly common and are found at all stages of elaboration. But the principle is always the same; the barriers are set across rivers or streams up which there is known to be a migration, usually a spawning migration, at a certain season of the year, which is almost invariably the season when the rivers come down in spate. The barriers are interrupted at intervals by gaps, into which basket-traps, fitted with non-return valves, are put. There may also be larger traps at the shoreward ends of the barrier, for fish usually travel close to the banks. An elaboration of this catching method may be the provision of horizontal screens on the upstream side of the barrier, to catch fish which have tried to leap over. Plates 14 and 15 show a fish barrier in Kenya.

Non-return Traps

The next variety of entrapping structure to be considered is that which permits the free and voluntary entrance of fish, but which hinders or prevents their escape by a structural non-return device. These also are the commonest of fishing devices, and are in use among the most primitive fishermen. They are baskets of wickerwork made from the most handy local material. A funnel-shaped valve is fitted into the open end of the basket; the funnel tapers to a narrow hole large enough to allow of the passage of the fish expected to be caught. The withes at the hole may project into the trap in such a way that a fish in the trap will tend to jab itself against these sharp inwardly projecting points; but, in any case, it seems that a fish trying to escape from such a trap cruises round and round the walls, and so tends to miss the way out, since the narrow orifice through which it entered the trap is clear of the walls.

These traps may be used by themselves, or in conjunction with barriers; they may be baited or unbaited. They are often set in channels among reed-beds.

A non-portable trap working on the same principle may be staked in a suitable position. They are to be found, in the dry season, standing forlornly among the millet and maize fields on the banks of the Zambezi. They look at first sight like small booths, being built of vertical screens arranged in a square or heart-shape, but without a roof. One of the walls, in the case of a square or rectangular trap, or the ends of the screen, in the case of a heart-shaped trap, is bent or recurved inward, so that, as with the valved portable trap, the fish finds it easier to enter than to get out again. These fixed traps may be placed in ditches or in narrow depressions which, in the flood season, become channels of water along which fish move. Fixed traps, like portable traps, may be used in association with screens and fences which steer the fish into them. They depend on the random movements of the fish.

14. Fish weir on the Nzoia River, Kenya.

15. Fish baskets and clap-nets used in the fish-weir.

16. A cast-net in use, Nigeria.

17. A lift-net on Lake Kivu, Congo.

LIFT AND DROP ENTRAPMENTS

Lift-nets and Cast-nets

Burdon's next category of entrapping structures are the lift and drop entrapments, which he defines as "structures, usually consisting of a sheet of meshed fabric, which are raised or lowered to trap fish above or below the gear".

In this class come the lift-nets, of which there are many examples. The most elaborate was seen on the West River in China. This was a big sheet of netting, held open in the form of a rectangle, by spars, and carried on a sampan of considerable size. The whole net was so hinged that it could be lowered into the water from the sampan and be lifted by a turnbuckle. The net was braided so that the centre of the net hung lower than the margins. A simpler form is the *Filogba* of Nigeria. Here the net is hinged to the side of a canoe, and is lifted by a skilful heave, each of the two operators using his foot as a fulcrum, a fine feat of balancing. This net is lifted on sight of fish seen passing over it. On lifting, the fish just slide down the net into the canoe.

A simple lift-net in use on Lake Kivu is shown in Plate 17.

Smaller lift-nets may be simply squares of small-meshed netting held open by two bamboos made fast diagonally to the four corners, and lashed together in the middle. The net is suspended from a rod like a fishing rod, and is used by a single operator in a canal or slowly-flowing river. He lifts his net at intervals, or when he sees fish over it. He may or may not use ground-bait.

Small lift-nets are shown in Plates 26, 57, and 61. A more elaborate and effective lift-net, used in conjunction with lights, has recently been introduced on Lake Tanganyika (Plate 37).

Into this class also come the hand-nets. In the fishery for the little anchovy-like *Dagaa* of Lake Tanganyika, the fisherman has a fine-meshed net mounted on a frame of the shape of a tennis-racket, with a long handle. The fish, attracted by a light, are scooped out (Plate 35). Hand-nets, usually one held in each hand, are used by men wading in rivers, to catch fish ascending. They are more effective when a line of men works the river abreast, Plate 27.

The most important fishing device in this class is the cast-net. The late Mr. P. I. R. MacLaren wrote a most interesting account of the geographical distribution of this net, and the variations in

HTIF

its structure.[72] It is well known in the Far East, and in the West Indian Islands, in India and in West Africa, where the fishermen use cast-nets of great size. It is also known on the East African coast, no doubt brought there by Arab influence. But it is not known in either East or Central Africa, except where used, usually in an amateur capacity, by some Asian immigrant. Though used in Egypt from the earliest civilisations, it does not seem to have reached the Nilotic peoples of the Upper Nile, nor beyond that to Uganda. It is so familiar a device that there seems little need to describe its use. Briefly, it is a circular net, tapering to a point, to which a cord is attached. The fisherman holds this cord in his hand, or fastens it to his wrist. He throws the net with a slight twist, and since the circular periphery of the net is weighted with leads or a chain, the centrifugal force imparted by the twist causes the net to spread out and fall in a circle. Plate 16 shows a cast-net being thrown. The weights carry it down to the bottom, and the fish inside are enclosed when the net is withdrawn by its cord. There are at least three ways of throwing the net, and many variations in structure. One variation, not much used, is the pursing cast-net, in which the bottom of the net is closed by a circular cord after the cast. In skilful hands, it is a most effective fishing gear; it increases the chance of success by the fact that each throw takes only a very few minutes, so that a large area of water may be tried, with the best chance of finding good fishing. There is great scope for the introduction of the cast-net among the fishermen of East and Central Africa. In Ghana, the people newly settled on the rivers cleared of tsetse are being trained to make and use the cast-net, among other techniques. In East Africa, there are instructors ready to hand among the coastal Arabs.

ENTANGLING STRUCTURES

The next group of fishing gear distinguished by Burdon are "structures of meshed fabric in which the fish jams or entangles itself in the actual fabric".

Gill-nets and Tangle-nets

This group includes the gill-nets, which have for a long time been made of local fibres spun by hand, a process which gave very irregular meshes. More recently such nets have been made from fibres teased out of worn-out motor-car and lorry tyres. But the availability of ready-made sheets of machine-made netting at a reasonable cost has led to a spread of the method. Indeed, it is being actively fostered by fishery development schemes. In its latest form, the gill-net may be made of synthetic fibres such as nylon and terylene. Gill-nets in use are shown in Plates 18-20.

Usually, the sheet of netting is mounted on ropes in such a way that the netting is set in by one-third, that is, for example, 30 yards of netting are mounted on 20 yards of rope. The result is that the meshes hang in a diamond shape and they snare fish which swim against them and push their heads through the mesh. If the girth of the fish is greater than the stretched diameter of the mesh, the fish will be held fast. In practice, if a fish can thrust most of its body through, it will usually succeed in getting through altogether, because not only is the mesh slightly flexible, but the muscles of the fish are flexible, and a fish can swim forward very powerfully. It is most common to find fish caught just behind the gills, whence the name of the net. A fish which can thrust its head no further than the hinder end of the gill-cover, where the body becomes thick, will not be able to escape for the two reasons, that the gill-covers may, by opening in the normal respiratory movements hold the mesh, and secondly, because a fish can usually swim backwards only weakly. The catching performance of the gill-net can be increased by beating the water (Plate 20).

It follows from the ensnaring action of this net that a diamond-shaped mesh is suitable only for a fish whose body has the normal oval shape in cross-section. It gives a poorer performance with fish which have a flattened or triangular cross section. For the efficient capture of such fish, meshes of a special shape would be needed. It is one of the many difficulties of legislation purporting to fix a legal mesh size as a conservation measure, that a size decided upon with one particular fish in view, may have quite different effects on other fish of a different shape, and few fisheries depend on one fish only. One has to consider the effect on all the fish, for none live in isolation or are independent of one another. The effect of a mesh of a given size must also be affected, in any one kind of fish, by the condition of the fish. A thin fish will pass through a mesh which will hold the same fish in good condition, or big with roe.

The gill-net is therefore a selective gear, rejecting both fish small enough to pass, or to force their way, through the mesh, and fish so big that they cannot get their heads far enough into the mesh to be noosed. Selection cannot be very sharp, for the fabric mesh, and still more the body of the fish, is supple and can "give" a little. This is especially true of nylon nets.

When a sheet of similar netting is hung more loosely on the ropes, say in such a way that the 30 yards of netting in the above example are hung on 15 yards of rope, the meshes no longer have a diamond shape but hang in very slack and loose form. They will still catch fish, and indeed may be more effective than the gilling mesh, but they work in a different way. Fewer fish are taken by the gills with their heads thrust through the meshes. Most are now taken entangled up in the netting, and sometimes completely wrapped up in it. In this form the net is called a tangle-net. It is not always known how a fish comes to be tangled up; probably the fish brushes along the net so that some projecting spine or roughness catches on the loose twine. The fish may then spin round in an effort to free itself, and become completely entangled. Fish with spiny or rough bodies are more prone to capture by tangle-nets, but all kinds of fish may be taken.

Both gill-nets and tangle-nets may be fished on the bottom or at the surface, or at any intermediate depth. The nets may be moored or secured to stakes, or allowed to drift freely. In many cases, as for example on Lakes Edward, George, and Mweru, the net may be laid and then the canoes may beat the water so as to frighten the fish into the meshes (Plate 20).

ENGULFING STRUCTURES

Burdon describes this group of fishing gear as "structures into which fish enter voluntarily or are driven as the result of scaring, the mouth or entrance to which is then closed". To this class belongs the *clap-net* of Lakes Rukwa and Tanganyika. This is a triangular net mounted on two diverging poles, and fished from the bows of a canoe. The fisherman squats in the bows, slowly paddling forward, with the net slanting into the water in front of him. When he feels a fish strike the net, he quickly lifts the net out of the water, at the same time closing the two poles so that the fish is held between them. A clap-net on Lake Rukwa is shown in Plate 45, and a small clap-net is shown in Plate 15, and on the dust cover.

INVESTING STRUCTURES

Burdon's last group are the investing structures "which are dragged or hauled through the water, investing or enclosing any fish which are encountered. It also includes those gears which are set around a shoal of fish, thus enclosing it, capture being accomplished subsequently by pursing the bottom of the net, or by the use of subsidiary fishing gear." This group includes seines and trawls, the most elaborate and expensive gear used in the fresh-water fisheries.

Seines and Trawls

There are great variations in the size and make of beach seines. Essentially, they are long sheets of netting, with ropes to support the netting at the head and foot, and with the ends supported by poles. There may or may not be a bag in the centre, into which the fish are swept. It is used where there is a smooth and fairly level beach on to which it can be drawn, and where the water to be fished is clear of snags.

Hauling ropes are attached to the poles at each end of the net. The method of operation is for the net to be piled in the stern of a boat or canoe, which then leaves the beach, paying out one of the ropes which is held on shore; the boat then describes a semicircle first paying out the one rope, then laying the net, and finally returns to the beach, paying out the second rope. The two ropes are then hauled in, and the fish lying between the net, the beach, and the two ropes are caught. Fish are able to escape sideways over or under the ropes; so there may be men in the water to splash and trample, and so scare the fish back into the net. Or in some cases, as for example on Lake Tanganyika, bunches of grass may be attached to the ropes to act as scarers. Or the ropes themselves may be shaken and thrashed on the water. The hauling of a beach seine on Lake Albert is shown in Plates 21 and 22.

As the headrope of the net is furnished with floats of cork or light wood, while the footrope is furnished with weights, the net extends from the surface of the water to the bottom, and can therefore only be effectively operated at the depths appropriate to the height of the net from headrope to footrope. It is not always an easy gear to work. If the footrope snags on rocks or stones, or becomes caught in a sunken tree-stump or bough, the haul must be stopped until men, wading or diving, are able to clear the footrope. Where there is much submerged water-weed, the footrope may roll up and the haul be spoiled. It is an effective gear, but has three limitations. First, it can only be used off a clear beach; secondly, it can only be used in depths of water suited to the particular net in use, since the footrope must be on the bottom; and thirdly, it requires considerable man-power, varying, naturally, with the size of the net. Even a small net will need six men, as well as a boat or canoe.

Unlike the gill-net described earlier, the seine selects fish in one direction only. All fish too large in girth to pass through the meshes will be retained. The size of fish which a seine will catch can be controlled by the size of the mesh, though if the net has made a big catch, so that the meshes are choked with fish, this net-selection may be masked.

The first cost of a seine may be high, for it has to be made of strong netting. It is particularly prone to damage, and so needs the attention of skilled menders. It may be made of locally spun fibre, such as that from the baobab tree, or the Agave or Sanseveria; or it may be made of rubberised twine taken from old lorry tyres. But nowadays, they are made of factory-made twines, or may even be bought ready-made. Perhaps its weakest point is the labour force needed. If this is unreliable, the net may be immobilised. This is why those who assist in the hauling of a seine always have some of the catch, as an inducement.

Screens of split bamboo or reeds or a number of baskets lashed together may sometimes be used in the same way as a seine; that is, the screen may be laid so as to enclose a likely piece of water, and then be slowly advanced towards some area where the fish can be concentrated for capture, perhaps by the use of a very small seine or by cast-nets.

Open-water Seines

There are seines designed for use in open water, which are not hauled on the beach but on to the boat or vessel. A simple version of this is the *Chilimila* net of Lake Nyasa (Plate 32). This is a very deep net, which when shot lies like a vertical curtain, with the upper margin supported at the surface by floats, and the lower margin sunk by stone weights. It is shot by two canoes, which may drag the net for a short distance, splashing the water vigorously to scare the fish towards the net, while hauling the net in such a way that the footrope comes up faster than the headrope is shortened. The result is that the net reaches the surface in a nearly horizontal position, with a deep sag in which the fish are held. The two canoes then come together, with the sag or bag of netting between them, and the fish are baled out into the canoes. It can be used in 20 fathoms of water, but is not a true deep-water net, as it seems to be most effective where the footrope can reach the bottom. However, it is one type of indigenous gear which is capable of modernisation. A similar net has been seen in use in the sea-fisheries of Aden, and it is just possible that it was introduced to Lake Nyasa in the Arab slave-raiding days.

The best-known open-water seine is the Danish Seine or Snurre-våd. This is a marine gear, and it is only necessary to mention it because it has been tested in Lake Victoria by the Fisheries Service, but did not give better results than the trawl (see below).

Encircling seines can only be used in shallow water. They are a simple sheet of netting, with the usual floats at the head and weights at the foot, which is shot in a circle around a shoal of fish, thus confining it. The circle may then be narrowed by the gathering in of the ends of the net until the fish are enclosed in a space small enough to be collected by small nets, scoop-nets or cast-nets. Sometimes the fish, once enclosed in the circle of netting, may be caught in a different way. Fishermen may jump into the circle of net, and by making sufficient uproar, stampede the fish into gilling themselves in the meshes.

Purse Seines

Purse seines can be used over deep water. They are seines in which there are metal rings on the weighted footrope. Through these rings a stout rope is rove and when a shoal of fish has been enclosed in the net, the bottom of the net is closed or pursed by the hauling of this pursing rope. The escape of the fish by diving out of the circle is thus prevented, and the rest of the operation of hauling is to narrow the circle of net until the fish can be baled out. It has only been seen in use in the southern shallow bights of Lake Nyasa, in a modern fishery, European-owned and managed, where the net is used in conjunction with the echo-sounder. It has recently been introduced to Lake Tanganyika (Plate 38).

Trawling need not be described in detail, as it has only been tried experimentally in freshwaters. The trawl is a big bag of netting, with the mouth held open either by a beam of wood, or more usually by the action of two kites, the trawl-boards, which stretch the net open when the net is dragged through the water. The trawl can only be used effectively from a power-driven boat, and both the first cost and the running expenses of this fishing method are considerable. In the sea it catches most of the world's fish-supply, but it is not known as commercially successful in freshwaters. It has been used successfully by the Belgians on Lake Tanganyika and by the British on Lakes Victoria and Albert for surveys of the fish stocks, and it may yet come forward as an important fishing gear when increasing industrialisation makes available the markets and the capital which this gear requires for its economic use. Very substantial catches were made with a trawl in the deeper waters of Lake Victoria, but no large-scale commercial use could be found for the fish, chiefly *Haplochromis*, which were caught.

A more recently successful marine trawl is the midwater trawl. This is usually pulled by two motor fishing-boats which keep the mouth of the net open by their separation. It has proved very successful for small midwater fish such as sprats, used on the indications of fish as shown by the echo-sounder. The author believes that this gear has a future on the great lakes for the capture of the small shoaling fish, but like the usual bottom trawl, it must await a further stage of industrialisation. Trials on an exploratory scale have been made on Lake Victoria.

PRESERVATION AND MARKETING

This brief account of the principal ways of catching fish may be followed by an account of the most common ways of preserving the fish caught. The need for this arises, because fish may be caught in quantities much greater than can be disposed of at the time and place of capture, and because fish are very perishable at the high temperatures prevailing in the tropics. From the point of view of production, it turns raw material into a product of commerce, which can be sold or bartered and distributed over a much wider area than the scene of the fishery itself.

Drying

Drying the fish is the simplest way of preserving it; when the flesh loses most of its water, the process of putrefaction is retarded. In the simplest case, that of very small fish such as the *Dagaa* of Lake

Tanganyika, or the *Haplochromis* of Lake Victoria, the fish may just be thrown out and spread over the hot sand to dry out. They are then put up in bags, in the case of the *Dagaa*, or mounted on frames, in the case of *Haplochromis* (Plate 24). There have been complaints about the amount of sand sticking to the dried *Dagaa*; this amounts to an adulteration which may be a significant part of the weight paid for.

Larger fish, with thicker bodies, must be split open and gutted, so that a thin layer only is exposed to drying. An attempt to dry a thicker layer would result in the putrefaction of the inner parts of the flesh. Very large fish must not only be split and gutted, but the thicker parts of the flesh must be deeply scored with transverse cuts, so as to increase the area exposed to drying (Plate 23).

Smoking

Especially in humid conditions, the heat of the sun may not be enough to secure rapid drying, and so there may be drying over or before a fire. Where the fish are dried over a fire, the fish may not only be dried but smoked, or even partially cooked (Plate 25). The smoke itself may have some antiseptic properties, but usually such fish will keep good for only a few days, and may have to be re-smoked either by the fishermen or by the merchant who has bought it.

Salt-drying

Where salt fish is acceptable to the consumer, and where salt is available and cheap, the fish may be both salted and dried. Salt has some antiseptic power, but in drying fish, its main function is to draw the water out of the flesh as brine, and so hasten drying. The fish are either baled in heaps with salt, after splitting and gutting, or rubbed with salt. The latter has to be done with very big fish; in the former case, the salt draws out water from the pile of fish, which runs away as brine. The fish are then finished off by sun-drying or smoking. A modern salt-fish drying establishment is shown in Plate 41.

Fermented Fish Products

Fermented fish products seem to be used only by the more sophisticated countries. In Egypt and the Sudan, small fish are salted in four-gallon ex-petrol or paraffin drums, in such a way that considerable fermentation takes place, giving a product, *faseekh*, with a very powerful and, to many people, rather foul smell. In the Far East, fish may likewise be fermented with salt; but, in this case, it is the liquor which rises from the fermenting fish which is bottled as a relish for use as a sauce. It is rich in amino-acids and minerals, and is undoubtedly a very valuable food supplement. A brief description is given on page 145.

Ice and Refrigeration

Nowadays, with the advent of improved transport and small ice-making machines, the use of ice to preserve the fish while they are transported to market is growing. On Lake Victoria, motor-boats equipped with insulated ice-boxes tour the Kavirondo Gulf, buying the fish from the Africans, and bringing them to railhead at Kisumu for despatch to market in Nairobi. Where there are roads, lorries may collect fish either dried or fresh. Finally, the ubiquitous bicycle is used by thousands of small hawkers who buy the fish at the waterside and take them for retailing in the villages. The bicycle has only a limited carrying capacity, but it can travel along bush tracks inaccessible to other wheeled vehicles. The provision of access roads may result in a great expansion of a fishery, by opening up markets hitherto inaccessible. A recent case is the opening of a road down the escarpment from the Masaka-Bukoba main road to Igoma on the shore of Lake Victoria. This road now gives access for lorries to a series of productive fishing landings, which will now find a greatly expanded market for fish. As these landings were limiting their fish supplies to the available transport facilities, the road will lead to a greater fishing effort, and so to increased supplies.

On Lake Mweru in Rhodesia, where there is an assured market for fish among the workers on the Copperbelt, the provision of ice-making plant at the lake side has led to a spectacular increase in the output of fish.

The writer saw lorries by the lakeside at Mweru and Kariba in which fresh fish were being very well packed in ice for transport to the Copperbelt towns. These are good cash markets, which have given the stimulus to the middlemen to improve the preservation and distribution of fresh fish.

Lake Rukwa, in Tanganyika, is an interesting case of a good

source of fish underdeveloped because it is remote from markets. During the height of the gold rush on the nearby Lupa Goldfields, there was a handy market; but now that this has died away, there is little except the long haul over an indifferent road to the main central railway line at Itigi. Capital has been invested in trying to work up a fishery on Lake Rukwa, but so far it has failed on the question of markets. Ultimately, the answer may prove to be an improved road and an ice-making plant.

One of the many benefits which will follow the successful introduction of power-driven fishing-boats in the inland fisheries, will be the ability of the fishermen to take their catch to some especially favourable landing place, where, for example, an access road opens up a good market. The better prices they would receive at such a landing would be a stimulus to increased production, and would increase the proportion of fish landed fresh to the proportion preserved in the various ways described above.

A Sesse canoe, modified to take an outboard engine, is shown in Plate 31.

Chapter Ten

THE RIVER FISHERIES

FISHERIES in the rivers are strongly affected by changes in water-level. Tropical rivers seldom keep at the same level even in the dry season. There is the effect of evaporation and the gradual drying of the land, varied by the local effect of occasional rains; and there may be the effect of the draw-off for irrigation. But the major phenomenon is the annual flood season. This, or rather the beginning of the subsidence of the floods, is the busy time of the river fisheries. Therefore these fisheries are strongly seasonal, and so are the fishing centres, which are often temporary camps. As the supply of fish is available during a few months of the year only, there is always an ancillary drying or salting industry.

Chevey and le Poulain[78] quote an interesting note on the River Mekong, in Cambodia, which seems to be true of the greater tropical rivers generally. They point out that, in a river of temperate climates there is a definite valley, or *thalweg*, sloping down to a definite river bed, which is usually a single channel. When heavy rains occur the water drains from the valley into the river. Moreover, heavy flooding is regarded as a disaster in a temperate river valley. It is unexpected, unwanted and unprepared for, and it leaves widespread destruction in its wake.

On the other hand, the great tropical rivers have a much less well-defined *thalweg*, and the banks tend to be higher than the rest of the river-valley. In extreme cases, definite levees are formed, and these may have to be maintained artificially. The author recalls standing on the levee of the West River in Kwangtung, many feet above the plain and looking down, on one side to the pale green river, on the other, to the pastel green of the paddy fields, the sugar-cane and the fruit and mulberry trees.

THE FLOODS

Even where artificial levees are not made, the river banks tend to be higher than the rest of the valley, because of the deposition of silt where the current is slowed down by the friction of the banks. When flooding occurs, the river overflows into the valley and forms vast lakes, lagoons and marshes. But such floods are regular, expected, prepared for and beneficial. The people either make their homes on the raised river banks, or have homes, often on stilts, to which they can migrate when the flood season comes round.

In the next chapter are described the fisheries in the floods, which are the biggest freshwater fisheries in the world. In the present chapter the minor, but still important, fisheries in the rivers themselves are dealt with.

NYANZA PROVINCE RIVERS

Whitehead[76] gives a most useful description of the river fisheries of the Nyanza Province of Kenya. He also finds that "the greatest single factor affecting the river fisheries is the occurrence of the twice-yearly floods. The majority of the fishing methods used are adapted to the catching of fish moving in a non-random manner, and are aimed at the vast numbers of migratory fish at flood time. The dry season fishing effort is small when compared with the many and ingenious fishing devices which make their appearance during the rainy months. The fishing industry is in fact entirely dependent on these floods, and a failure in the rains affects the fishing quite as strongly as it affects the growing of crops, though less directly." The slack nature of the non-flood fisheries in the case of the Nyanza river fisheries may be due to the fact that Lake Victoria, into which the rivers run, provides a safe refuge for the fish when the river water is low. It will be shown later, that in the bigger rivers, though the off-season fisheries are much less than in the floods, they are far from negligible.

Barriers

In Lakes Victoria and Nyasa, spates in the rivers, which can occasionally occur in the off-season, may cause a run upstream of migratory fish similar to the well-known migration of the salmon. The most effective form of fishing gear used in the Nyanza Province fisheries is aimed at the capture of these migrators. It is called the *kek*, and is a barrier of sticks, often strengthened with stones, which is built across a river. Like the long leader-fences used in fish traps in the sea and in estuaries, their object is to guide the fish into enclosures fitted with non-return devices, or fitted with movable traps having non-return valves. The *kek*, however, stretches completely across the river, and the traps can face both ways, that is they can catch fish both ascending and descending. At the ends of the *kek*, where it touches the banks, there may be a larger enclosure with a non-return device.

A recording of the catches made by one *kek* gave surprising results. During one month (April) from this *kek*, fourteen tons of fish were taken, and during a five-month period, forty-four tons. Some interesting facts were noted; for example, that *Tilapia variabilis* tended to migrate mainly in daylight, whereas the larger *Barbus* seemed to prefer the night-time, and so tend to be found in the traps in the early morning. Further data on the performance of a *kek* will be found on page 206.

The construction of a *kek* seems to be no small feat of simple engineering, calling for a considerable combined effort, and Whitehead says that the effectiveness of the fishing industry depends on the present social organisation of the people. For instance, whereas the traps are individually owned, the fence or barrier is the result of a combined effort by all; and not only the first construction, but the running repairs, must be a considerable task. The gradual breakdown of tribal society, which is going on at the present time and which is probably due to improved communications and to mass-enlightenment due to radio and cinema, may ultimately make it difficult to continue such communal forms of fishery.

The *kek* is not a standardised fishing engine, and may show considerable variation. When the author visited the Nzoia River, the *kek* described by Whitehead had been swept away. This *kek* seems to have been made of strong reeds lashed together. But he visited a much more formidable *kek* higher up the same river. This was a massive barrage of boughs and stones, strong enough and heavy enough to dam back the river so as to give a head of water of several feet (Plate 14). In this barrage were many sluices, and through these sluices the water roared down in cataracts. Fish ascending the river swam up into the sluices, where they were either caught in clap-nets, or, if they turned in the sluice to rush back to the river below, they were caught in funnel-shaped basket traps set in the cataract below each sluice (Plate 15).

At the time of the author's visit to this *kek*, in June 1960, the chief fish being caught was the *Barbus*. At this time, there was no question of catching fish descending the river, for the upstream mouths of the sluices were barred by grilles. But it is possible that, at a lower level of the river after the rainy season, the grilles might be removed so as to make it possible to catch fish descending.

Most of the *keks* built on the larger rivers are built and owned by the families who own the land on either side, their respective rights terminating half-way across the river. The single enclosures into which the fish are guided by the barrier are individually owned; but the larger enclosures at the shorewards ends are owned communally by the family, and the fish are shared out among the members.

The marketing of the catch is by direct sale, usually to hawkers on bicycles, who retail the fish among the nearby villages.

Apart from the *keks*, simple traps are used in quiet stretches of the river. These are of the type used all over the world. They are essentially cylindrical or conical baskets of wicker-work with a small gate at the blind end to facilitate the removal of the fish caught, and at the other, open end, is a conical valve, usually ending inwards with the withes or reeds projecting into the trap like *chevaux-de-frise*, so that fish entering are hindered from getting out again.

Gill-nets are commonly used, both of 5-inch mesh for the big *Barbus*, and 2½-inch mesh for the *Labeo*. Hand-scooping nets may be used for the smaller *Barbus*, and in fast-flowing rivers line-fishing is practised.

Line Fishing

The last method will recall the fishery for the big *Barbus radcliffei* at the Ripon Falls on Lake Victoria, which is familiar to so many people because it happens near a main road. The sight of large numbers of these big black fish struggling in the seething waters below the falls is a remarkable one and so is the sight of the many fishermen, mainly Africans, fishing for subsistence and for sale, but also the occasional European fishing for sport, casting their lines down the cataract. The *Barbus* can be seen making repeated attempts to jump the low falls against the roaring green water. The completion of the Owen Falls Dam, and the consequent disappearance of the Ripon Falls, has transferred this fishery to the spillways and tail races of the turbines. A procession of *Barbus* struggle up the tail races, and a succession of dead *Barbus* drift downstream, killed in the turbines. There seems to be scope here for some kind of diversion weir, which will shepherd these big fish into some staked trap, where they can either be sold as food or, if it is proved that their migration into Lake Victoria is necessary for the well-being of the fisheries there, they could be conveyed to the river above the dam.

Production by the River Fisheries

In Whitehead's description of the fisheries of Nyanza Province, it is recorded that as much as 1,000 tons of fish may be caught in the fifteen-mile stretch of the Nzoia River between Luambwa and Lake Victoria, and even this is a conservative estimate. The Nzoia at Luambwa is some 70 yards wide. If it is assumed that it has an average width in this stretch of 200 yards, then the fifteen-mile stretch will have an area of some 1,100 acres. It would be very unlikely that such a river could carry a stock of fish equivalent to 2,000 lb. per acre. Clearly, as Whitehead says, the fishery must tap stocks which have grown in the wider waters of Lake Victoria, or in the headwaters and floodlands upstream.

The rivers in the whole of the Nyanza Province are estimated by Whitehead to give an annual crop of at least 3,000 tons, valued at some £300,000, an impressive figure whose magnitude was not suspected before. Whitehead has done a valuable service in setting the importance of the inland fisheries of Kenya in the right perspective.

LAKE NYASA AFFLUENTS

Lowe[73] gives a brief description of the river fisheries at the northern end of Lake Nyasa. These are all short rivers rising in the Southern Highlands of Tanganyika and running without many meanderings across the alluvial plain into Lake Nyasa.

Barriers similar to, if not identical with, those described by Whitehead, are put up across these rivers, chiefly to intercept the migrations of *Barilius microlepis*. This fish runs up the rivers to spawn when floods come down, and the barriers are intended to guide the fish into enclosures equipped with non-return valves. In the Nyasa barriers, the fish passing upstream are the ones taken; those descending the rivers later are caught in box traps facing

18. Gill-nets set in a backwater of the flooded Zambezi.

Gill-nets being
ed on Lake
vasha.

20. Fish being beaten into a gill-net on the Kazinga Channel, Uganda.

21. Beach-seine being hauled at Lake Albert.

22. Catch of beach-seine being sorted.

upstream. Lowe gives some fine photographs of the barriers, but was unable to see the box traps in use.

It is significant to note that there may be many of these barriers, one above the other, on the same river. Whitehead found five of these on the fifteen-mile stretch of the Nzoia and Lowe-McConnell found eight of them on the fifteen miles of the North Rukuru River in Nyasaland. These facts suggest that these barriers are not very effective. Very large numbers of fish must pass each barrier, or it would not be worth the cost and effort of making barriers, as many as eight in number, upstream of each other. Possibly at certain river levels the fish may be able to jump the barriers. Then, when the river rises above a given level (and rivers can rise very rapidly) there may be a passage for the fish around the ends of the barrier alongside the banks. In very heavy floods, the barrier itself, built only of reeds supported by poles and stones, may be damaged or even swept away. Such occasions, occurring at peak flood, would allow of the passage of large numbers of fish.

So strong may be the flow of these rivers, that a structure much stronger than any which could be made by primitive tribesmen would inevitably be swept away at times. The stress is not only through the violence of the current, but also by the accumulation of logs, rafts of reeds and other debris, including stones and boulders rolled along the river bed. These accumulations increase the damming effect to the point where the dam must burst. But even so, the barrier may resist the current to the point where there may be strong erosion under the banks.

This erosive effect seems to be the chief danger in the presence of these weirs in rivers. By encouraging erosion, they help to form mudbanks lower down the river, which again must promote flooding and changes of river course. Very formidable fishing stakes are used in the rivers of the Niger Delta. These are formed from wooden piles of some strength, driven deep into the ground. The piles form the two arms of a V facing upstream, fish and prawns being guided by the arms into a trap at the apex. In this case, the fish and prawns are guided passively, drifting down the current, rather than actively swimming against it. But the stakes lead, through the turbulence they cause, to erosion of the river-bed, and the deposition of the soil downstream. Once deposition has reached the point where the mudbank is exposed at low water, vegetation will establish itself, which, by catching silt, will still further raise the level until an island

ITIF

is formed. This island will divert the river channel, perhaps causing erosion elsewhere.

This danger is not so great where the flow of the river is sluggish. In the Andoni River in the Niger Delta, fish-fences form an almost continuous puzzle stretching for miles. The catches of each fence seem to be only marginally economic, yet the total catch must be considerable. In some of the Malayan rivers, fences made of reed or chicken-wire are frequent, and these may cause flooding at times of slack flow because they become choked with growths of the water-hyacinth, *Eichhornia crassipes*. No doubt a spate would knock them over, in this choked condition, but they can cause flooding in the valleys.

A very well-known fish barrier of modern design is in the River Bann in Northern Ireland, where it is used for the capture of eels. It is a substantial permanent structure and the fishery is run on modern lines. But there were, especially in former times, a great many other such barriers across rivers; indeed, the remains of the old timber baulks are still encountered in such rivers as the Deben. Because the fishing interests of riparian owners upstream might be affected if any one weir were too efficient, it came to be enforced, or at least stipulated, that a gap be left in the barrier, known as the Royal Gap, in midstream. This principle of a gap, to prevent a too efficient action of a fish-barrier, was incorporated in the fishery laws of Nyasaland in 1931 and is still in force. It requires that a gap must be left in midstream of about five per cent of the width of the stream, provided that the District Commissioner may, at his discretion order that the width of the gap be varied. It seems a little doubtful how far a gap in midstream would help because fish have a tendency to migrate close to the banks. Further, where the action of the barrier depends on the damming back of the stream, to the point where there is a small head of water, a "Royal Gap" would make these barriers useless. But the object of the "Royal Gap", as applied in these cases, is to try to secure that some of the fish, at all events, safely pass the barriers to the spawning grounds and so perpetuate the fishery. But the fact that there are often many barriers on the same river, one above another, is proof that there is a very large escapement already. If there are only nine barriers in the course of a river, the reason why there is not a tenth is not because no fish pass the ninth, but because not enough fish are known to pass to make it worth the expense of putting up a tenth. Yet tropical fish are so prolific that even a small escapement of adults will provide as many young fish as a small river will support. It seems, in any case, that the "Royal Gap" legislation was not always being enforced.

The inclusion of this clause in the Nyasaland Fisheries Legislation of 1931 was justifiable in the then state of our knowledge, but there is a strong case for an experimental test of the need for this law. If a large number of the fish entering the first barrier and caught there were marked with a tag or identified by fin-cutting, and again released, the return of the tagged fish from the higher barriers would provide data for a calculation of the actual escapement from barrier to barrier. Or a special weir could be built above the last "commercial" weir, and a count made of the fish caught there and of their state of maturity. A valuable pointer could be obtained from a single experiment in one river during one fish-run. Without some reassurance that the "Royal Gap" is needed, it seems undesirable to enforce a law that may prove difficult and costly.

It is too often assumed that fishing methods are harmful. They are harmful to the extent that any fishing at all will introduce a new mortality risk to fish which may already have many. But against this is the great fecundity of most fish. Each fishery must be considered on its merits; what seems wrong is for the assumption to be made *a priori* that a fishing method is harmful to the stock. As will be described in the next chapter, fish fences or barriers have been in use in Burma for generations.[77] A report of 1878 expresses the most serious concern as to the future of the fisheries there in view of the destructive powers, as supposed, of these engines. Yet the fisheries of Burma still flourish.

Scoop-nets

Lowe[73] mentions two other methods of fishing in the rivers entering Lake Nyasa. One is the hand scoop-net, which is usually used one in each hand (Plate 27), and the other is a single large scoop-net mounted on a handle. The fisherman stands on a platform built on the side of the stream and simply scoops up fish seen to be ascending (Plate 26).

Fish wishing to ascend the rivers have to pass the following obstacles: (*a*) seine nets at the river mouth, (*b*) numerous crocodiles lying off the delta of the river, (*c*) fishermen with a scoop-net in each hand chasing fish in the shallow water, (*d*) fishermen with large scoop-nets fishing from platforms built every 50 yards or so along the banks, (*e*) one or several of the barriers described above, and finally (*f*) fish netting parties, in which all the men of a village form a line across the river, with a scoop-net in each hand. Livingstone, who saw all this in the 1860's, marvelled at even the most sagacious fish being able to get up the river at all without being taken.

THE ZAMBEZI

The late Mr. MacLaren has written an account of the existing native fisheries of the Middle Zambezi.[72] The inhabitants of the Gwembe Valley were not natural fishermen and their fishing was primitive and desultory. The reason for this has not been explained, for there was good fishing to be had in the river. The native methods employed screens set across backwaters and tributaries, but often without the refinement of a trap set in a gap in the fence. The fish might merely be stranded behind the fence when the water falls, and were then speared or scooped out with baskets. Occasionally valved baskets were used to catch fish actively, either long baskets used for dragging or conical baskets used for plunging. Hooks were only occasionally used.

Jubb (unpublished note) supplements this description by a brief account of the fisheries of the southern shore of the Zambezi. He states that fish-weirs or fences were used extensively to intercept migrating fishes and that basket non-return traps were inserted in openings. The entrances to backwaters were often closed in with fences and the entrapped fish baled out with baskets. In deep pools non-return traps were baited and set on the bottom. Home-made seine nets were used and gill-nets set on stakes across the entrances to backwaters, lagoons and small tributaries. Set lines with hooks baited for predators, especially *Clarias*, were used when hooks were available. Small *Barbus* and *Tilapia* to be used as bait were caught in scoop-nets. On many occasions he had seen a fine catch of *Tilapia mossambica* made by native children using nothing more elaborate than a bent pin, fibre string, a rod of sorts and a boiled concoction of ground millet.

All this is now past. The Gwembe Valley has become Lake Kariba, and the Africans have developed in less than two years into commercial fishermen, setting nylon gill-nets among the drowned trees, and making excellent catches of *Tilapia*, *Distichodus*, *Hydrocyon*, and other fishes.

MODERN RIVER FISHERIES

In Africa more modern fishing methods are coming into use on the rivers. On the Luapula River, on the Rhodesia-Congo frontier, gill-nets, formerly made of cotton or flax but nowadays of nylon or terylene, are used. They may be used at night from dugout canoes, and the canoes may have a fire lit in a sconce in the bows, though it is not certain whether this is to give the fishermen light, or to attract the fish, or to help to keep off mosquitoes. Several canoes may join their nets end to end, and the fish may be driven into the nets by a combined drive, the fishermen splashing the water and plunging into it spears tipped with a bell-mouthed iron cup which makes a loud plop. This fishery is being modernised and gradually mechanised under the guidance of Fishery Officers, who have succeeded in introducing planked boats using outboard engines.

There is a valuable fishery on the River Volta, in Ghana. Primitive fishing methods do not seem to have survived here, because the river valley has been so infested with sleeping sickness that there were, until recently, few permanent riverside inhabitants. The rivers, especially the White Volta and the Black Volta, and their larger perennial tributaries have, however, been fished for several generations by migrant Tonga fishermen from the towns of the lower Volta. Ignoring the risks of waterborne diseases, they alone have fished these rivers. No fewer than 390 groups of them were working on the rivers in 1949, and there is no evidence that there are any fewer today. The fish they catch are smoked to preserve them for sale on the markets of Ashanti.

The season of best fishing is from January, when the previous flood has subsided, to June or July, when the rivers again begin to rise with the onset of the rainy season. The rivers have mainly rocky bottoms, so the chief fishing method used is the set gill-net. These migrant fishermen are familiar with the fishing methods in use on the Volta estuary and on the sea-coast. The fishing community there is technically well-advanced, so the migrant fishermen use seine nets and gill-nets of modern design.

In order to help conserve the stocks of fish in the rivers, the Ghana Fisheries Department lays down certain regulations. The seines usually have wings 80 yards long, this being the maximum permitted length, and they must have a mesh in the bag of the net, where the fish accumulate during the haul, not less than 2 inches stretched mesh, i.e. with sides not less than 1 inch in length. The gill-nets are likewise regulated. They must not exceed 12 feet in depth and the mesh must be not less than 2 inches. The nets themselves may be from 30 to 150 yards long. They are fixed to stakes driven into the banks or into the river bed, or are buoyed and anchored with stones; they are therefore called set-nets. The set-nets are usually shot at dusk and lifted at dawn, but the seine nets, which are dragged over the bottom of the river to the bank, are worked by day. Because of the rocky nature of much of the rivers, and snags due to sunken trees, most of the fishing is done by gill-net, which, though liable to be torn when it fouls a snag, is more easily extricated and mended, and above all, will still catch fish with the undamaged part. A seine, if torn, especially if torn in the bag, will lose all its fish.

Obviously, this kind of fishing can only be done when the rivers are in moderate flow. A fast current will either sweep a gill-net away or cause it to lie at an angle or to belly out in a way which prevents it from gilling the fish properly. This it will do only if the net hangs vertically and loosely, so that a fish which swims into the net will be gilled. Seine nets can be worked in a moderate current, but to do so needs a long stretch of river clear of snags on the bottom and with clear banks on to which to bring up the net. This is because, as the net is hauled back to the bank after being shot in a semi-circle in the river by a canoe, the men must move down the river as the net is carried down; otherwise the net will not remain open as it is hauled, but will bunch up and catch nothing. But at low river level there are always more or less extensive backwaters where the water is quiet and where both seines and gill-nets may be used.

Some valuable sample data were collected by the Ghana Fishery Department of catches on the Volta River (Ann. Repts. 1948 to 1957). It is difficult to over-emphasise the value of reliable figures and where they can be found they give reality to a description of fisheries which nothing else can give. Seine catches were carefully recorded at three fishing stations. The records showed, for example, that at a station at Kpandu, the average weight of fish caught per haul has varied, over the years 1945-50, between 11·1 lb. and 32·6 lb., with no definite trend towards either an increase or a decrease. A stable fishery is indicated, with fluctuations from year to year, to be sure, probably due to natural causes such as varying river levels. These are not very high yields. If it is assumed that six hauls are made per day, the team of fishermen would have only 120 lb. of fish for a day's work. Smoked and dried, this would amount to only about 30 lb., worth perhaps 60 shillings. At other stations the average was better. At Yezi, the most northerly station recorded, the catch per haul in the years 1948-50 averaged about 38 lb., and included 15 per cent of the valuable Nile or Niger Perch, *Lates*, of an average weight of 15 lb.

In recent years, a successful campaign has been waged in Ghana by the Department of Tsetse Control to clear the river banks of the tsetse fly which is the carrier of sleeping sickness, and in consequence, the folk who used to have to live remote from the rivers are now settling along them. The Fisheries Department therefore started a scheme to train as many of these newly settled people as wish to make a part-time or full-time profession of fishing. Most must necessarily be part-time fishermen, because they must cultivate their plots of land; but that again fits in well with the prevailing conditions, for during the rains the rivers are flooded and fishing is difficult.

As a result of these training schemes, it seems likely that fishing will become an integral part of the life of the northern territories of Ghana.

THE UPPER NILE

On the Upper Nile, the Nilotic people do little fishing in the main river, where their usual fishing methods are ineffective. In any case, during the dry season they are tending their cattle. Their great fishing season is at the time of the subsidence of the floods and will be described in Chapter XI. The fisheries of the Nile itself are being developed mainly by Arab fishermen from the north, and not by the local Nilotic people. They have been attracted to this trade by the high prices paid for sun-dried fish, especially in the Congo. The weight of fish exported in the sun-dried state rose from 716 metric tons in 1940, to 2,027 tons in 1951, with a value of some £E131,651. As it may take three parts of fresh fish to make one part of salt dried fish, the 1951 catch represents over 6,000 tons of fresh fish. Modern fishing methods are used, namely, gill-nets and beach-seines.

The southern fishermen set up temporary camps by the river: grass-roofed sheds in which the men live and in which the fish are stored after drying on racks in the sun. Some of the camps are small with one boat and five or six fishermen; some are larger, with four or five boats and twenty to thirty fishermen. At the fishing season the Nile is low and wanders among shallow islands of sand or gravel, with banks of reeds and floating islands of sudd. Birds abound—wild duck, cranes, herons, egrets and fish-eagles. The fish are caught either in gill-nets set at night, where the current is slow, or by day, when the fish have to be beaten into the nets by men wading or swimming. These must run no small risk from crocodiles.

Seine nets are also used. These may have a fine mesh for the capture of small fish, such as *Barbus* and *Alestes*, which are packed in 4-gallon paraffin drums with salt and allowed to ferment. The result is a very strongly-flavoured product known as *faseekh*. The smell is most offensive to European nostrils, but such strongly flavoured fish products are common in the tropics. They have a valuable function where the food of the bulk of the population consists of rather flavourless starchy foods. The "relish" then acts as a powerful condiment as well as a valuable protein supplement. It is not so long ago that the Yarmouth Reds, powerful enough in smell and flavour, were produced and eaten in England. It is quite possible that the condemnation of such tropical fish products by Western advisers, applying Western nostrils to their appraisal, is wholly mistaken. Modern methods of fish preservation, such as freezing in its various forms, give a rather flavourless product, of little help in getting down a bowlful of stodgy cassava porridge, or of millet or polished rice.

The larger fish are split, salted and sun-dried on lines between wooden uprights. When the fish is very big, the penetration of the salt may be helped by scoring the flesh deeply with transverse cuts. The principal species taken are *Citharinus, Distichodus, Lates, Labeo, Tilapia* and *Heterotis*. When drying is finished the fish are sewn up in sacks which are then collected by traders travelling the river in barges. The camps are financed by Sudanese merchants at Omdurman, but it is pleasing to know that the Nilotic fishermen are beginning to imitate the methods of the more advanced northern Sudanese, and a start has been made among them to organise sales on co-operative lines.

The chief defect of these camps is the careless dispersal of the offal and trimmings of the fish. Quite apart from the smell and fly nuisance, these scraps lying about encourage the breeding of the Dermestid beetles which are so destructive to dried fish. These beetles can reduce a bale of dried fish to a powder in a short time, and the loss must be borne by the merchant or retailer. Because of the disastrous effect that a bad infestation would have on the good-will of the valuable trade with the Congo, the Government of the Sudan has started the inspection of the fishing camps and of the baled produce.

WEST AFRICA

Cast-nets

The cast-net is much used in the river fisheries. When crossing the Niger while it was at high level the author once saw in the quiet bays out of the full force of the current, men in canoes throwing small cast-nets, while, on the banks nearby, women were waiting with baskets to buy the still-living fish and hustle them off to market. It is surprising that the cast-net, well known in antiquity (to the Greeks, the Romans who also used it in gladiatorial combat, and to the ancient Egyptians) has never penetrated to East and Central Africa, except near the coasts, where they may be used by Arabs or Indians. It is a very effective fishing device. A really large net, which might have a radius of 18 feet, would, in a perfect throw, cover an area of some 1,000 square feet, and be effective to a depth of perhaps 15 feet. In Sierra Leone, and in Nigeria, can be seen the throwing of a big and heavy cast-net from a tiny platform in the bows of a dugout canoe. In Plate 16 a big cast-net has just been thrown. One would think it as much as a man could do, merely to keep his balance on a platform hardly bigger than the soles of his feet, and that on a hollowed-out tree trunk without keel and of lop-sided shape. But they make perfect throws, and then lift the net, with its heavy leads and perhaps 30 or 40 lb. of fish, over the gunwale. These big cast-nets are also used in the upper estuaries of the rivers for the capture of the Bonga, *Ethmalosa fimbriata*, an anadromous shad. The fishermen will make temporary camps in order to follow the fish and will often take their womenfolk with them. The temporary camps take on something of the appearance of herring ports in the season, with their busy succession of canoes coming and going, and the temporary smoke-houses exhaling thin clouds of the fragrant smoke of the mangrove wood. Smells are very evocative, and for the author the smell of mangrove smoke always recalls the Bonga fishery at Shenge in Sierra Leone.

Lift-nets

In the Niger, below Onitsha, elaborate lift-nets are used. They consist of a rectangular sheet of netting spread out by a framework of bamboo and hinged to posts driven into the bank and with a long rope leading to the branches of a tree overhanging the river. The fishermen sits in the tree branches and when a big fish is seen passing over the net on its way upstream, the rope is pulled vigorously and the fish lifted out of the water. An attendant boy then removed the fish. The so-called *filogba* is another variant of the lift-net, which is much used on the Niger. This is again a rectangle of netting in a bamboo frame, but in this case it is attached to the side of a canoe. When fishing the net is lowered into the water, and when a fish or a shoal of small fish is seen above the net it is lifted by a remarkable feat of balancing. The operator and his assistant stand up in the unstable canoe and heave the net out, the canoe tipping over until water may pour in. But the fish is rolled into the canoe by the angle to which the net is lifted, and the net is then lowered for a further haul. This is only one of the notable balancing feats which seem to come so easily to men used to the behaviour of the dug-out canoe.

CHINA

In China and Hong Kong the lift-net becomes quite an elaborate engine. One seen in the West River in China was mounted in a sizeable sampan, the net being suspended in the water from a small derrick, and lifted by a tackle. But the principle of fishing is the same; the net is lifted either on the sight of a fish, or at random.

In the Kapuas River in Indonesian Borneo, Vaas[44] says that the fishing methods used are hooks, fish fences with traps, with and without bait, and two kinds of net. One is the cast-net, but the other must resemble the marine fish fences, or *kelongs*, of the coasts of Borneo. They resemble the *jermal* of Malaya, in that the fish and prawns are shepherded by the fences into bag-nets, which may be 30 metres long and 15 metres high. Spears and lances are often used at night from canoes carrying lamps. The fish chiefly taken in this way are the large predators. Finally, poison may be used. It is the opinion of Vaas that poison can suitably be used without harm to the fish stocks in the main river, in circumstances where the fish will die in any case through the evaporation of the water in the river ox-bows where they are trapped.

LAKE DISTRICT OF BORNEO

Saanin[57] describes an important river fishery in the Lake District of Borneo. The Cyprinid fish *Thynnichthys* lives in the lakes, but when the dry season comes round and the water level falls, acid and dark water enters the lakes from the surrounding lately inundated land, and the oxygen content becomes deficient. The fully grown *Thynnichthys* (30-35 cm. in length) then move from the lakes into the rivers, followed later by the smaller fish. As the dry season progresses, the water in the river also falls and becomes warm from the discharge of the lakes. Then the fish move upstream in search of cooler and better-oxygenated water. These migrations usually take place at night and in shoals. The shoals are fished for mainly with dip-nets of considerable size. Saanin writes that 3 tons of fish were taken in a single haul by a dip-net 15 metres long. Probably this is a form of lift-net. The total production of this fishery is very impressive; it may amount to 17,500 tons in a season. Cast-nets and gill-nets are also used. Three-quarters of the fish caught are salted down to make a product known as *repang kechil*.

BURMA

Fish-weirs are much used in Burma. They are set, not across the big rivers, but across side creeks in communication with the main river. Some good drawings of these are given in an anonymous paper.[77]

Posts are fixed upright in the bed of the creek, and if the current is strong, other posts are driven in a few feet lower downstream as buttresses to the uprights. Supporting struts of this kind are common enough in the fixed frameworks from which prawns are fished in the tideways of Borneo, Brunei and Malaya.

Cross-bars are tied on the upright posts and on this framework is lashed the fencing proper. This fencing is made from split bamboo or elephant grass stalks, with strips of cane woven through at intervals. A narrow space is left between each piece of bamboo, so that the water can pass through while the fish cannot escape.

The fence may have gaps in which non-return baskets are placed; in this, except for an obviously superior construction, it resembles the *keks* of Africa. An original idea is to cause the fish, while trying to jump over the fence, to drop into a horizontal cage from which it cannot escape. There are two forms of this. In both cases the fish-fence emerges well above the water except for a gap 8 to 10 feet wide. Into this gap is fitted either a horizontal platform of wickerwork, 10 to 20 feet long and with a high fence all round it, or else a tray is built well above water-level. Fish held up by the fence in their upstream migrations are probably inclined to cruise up and down the fence looking for a way through. Seeing the gap in the fence, they swim into this or jump over it, and then find themselves either imprisoned in the horizontal chamber, or else flapping high and dry on the tray. This trick reminds one of the "canard" net of Mauritius, similar to the one used in Egypt for the capture of the mullet, which have the habit of jumping out of a net when encircled. This net is an ordinary seine net, except that attached to the headrope of the seine at the time of shooting the net is a horizontal sheet of netting floating on bamboos. The fish leaping out of the net fall on to the horizontal net, and are collected by the attendant fishermen.

BRITISH GUIANA

The very primitive river fisheries of British Guiana have been described by Roth.[79]

Gorges and Hooks

Roth states that the Amerindians have always used "gorges" for the capture of fish, and indeed it is not so long ago that this primitive type of hook was used in Britain, for the "gorge" is included in the first editions of Davis' classic *Fishing Gear of England and Wales*.[147] A gorge is a sharp thorn or sliver of hardwood, made very sharp at both ends and with a thin, strong line lashed around the middle. The bait is attached to the gorge in such a way that the fish can swallow bait and gorge, but when the fish finds that it is still attached to the line and tries to pull away, the gorge is jerked so that it jams transversely across the gullet. It then takes the fish like any modern hook.

Nowadays, the Amerindians use hooks, which may have to be very strong to take some of the exceptionally large fish found in the South American rivers. They may be hand-forged. Roth quotes Dance, in describing how these big hooks may be used. A stout cord, having several fishing-lines with hooks baited and with a weight attached to one end, is let down into the water and the other end is tied to a small raft of floating wood. The motion of the raft up and down in the water is the signal of a fish caught by one of the hooks. Lau-Lau (one of the big Silurid fish of the Amazon and British Guiana) of several hundred pounds weight are frequently thus caught. Instead of rafts, empty calabashes can be used as floats.

Arapaima

A rather similar rig is used for the capture of the Piraracu, or *Arapaima*, which has been claimed as the biggest freshwater fish in the world, and which is said to grow to a length of 15 feet and a weight of 400 lb. The *Arapaima* is also one of the Siluroids and a fish of prey, its chief food being the Arawhana, *Osteoglossum arowana*, itself a fairly large Siluroid with a curiously flattened body, which may grow to a length of $2\frac{1}{2}$ feet (see drawing on page 67). To catch the *Arapaima* it is necessary first to catch the Arawhana. The bait Arawhana are impaled on large hand-forged hooks, each of which is attached to a float. When an *Arapaima* takes the bait and hook, the float is pulled under, but will reappear sooner or later, when it is seized and the fish played by the fishermen near enough to the canoes to allow of its despatch by harpoon and arrow. On visiting a landing-place close to the village of Yupakarri on the upper Essequibo River, the writer saw the skins and bones of many of the *Arapaima* lying on the bank where the fishermen had left them, for here it is the practice to fillet the fish. The fillets, each perhaps 3 feet long, were hanging out to dry in the sun like long strips of pink cloth. This method of catching *Arapaima* is only used when the river is low and where there are long quiet stretches of river with hardly any current. The fish seem to prefer to lie where deep water has been scoured out under a bank.

Bait

As bait the Amerindians use lures made from feathers, or cut from reeds or water-lily blossom. Baits for vegetable-feeding fishes may be fruits such as crab-nuts, seeds of *Hevea* or *Smilax* or the flower of the large white water-lily or the green pulp of the calabash fruit. Spiders are found to be effective bait, and so are certain ants; all these may be used also as ground-bait to attract the fish as well as on the hook to catch them. Similarly, the fish may be attracted by whistling, splashing the water or beating it with a rod.

Foul-hooking or jigging is used for catching a fish called the Yukunuri, when it is shoaling. The curiosity of the fish is aroused by beating the water, and the fish are then jigged for, with a number of hooks attached to a short thick rod.

Shooting and Spearing

Shooting and spearing are methods used in conjunction with ground-baiting or with the attraction of the fish by noises and splashing, or with the stupefaction of the fish by poison. Roth (loc. cit.) describes five types of arrow used for shooting fish. All the arrows are barbed; one has three barbed points and two are harpoon arrows in which the iron head, is detachable and is tied to a line held by the fisherman. When a fish is struck the fisherman lands it by hauling on the line. The harpoon thrown by hand also has a detachable head. It is identical with the harpoon used among the Caribbean Islands for spearing the small whale known as the Blackfish. As the Amerindians of British Guiana are related to the Arawaks and Caribs who once inhabited all the West Indian Islands, one may wonder whether the harpoon used among the islands is not the Amerindian harpoon taken over by the present inhabitants. Originally, the detachable head was made of deer-bone. As Brown[80] points out, the four cent stamp of British Guiana gives an excellent illustration of an Amerindian fishing with bow and arrow.

Poisoning

Poisoning is still in use, the plant used being chiefly a *Lonchocarpus* known to the Indians as Haiari, but a *Tephrosia* is also used. These plants are pounded to extract the juice, which is mixed with water or mud and poured or thrown into the water. Sometimes a natural pool is poisoned in this way, but more often a pool or lagoon where fish are known to be plentiful is dammed off by a barrier of stones or sticks, so that the fish cannot escape the poison or the fishermen. Once the fish are stupefied or killed, they are caught with arrows or harpoons, or by hand-nets or even with the bare hands.

It is notable, not only that fish poisoning in this way is universal among primitive people, but that they all use local plants which have in common the production of the drug rotenone. We can hardly believe that this method has been inherited from the common ancestors of all mankind, so we can only conclude that it has been independently discovered. In this the discovery of the action of rotenone resembles the discovery of stimulating drinks which, whether as tea, coffee, cocoa or yerba matè all contain the same stimulating drug caffeine, or one of that group of drugs. Rotenone can now be bought commercially in pure form, as well as in Derris extract of named strength. Raw derris root was tried at Malacca. It is bought (or can be collected) as bundles of brown, sticky, very pliant vines. These are pounded with a stick or stone in water, when a thick milky juice comes out. The pounded and softened vines are wrung out in the water until all the juice has been extracted. The milky emulsion is then scattered over the water. After an hour or two the first fish will be seen swimming violently about near the surface and after five or six hours all the fish are at the surface and are either dead, or so drugged that they may be caught by hand. The fish are perfectly safe for human consumption, so that the use of derris for clearing the wild fish from the Malacca ponds was very popular with the labourers. As a fish poison derris is rather expensive: estimated at $22 (or say £2 12s.) per acre at Malacca. Since then, we have used a far more effective fish toxin, namely Shell "Endrex" at a fraction of the cost per acre (see Soong and Merican[148]).

Rotenone is a respiratory poison, and the fish will in many cases recover if they are taken out of the water as soon as they are catchable, and are placed in a large volume of clean water.

Traps

Fish traps are used by Amerindians in great variety. There is the spring-hook trap in which the baited line is attached to a supple rod, bent so that it will spring upright when released. There is a trip device attached to the baited hook, so that when the bait is taken and the fish is hooked, the trip is released. The fish is then jerked out of the water clear of predatory fish or crabs (though not of predatory birds). This identical method is used in the delta of the Niger in West Africa.

A very simple trap consists of a hollow cylinder of wood stopped at one end and suspended about 2 feet beneath the surface of the

water by a line. The blind end is baited with a live fish. The cylinder
is so balanced that when a predatory fish enters to take the bait, the
cylinder tips up and the blind end sinks. The predator may not be
able to reverse and is taken. A similar simple trap is used on the
Niger for catching catfish. They are enticed into a narrow bamboo
tube in which they are held by their backward-pointing spines.

More elaborate traps are wickerwork cages with trap doors which
are tripped when a fish enters. Similar traps are seen in Nigeria. They
work on identical principles, similar to that of land traps for game;
they have the great advantage that the fish cannot escape, yet is
protected from predators. It seems likely that such traps, appearing
in almost identical form at places so widely separated, are among the
most primitive fishing devices known to mankind.

Nets were formerly not known to the Amerindians but nowadays
they may use stop-nets into which fish are driven by beating the
water. But nets are unimportant in the rivers of British Guiana.

Puddling

Puddling is practised by the Amerindians. The principle is to stir up
the mud until the fish are suffocated, and this effect may be helped
by the release of sulphuretted hydrogen from the mud. Not only may
the fishermen trample the mud with their feet but a heavy log or
small tree may be dragged about in the water. It may be that this
principle of suffocating the fish by stirring up the mud is at the back
of many of the big communal fish drives, so much a feature of
primitive tribal custom the world over.

Finally, Roth describes primitive hand-fishing methods, such as
tickling fish, and killing sleeping fish at night with cutlasses, using
torches to see the fish (a method used, incidentally, on coral reefs in
East Africa and the Pacific). The Amerindian fishermen may even
use the otter as an indirect means of obtaining fish. By watching the
places where the otter leaves its prey after capture, the fishermen can
confiscate the booty for their own use.

THE "NGOLA" OF THE CONGO

Mathieu[81] describes a substantial filtering device in use in the
River Congo, by which fish are swept passively by the strong current
into a palisade-like structure, ending in a sloping screen. This is the

23. Split fish being dried on racks, Lake Albert.

24. Dried *Haplochromis* put up for sale on frames, Lake Victoria.

25. A fish-smoking pit, Lake Edward, Uganda.

26. A scoop-net in use, Nyasaland.

27. Hand-nets, Nyasaland.

28. A *Ngola* in the River Congo.

ngola, and because it is set among rapids, some crude engineering skill is needed. Mathieu gives excellent photographs, which show how the palisades are fixed in crevices in the rocks, or between big stones (Plate 28). They consist of upright stakes about half a metre apart, buttressed with forked sticks, and secured to each other by horizontal bars, with diagonal sticks to form extra braces. Even so, the *ngola* is very frequently swept away even at low water, and few survive the floods; they have to be constructed anew.

The principle of the device is that fish swept into the narrowing gap between the palisades by the swift current are dashed against the poles, perhaps stunned, then carried by the current on to the inclined screen, from which they are removed by the men on watch (Plate 28).

Mathieu gives some statistics of catches. These naturally show a correlation with the fluctuations in water-level; each rise of water-level, which signifies a faster flow, results in an increased rate of catch. The principal fish caught are *Mormyrops*, *Distichodus* (2 spp.), *Labeo*, *Hydrocyon* (2 spp.) and *Gnathonemus* (2 spp.). The rate of production is not heavy, and each trap produced an average of about 63 kg. of fish during the season recorded. That is a small yield, remarks the author, for a device which takes 60 man-hours to put up. Nevertheless, it caught more fish in that area of the river than all other methods combined. It will be noted that the fish were apparently being passively swept downstream, and were not upstream migrants. Mathieu thinks that the infatuation of Africans for this not very efficient trap prevents them from using alternative methods effectively. Even nets take second place.

THE "DAY" OF INDO-CHINA

The most elaborate fishing device in use in the tropical rivers seems to be the *day* of Indo-china.[74] The Mekong River (one of the world's greatest rivers) comes down in flood in June, with the melting of the snows in Tibet and the onset of the local south-west monsoon, which brings heavy rain. When the river rises beyond a certain height, it flows back along a natural spillway, named the Tonlé Sap, into the Great Lake of Cambodia. The fishing in the Great Lake, which is the most productive freshwater fishery in the world, will be described in the next chapter. Here, however, after October when the floods begin to subside, the fish which have bred and grown in the Great Lake, and have grown fat on the rich feeding there, travel back down the Tonlé Sap with the receding water, to avoid the low water-level and high temperatures of November to May.

Many different fishing devices are used in the Tonlé Sap to catch these migrating fish, and the *day* is the most important, for by this method some 10,000 metric tons of fish are caught annually.

There is an excellent figure in the work of Seo Leang and Dom Saveun[74] which is reproduced here (page 95). The *day* is a type of stow-net, a truncated cone of netting, 60 to 100 metres long, and 25 to 40 metres across the mouth. The meshes at the open end are 4 cm., diminishing to 1 cm. in the bag. Such variation in the mesh size is very common, especially in nets used in the tropics. Similar stow-nets used in estuaries in Borneo and Brunei have very large meshes at the mouth, diminishing to a shrimp-mesh in the bag.

But the *day* is not fixed to stakes but moored by a system of anchors; the number and arrangement of the anchors depends on the size of the net itself, on the size of mesh in the net and on the force of the current.

The mouth of the net is rectangular; there are no floats on the headrope nor weights on the footrope. The net is kept open by a cross-bar of heavy bamboo lashed to two bamboo rafts, and by vertical poles of wood braced by a system of ropes or wires to the rafts, which are strongly anchored. There seem to be no turn-buckles by which the vertical poles, which keep the mouth of the net open, can be raised, so as to close the net when needed.

At least two sampans attend the net. One is moored to the bamboo rafts at the mouth of the net, and the men in it help to keep the mouth clear of snags and debris. A second sampan tends the bag. This sampan has a small turnbuckle by which the bag can be lifted. The fish swept into the net are retained by a long cigar-shaped basket of rotans woven over a series of strong circular rings and with rotan handles. The basket fits into a ring to which the narrow end of the net is laced. At intervals the sampan hoists the baskets to the surface, and the fish are emptied out. The river current is the agency which sweeps the fish into the net. This is interesting because it is much more common for fish to swim against a current, so that most river fishing devices face downstream to take fish coming up against the current. The *day* is not fixed to permanent stakes, probably because there would then be an obstruction of the channel, while, secondly, the large and sudden changes in river level would need an elaborate fixed framework.

Chapter Eleven

THE FLOOD FISHERIES

IN the beginning of Chapter X, it was said that the greatest river fisheries occur when the rivers flood and inundate the surrounding land. In this chapter these flood fisheries will be described. The land annually flooded varies greatly in depth and area. There are long deep channels and lagoons, often former river beds, generally approximately parallel to the main channel, and still linked with the main river by a more or less narrow strait. Such are called *khors* in the Sudan and *bengs* in Cambodia. In Cambodia the connecting strait is called a *prek*. There are other natural depressions in the land which form lakes when the floods come and which retain water for a long time after the floods subside. Between these deeper parts are more or less flat areas which are flooded to a depth, perhaps, of only a few inches, a kind of water-meadow, called *toich* in the Sudan.

THE SUDAN

Flying over the Sudan at flood time one can see the great areas of water-meadow, bright green with fresh grass, with only a glint of water in the thinner places to show that the flood water is present. The deeper *khors* on the other hand, show a deeper green and look like great tributaries. Evans-Pritchard[82] describes the flood plain of the Nile, in Nuerland, as follows: "This vast plain is threaded with depressions . . . which run in all directions and link up with the main rivers. Where continuous, these depressions have the appearance of small rivers, though water seldom flows in them. While rain is falling on the country, the main rivers flood into these depressions, making a network of waterways which prevent drainage from the saturated earth, so that the rainwater everywhere lies in deep puddles which slowly extend until . . . the whole country, except for the higher ground, is inundated." He describes a journey across this country during the flood season. "On a tour of Western

Nuerland in October 1936, a fairly dry year, we walked about continuously in several inches of water for seventeen days, apart from having to cross numerous depressions."

The Jonglei Investigation Team[83] sums up the benefits which come from the annual flood as follows: "The Nile therefore produces for the inhabitants, by a simple process of natural irrigation, adequate pasture for their animal stock, and plentiful supplies of fish, when such vital assets are not available elsewhere . . . some 700,000 people and 800,000 animals are in one way or another dependent for their very existence for from four to five months of the year on the flood-plains of the river."

THE NUER OF THE UPPER NILE

Evans-Pritchard[82] made a study of the Nuer people of the southern Sudan, who live in the flood plains of the Nile and its tributaries. They are predominantly cattle-raisers and have to make use of a mixed economy, since their herds do not supply them with all the food they need, especially in the dry season, when the supply of milk diminishes. They do a little agriculture, chiefly of millet, but the crop is uncertain. Fish is the great supplement to the diet of the Nuer, and enables them to survive years in which their crops fail, or when there are epidemics among the herds of cattle. In choosing sites for their encampments, the opportunities for fishing are as important as water and pasturage. They pretend to despise fishing, even those tribes with so few cattle that they have to depend mainly on fishing; yet they enjoy fishing and the feeling of well-being given by a full diet of fish. Tribes and tribal sections jealously guard their fishing rights.

Here, again, it is the seasonal flooding of the river which allows the Nuer to kill fish in such large quantities. At high water the fish leave the river and move into the shallow lagoons and water-meadows where they are easily accessible to simple methods of fishing. The best fishing months are November and December, when the rivers begin to fall and the streams and lagoons begin to dry out. The Nuer then dam the shallows at suitable points, and the fish may be speared in their efforts to break downstream. Fishing at the dams is mainly at night, fires being lighted behind the line of spearmen, who fix their attention on a line of reeds planted upstream of the dam, and plunge their spears where the fish reveal themselves by the movements of the reeds. There is also much spearing of fish in the flooded water-meadows, the fisherman spearing where he sees a fish ploughing its way through the grass.

As the dry season advances, and great numbers of fish are cut off in lagoons and backwaters which have lost their connection with the main river, there are communal drives or battues, in which gaffs, spears, and baskets are used by the whole tribe, and all the fish are taken. Probably no harm results, for the fish would die in any case, due to the drying up of the water.

Evans-Pritchard shows that fish, taken in these simple ways, have a vital place in the calendar of Nuer activities and migrations. During the wet season, the Nuer grow their grain and meat, and are then living on patches of drier ground above flood level. As the floods subside, the Nuer drive their cattle down to the emerging water-meadows, where there is a rich grazing of young grass, and so there is plentiful milk. Thus, during the wet season, the Nuer have millet for porridge and beer, and towards the end of the wet season abundant milk and some fish. These months, from September to December, are the months of plenty.

But then the dry season begins; grain and meat become scarcer, and the supply of milk declines. It is then that fish become the mainstay of the Nuer, for with the dry season, fish become more and more vulnerable to the simple fishing methods described. Fishing is not so much an industry as an essential part of the Nuer way of life.

OTHER NILOTIC TRIBES

A further account of the fishery in the flood region of the Nile is given by Stubbs,[85] who deals with the Nilotic tribes other than the Nuer. He points out that the fishing rights are owned by individuals or clans, who may collect tribute from strangers fishing their waters.

The Nile rivers have banks generally higher than the level of adjacent land, and the tribesmen may cut channels in the banks, to lead the water into low-lying basins, where fish grow and spawn. They are caught in simple wicker traps set in the channels when they try to regain the river.

In the water-meadows, the fish are speared either blindly or at sight. They may be detected by movements in the standing grass; at night they may be speared at sight with the aid of torches, in the sandy shallow stretches of water which lie between the deeper pools.

The women may catch fish in the shallow water by plunging with a conical wicker basket which has a hole in the top. If a fish is enclosed in the basket, it is removed through the hole. A simple hammock-shaped lift-net may be used by two people. It may be 5 feet long and 3 feet broad, of a 4-inch mesh on a rectangular frame. A barbed-headed gaff may be used, with which the water is swept blindly; if a fish is struck, the head of the gaff becomes detached. As it is attached to a line held by the fisherman, the fish is secured.

An interesting and unusual "fishery" is for the Lung-fish, *Protopterus*, which burrows into the mud as the waters dry up, and encloses itself in a cocoon. The Dinka herdsmen search for them by prodding the hard-baked mud, the burrows being detected by the hollow sound, and the fish are dug out. They are always found in prime condition.

One tribe, the Zande, are said to put earthen dams across the shallower parts of the flood meadows, and later obtain the fish by baling out the water (Colour Plate V). Stubbs comments that this is a first step towards fish farming.

The only method of preserving surplus fish is by sun-drying. The small fish caught in traps are cleaned, sun-dried, and then broken up by pounding in a mortar, and packed in cone-shaped baskets weighing about 50 lb. each. The outside of the basket is treated with locally manufactured potash as a protection against insects. The bigger fish caught in the winter are cleaned, cut into strips, and sun-dried. Fish oil may be extracted from the fatty organs of some large fish, the Mormyrid fish being especially useful for this.

These preserved fish are traded for by merchants; but by far the greater part of the catch in the flooded lands are eaten fresh, and the quantity so used must be great.

THE GREATEST FRESHWATER FISHERIES

From the fishery point of view, the greatest river fisheries, and indeed the greatest inland fisheries, take place as a consequence of the annual floods. The fish which had, in the dry season, been confined to the shrunken rivers, now find their living-space enormously increased. Moreover, it seems that their reproductive cycle may be attuned to this factor. Chevey and le Poulain[78] found that the fish of the Mekong River are ripe for spawning at about the time when the floods begin. In the Rupununi Savannahs of British Guiana in April 1957, shortly before the rainy season, it was noted that a large proportion of the fish examined had their ovaries very near ripeness. Spawning would take place as soon as the rains came, and their narrow lagoons swelled out over the land. Moreover, as pointed out in Chapter III, the flooded land not only provides living space, but abundant food. Therefore, not only can the fish themselves spawn and quickly recover their condition and grow, but their offspring are spawned where there will be the maximum food for them and, by the spread of the waters, the least interference from predators.

A possible or probable exception to this fertility in the floods may be the papyrus swamp. In Chapter II, the work of Carter was quoted showing that oxygen is very deficient in such swamps. When papyrus swamps are flooded, unless there are open channels through which oxygenated water can flow directly into the lagoons among the swamps, it seems unlikely that fish could spawn and flourish there, except for the few air-breathers. On the contrary, the deoxygenated water may be swept out of the papyrus swamp by the flood water, and inhibit fish life wherever it is carried.

One interesting point is quoted by Chevey and le Poulain.[78] The *prek* or channel which connects the *beng* or hollow with the main river may have a shallow sill, and the same applies to the Grand Lac of Cambodia, which has, at Snoctrou, a shallow bar, where the lake is connected with the Tonlé Sap which drains it into the Mekong River. When the river starts to fall at the end of the flood season, the level of the water in the *bengs*, which may be extensive systems of interconnected depressions, may become higher than the level of the falling river. They therefore drain back into the river, thus helping to maintain its flow.

Similarly, when the main river rises at the beginning of the floods, the water flows down the *preks* to fill the *bengs*, including the Grand Lac, thus helping to abate the rise of level of the main river. The floodlands on either side of the main river, in fact, may act as natural regulators.

But since there is a shallow sill in the *preks*, a stage is reached, as the river falls, where the sill dries out. The *bengs* are then still flooded but have now lost their connection with the main river. They may gradually evaporate, the shallow parts emerging first, to be intensively cultivated with maize. Finally, only the deepest parts still hold water and here, of course, all surviving fish which have failed to regain the main river in time, become concentrated. At the deepest-lying parts of the flood-plains artificial fish ditches may be dug, some as much as 100 metres long and 4 metres deep, to collect the last survivors for certain capture. A map given by Chevey and le Poulain shows that there are hundreds of these fish ditches.

The catch of fish for the Grand Lac area of Indo-china in the few months between the fall of the flood and the end of the fishery in June, is estimated at 120,000 metric tons per annum. There are naturally no statistics for the weight of fish consumed by the large numbers of fishermen, ancillary workers and their families, but the grand total can hardly be less than 150,000 metric tons. No statistics are available for the catches of the flood-fisheries of the Nile, though the Jonglei Investigation team estimated it at about 3000 metric tons by the very primitive native methods used there. Blanc, Daget and d'Aubenton estimate the production of fish in the delta of the Middle Niger at 45,000 metric tons. Those of the Kapuas River in West Borneo are estimated to yield 17,500 metric tons. These are impressive figures in any fishery statistics.

THE MEKONG AND THE GRAND LAC OF CAMBODIA

Chevey and le Poulain give a detailed description of the freshwater fishery of the Mekong in Cambodia. The joint effect of the melting of the snows at the headwaters of the Mekong, and of the heavy monsoon rains in Cambodia itself, can increase the flow of the river from 15,000 to 60,000 cubic metres per second. Such an increase in volume cannot be flushed away to the sea, so the level of the river may rise by 15 to 18 metres, and in places by as much as 30 metres. The land on either side of the river floods and the people live on the raised banks. The Mekong backs up the Tonlé Sap, the channel which links the Grand Lac with the Mekong. The level of water in the Tonlé Sap rises to the point where it flows over the bar at Snoctrou and floods the lake. At low water, with the Snoctrou bar dry, the Grand Lac has an area of about 2,700 square kilometres. At maximum flood, the area becomes more than 10,000 square kilometres. But the area flooded, apart from the Grand Lac, is hardly less in area, judging from the maps.

I. Sugar-cane field under flood-fallow, British Guiana.

II. Some of the fish from a lagoon on the Rupununi Savannahs, British Guiana.

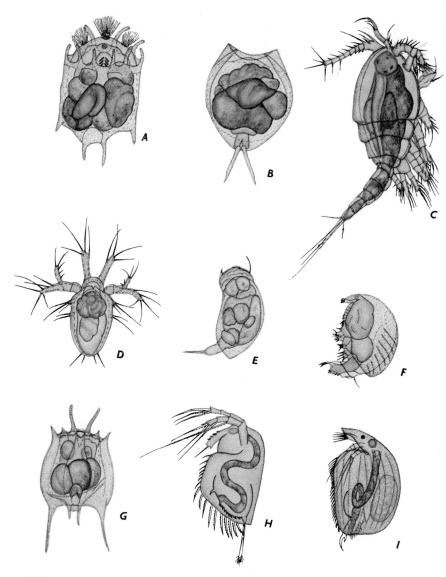

III. (*Hand painting*). Some tropical Zooplankton organisms from a fishpond at Malacca.

A. *Brachionus* sp.—Rotifera (×315).

B. *Cathypna* sp.—Rotifera (×315).

C. *Cyclops fimbriatus* Fischer—Copepoda (× 225).

D. Nauplius of *Cyclops* (×315).

E. *Colorus* sp.—Rotifera (×1170).

F. *Chydorus* sp.—Cladocera (×315).

G. *Brachionus* sp.—Rotifera (×450).

H. *Macrothrix* sp.—Cladocera (×225).

I. *Alona* sp.—Cladocera (×225).

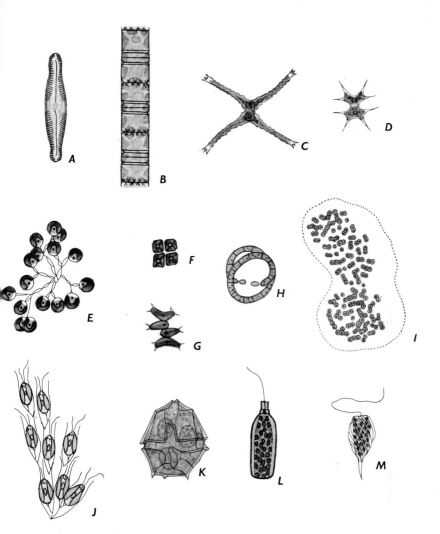

IV. (*Hand painting*). Some tropical Phytoplankton organisms from a fish-pond at Malacca.

A. A diatom *Pinnularia braunii* (Grunow.) Cleve (×825).

B. A colonial diatom *Melosira italica* (Ehr.) Kuetz (×825).

C. A desmid *Staurastrum chaetoceros* (Schroed) G. M. Smith (×460).

D. A desmid *Arthrodesmus octocornis* Ehr. (×460).

E. *Dictyosphaerium pulchellum* Wood (×460).

F. *Crucigenia tetrapedia* (Kirch) West & West (×460).

G. *Scenedesmus sp.* (×460).

H. *Anabaenopsis tanganyikae*, a blue-green alga (×460).

I. *Microcystis aeruginosa* Kuetz, a blue-green alga (×460).

J. *Dinobryon sertularia* Ehr., a member of the Chrysophyceae (×460).

K. *Peridinium volzii* Lemm., a freshwater dinoflagellate (×460).

L. *Trachelomonas volzii* Lemm. var. *cylindracea* Playf., a euglenoid (×460).

M. *Phacus pseudonordstedtii* Pochman, a euglenoid (×460).

V. Baling out water with a bucket from a swamp in Malaya, so as to catch the fish.

VI. Subsistence fishing with rod and line, Malaya.

The regions flooded are mainly forest around the Grand Lac itself, and the trees may be flooded to a depth of many metres. Outside the Grand Lac, the flooded land must be largely clear of trees, for it is described as important maize-growing country.

The fish in the river follow the rising flood-water into the flood plain and forest. While the water is rising, fishing is prohibited as far as possible. This seems a sensible measure, for the fish, after growing and reproducing in the floods, represent a fish potential many times greater than when they first left the river. Worthington, quoted by the Jonglei Investigation Team, likens the river in these cases to the stock ponds, and the flood to the growing ponds of a natural fish-culture. It is a general principle which should be observed.

An example of this principle can be quoted from the author's own experience. In Antigua (Leeward Islands), there is a lagoon of about 100 acres linked to the sea by a narrow passage. Across the passage, a fish-fence of chicken-wire was built in such a way that fish could freely enter the lagoon past the fence but would be caught on the escape out of the lagoon. Such a device reaped the benefit of the increment of growth made by the fish during their rich feeding in the lagoon, while a natural re-stocking from the sea was not hindered. The catches made by this fence were good, but local fishermen who tried to imitate it made the mistake of putting the trap so that fish were taken as they tried to enter the lagoon, and it is not surprising that their results were poor.

Fishery Leases

The flooded areas in Cambodia are leased out to farmers, using this word in the sense of people to whom the land is farmed out and not in the narrower sense of one who tills the land. Presumably all this part of Cambodia is State land, for in the early days the king himself leased out the land to a few favoured people, usually Chinese. These in turn sub-let at a profit, and finally as many as eight stages of sub-letting might intervene between the State and the actual exploiter. The opportunities for abuse were obvious, and in 1908 the authorities put a stop to the system and substituted two kinds of fishery only, namely, State concessions and free fisheries. Revenue was raised on the fishing devices by a tax and Cambodia was divided into fishing lots defined in a precise way. Chevey and le Poulain show these lots in a series of maps. Clearly, they vary much in shape and area and must have more regard to their fish-producing potential than to their actual area. Some lots, favourably placed between the main river and a considerable area of flooded land, appear to be quite small.

The income derived from the leasing of the fisheries has fluctuated, and must reflect the state of business as well as the availability of the fish. Undoubtedly, also, the varying height of the flood will influence the fishery and therefore the demand for leases. In the years before World War II, there was a declining tendency in the income from leases, which caused some concern. Some of the figures are given below.

Years	Income (*piastres*)
1923-6	710,000
1929-30	1,355,000
1932-4	367,000
1936-8	275,000
1938-40	600,000

It was feared that this fall in revenue might be a result of a declining revenue to the entrepreneurs due to over-fishing, but no statistics of catches to confirm or deny this have been seen, and the figures for exports of dried fish, of which all but about 3000 tons are from the fresh waters, show no downward trend.

Year	Exports of dried fish (*metric tons*)
1929	28,074
1931	25,830
1933	21,099
1935	20,873
1937	23,741
1938	26,651

It seems likely that these figures reflect as much the trend of trade as any change in the availability of fish. The figures show a decline from 1929 to 1935, reflecting the world slump of that period, and a recovery from 1935 to 1938 when world economy likewise showed a recovery.

Chevey and le Poulain admit the prevalence of cheating in the returns made for the use of the licensed fishing gears and therefore presumably in the taxes paid. A lack of comprehensive statistics is a general handicap when dealing with tropical fisheries. It is true that statistics are sometimes difficult to collect, and may involve a costly paid staff for which governments are not always willing to find the money or to set up the organisation needed. Yet when a major question of fishery policy arises, decisions which may cost hundreds of thousands of pounds may have to be based largely on guess-work, for lack of statistics which would have cost only a few thousands of pounds to collect.

In 1907, and again in 1935, the fisherfolk of the Grand Lac complained of a reduction in the yield of fish, in both cases to try to obtain a reduction in the taxes. The complaint of 1935 came at the end of two or three years of declining production; yet between 1936 and 1939 there was a recovery to the level of previous years. Lemasson[84] in 1949 still put the annual catch at 100,000 tons per annum, but says that most of the fish were then sold in the fresh state, so that exports of salted and dried fish were reduced to 2000 tons. He points out that fresh fish are more profitable than salt fish; moreover, the traditional Indonesian markets for the exports were then in a very unsettled state.

Chevey and le Poulain show that the high price of maize may have had an adverse effect on the fisheries. Flood forest cleared for the growing of maize may be less productive of fish than the forest, with its tangle of branches on which epiphytic plants, which form the basic food of the fish, can find a good substratum for growth. The production of maize in Cambodia increased from 50,000 metric tons in 1929, to 400,000 metric tons in 1938.

Fishing Methods

The fishing implements used vary from simple harpoons and spears, hand-lines and traps, to simple nets, cast-nets, seines and lift-nets. By far the most important fishing device is the barrage, built of split bamboo fencing in rolls of convenient length, mounted on poles driven into the bed of the river or lake and laid out either to confine fish in a certain space, or to lead them into various kinds of non-return traps. The vast size of some of the enclosures, the great amount of material needed, and the large number of workers, speaks for high organisation and a long-established tradition of skill and hard work; in complete contrast to the subsistence flood-fisheries of some parts of Africa and South America.

To work a single concession of flood-forest, about 20 km. in circumference, the following materials are needed: 3 large fishing-junks, 5 smaller vessels for carrying bamboo fencing, 10 sampans or dinghies, 40,000 stakes, 20,000 metres of split bamboo fencing and the employment of 50 labourers.

It is necessary to distinguish between the fisheries in the flooded river valley, and those in the flood-forest of the Grand Lac.

The Flooded Valley

In the flooded valley, the concessionaire will put barriers across the channels at the riverward side of his concession as soon as the flood starts to fall. Thereby he prevents, so far as possible, the escape back to the river of the fish which have entered his concession with the rising water. These barrages may be moved back, that is, away from the river, successively as the water-level falls, until the fish are confined within the inner lagoons. There they may be fished with shallow seine nets. Alternatively, the channels may be swept with nets or by a moving barrier, slowly and often over a distance of several kilometres, to a *chambre de capture*. This is a square enclosure with a non-return valve at the entrance, so that the fish cannot escape but may be caught at leisure.

These barriers are made from split bamboo, reeds or strong grasses, fastened together with three or more lines of twine. They are made in convenient lengths so that they can be joined end to end to make a barrier as long as may be needed. They are also used to make the *chambres de capture*, and indeed most of the fishing devices which will be described below. This type of fishery is characterised by the use of these fences rather than nets.

The lagoon may be fished by a device known as the *samra*. It is installed at the height of the flood and dismantled towards low water in February. Poles as long as 8 to 10 metres are driven strongly into the bed of the lagoon, usually parallel with the bank, and joined together by floating bamboos. The space between the poles is filled with brushwood, or with water-hyacinth, which is kept in place by the floating bamboos. After some months, fencing or nets are hung from the poles, surrounding the brushwood. Fish will have gathered in the shelter of the brushwood, possibly also for the food materials which may be found, or will have grown there. On the completion of the barrier around the poles, the brushwood is removed and thrown on the bank. The fish, robbed of their cover but entrapped in the screens, are caught in movable fences dragged on to the bank, or they may be driven into a *chambre de capture*.

This simple device has been seen at least twice elsewhere. In the Lekki Lagoon in Nigeria, a circle of stakes may be driven into the mud at the bottom of the lagoon and the space between filled with leafy branches. After some weeks or months, the circle of stakes is hung with an encircling net, and the fish, which have made their habitation in the shelter of the brushwood, are trapped. The branches are removed by men wading, and the fish are caught by cast-net or by a small run-around net.

Barrages of earth may be made across narrow channels. First, stakes are driven in a double line across the channel. Then lines of wattles or even planks are laid between the stakes and the space between filled with clay to make a water-tight dam. A similar dam is made some distance away, and the water enclosed between the dams may be baled out by baskets on an endless rope operated by hand or by treadle. When the water has been baled out, the fish are easily removed. The whole of a creek may be fished by successive barriers in this way.

We are here not dealing with subsistence fishing, for the driving of strong stakes, and the making of successive coffer-dams, the setting up of long barriers, and the digging of deep ditches for the con- centration of the fish, need capital, experience and labour on a large scale. Even more is this the case with the much larger barriers and earth dams which include traps and *chambres de capture* in their construction. There are a variety of these. There may be earth dams with neat revetted channels, each channel containing a basket trap; some of these are substantial works. There are the barriers of split bamboo placed across channels one above the other, with two types of net trap in them. There is the cylindrical trap, torpedo-shaped, with a small non-return valve on its under side, which is jammed into a hole in the barrier. Another variation is a barrier, past which the only way of escape is through a non- return valve into a rectangular enclosure. In this enclosure is a battery of vertical cylindrical traps, with the non-return valve along the whole of one side. These traps may even be stacked on top of one another until they fill the whole of the enclosure.

Some of the barriers give entry to *chambres de capture à capture flottante*, which are supported at the surface by logs. Fish trying to pass the barriers find themselves stranded on these horizontal platforms, and are swept off by landing nets. The fish may be placed, still alive, in floating cages in which they are towed away to market.

The Flood Forests

When the flood is at its height in the Grand Lac, and the forests around it are deeply inundated, there is little fishing except by a few poachers who may set illegal small fences in clearings in the forest. But when the water begins to fall, there is a season of joy for man and beast. The forest animals, such as wild boar, deer and elephants which have been driven out by the flood, regain the forest, and for the fishing community it is the beginning of the most active phase of the fishery. The only creatures not to share in the general rejoicing, say Chevey and le Poulain, are the luckless fish.

Into the drying forest come travellers in wagons, not only from other parts of Cambodia, but from Thailand. They bring general provisions and goods, which they will exchange for dried fish. There is fishing with harpoon, net and trap in the forest clearings and the streams. But chiefly it is the busy time for the concessionaires of the fishing lots into which the lake margins and the flood-forest are divided.

Each concessionaire has a large staff, not only of fishermen but also of boat repairers and general labourers. During the dry season these men repair the boats, cut poles, make fencing and cut straight paths in the forest in which the fish fencing may be staked. When the water begins to recede, sampans are sculled up these paths and the poles and fencing are laid. These fences are laid, not only around the margins of each concession, but in the lake itself; each concession is therefore fenced off both at the sides and towards the lake.

As the water falls, the fish must leave the forest. Guided by the fences, they find themselves barred from the open lake by the end-barrier. Now large *chambres de capture* are set up and filled with brushwood, as an artificial substitute for the flood-forest, until the fish are ready for capture.

Yet another fishing device comes into operation as the water falls still lower. Outside the concessions and at right-angles to them in the lake, are ranks of traps of a different kind. Each has a long straight leader to divert the fish in the lake into a *chambre de capture*. To make the leader yet more effective there may be two wings, making, with the leader, the shape of an arrow-head when seen from above.

Chevey and le Poulain sum up the trials of the fish in the Grand Lac as follows: at the moment when the water starts to recede in the forests, the fish are caught by the barrages set up in the creeks and the interior of the flooded forest. They may become stranded in the flood forest and be caught by the subsistence fishermen. Those which escape stranding find themselves in turn held up by the stakes and fences of the fishing lots, placed at the exits of the forest. Even so, however, a few escape into the lake where they may be caught in the arrow-shaped traps. The rest follow the falling water, and are caught in the great barrages or batteries of *days* in the rivers. Finally, a remnant take refuge in the *samras* in the open lake set for their reception, where they will be captured at low water It is truly astonishing how any fish escape; yet they must do so, for there has been a fishery every year for centuries.

Perpetuity of the Fishery

Sao-Leang and Dom Saveun[74] show that there has been little change in the fishery in recent years, as compared with Chevey and le Poulain's account in the late 1930's. In 1954, as before in 1907 and 1938, fear was expressed for the future of the fishery, and again the statement was made that the fishery might be declining. It is true that, according to the annual statistics published by F.A.O., production of fish in Cambodia was 61,000 tons in 1954 and only 28,200 tons in 1955, but no explanation is given of these figures. What is new in the account of Sao Leang and Dom Saveun is the greatly increased clearance of the flood forest for agriculture, which not only destroys a part of the source of food for the fish, but leads to erosion and, by the deposition of the eroded soil in the lakes and lagoons, is tending to fill them up. Both factors must be adverse to the fishery. The remarkable fact is that the fishery goes on, for these recent authors speak only of signs that the fishery has become impoverished in the last few years, and these are almost the words used in 1907, nearly fifty years earlier.

Preservation

Nowadays, it seems that a high proportion of the fish are sold alive or fresh. This may be a consequence either of an increase of population, the advent of cheap ice or refrigeration, or of the instability of the Indonesian market for salt-dried fish. But the chief product of the fishery has been in the past dried fish for home use and for export.

These dried fish may be produced on a small scale by family businesses, and the small quantity of smoked fish produced is also made by the small family concerns. Most of the dried fish is made by the big concessionaires, who may have large establishments, including fish-preparing sheds built on piles in the lake. Chevey and le Poulain describe these and the urgency with which a catch, at whatever hour of the day it is brought in, is prepared.

At the sound of a gong all hands turn out, the wealthy concessionaire and his fashionable daughters turning-to with the coolies and women splitters and salters. The fish are gutted and the heads are removed. They are then placed in baskets to ferment from 12 to 36 hours. This is to make the fish ready for salting and to make the flesh whiter and of better flavour. They are then split, washed, and placed in vats with salt. Finally, they are spread out on the drying platforms. The merchants come in their junks and buy the fish on the spot, to transport it to the big depôts at Pnom Penh, whence much of it used to be exported to the Indonesian markets and Singapore.

A number of other fish products are made. The guts and heads of suitably fatty fish, and whole fatty fish, are boiled in cauldrons and the fat skimmed off as it rises to the surface. As much as 4,000 metric tons of fat have been produced in one season, mainly for export to Europe.

In addition, a variety of fish sauces and fish puddings are made. The fish sauces are the national condiment of Cambodia. They may be prepared from the whole fish, which is the cheaper kind of sauce, or from fish fillets, which make the more expensive kind. Or, after fermentation, they may be mixed and again fermented with rice, to make a kind of pudding. This last recalls the *blachan* of Malaya.

Prahoc is made from small fish. The heads are cut off, and either rejected or saved for making oil. The headed fish are placed in a wicker basket and trampled to remove the scales and to empty the intestines. The basket and fish are then washed in the water of the lake or river, for half an hour until the fish become clear and scaleless. They are then put under stones placed over banana leaves to press out the surplus water. The fish are then mixed with coarse salt in the proportion of 2 to 3 kg. of salt to 20 to 30 kg. of fish. When the fish are well impregnated with salt, they are spread out on mats in the sun for 24 hours. They are then pounded to a salty paste, which is packed into jars of unglazed earthenware of 60 kg. capacity. These are left open to the sun by day, and covered at night, for as long as a month while fermentation takes place. Each day, the juice which rises to the top and which constitutes the *Prahoc* sauce, is skimmed off. After about a month, the separation of the sauce is complete, and the residue may be sold as manure.

These fermented sauces are common in the Far East. They are used with rice dishes, and are put into little platters beside the rice bowl. Pieces of fish or meat may be dipped in the sauce, or the sauce may be poured on to the rice. The sauces may be made from soya bean as well as from fish and prawns. All depend on the controlled fermentation of the pounded product with the correct amount of salt. Usually, after the correct duration of fermentation, it becomes possible to ladle off the clear brown liquor which rises to the top, though the fermentation may last for weeks or even months. The liquor has a pleasant salty Bovril-like taste, and is very rich in amino-acids.

THE FLOOD FISHERIES OF BURMA

The flood fisheries of Burma are very similar to those described for Cambodia, and the fishing depends on fences and traps made of some kind of wickerwork, such as split bamboo or reeds. Once the fish are enclosed in the fences, nets may be used. Even the device of using brushwood shelters to cause the fish to become concentrated for capture is used here also. Small branches of trees are put down, either near the bank, or in the centre of a creek where the fishermen know the fish are likely to come at night. Before morning, a fence is suddenly dropped around the brushwood, which is then removed and the fish caught with the cast-net.

As in Cambodia, the fisheries are leased and the boundaries of each fishing defined. Some of these fisheries, in flooded lakes and hollows, may be many miles from the main river. It is interesting to note that, in 1886, there was some anxiety about the supply of fish, the general opinion being that the fish were being found in smaller quantities than formerly, especially in fisheries some distance from the river. But the local fishermen did not ascribe this to overfishing but to river works, such as embankments, which impede the flood waters from spreading out over the valley and up the creeks into the lakes and depressions, and also to the increase of traffic on the river. Fisheries close to the river are liable to constant change; a new sandbank, or the cutting away of a portion of the bank, might destroy a fishery in a single season.

BAROTSELAND

Barotseland, in Rhodesia, has a flood régime similar to that of the Nile, based on the Zambezi. The fishery plays an essential part in the life of the people, who occupy the flood plains in the dry season but move to the higher ground at the margins of the plain in the wet season. In every month of the year except February, March, April and May, fish are plentiful. There is individual ownership of fishing sites, which are usually associated with the ownership of cultivated mounds in the flood plains, but there are also large areas of free fisheries.

August and September are two of the busiest months, for the water in the flood plains is then falling. Gill-nets are then extensively used, and also what Gluckman[86] calls "trawl-nets". From his illustration, these seem to be gill-nets which are dragged some distance by three men in a canoe at each end of the net. Probably the manœuvre is to increase the efficiency of gilling. In a later context, "trawl-net" clearly refers to a genuine seine-net.

Of these seine-nets, Gluckman says that only the important chiefs could command the labour to use the larger ones. The greatest of these was so large that it stretched far across the Zambezi, where it is half a mile wide. It was used on the river, but also in extensive flooded lagoons. Hundreds of people were needed to drag it and everyone who helped got so much fish that he might need the services of porters to carry his share away.

Seines and gill-nets are used mainly in the public waters. Privately owned fisheries are mainly in the shallower parts of flooded depressions. At higher flood they are fished by weirs, dams and traps, but when these depressions start to dry out, battues are held by big gatherings of men and women. The owner of a small pan with little weed would notify the district men that on a certain day they could come with plunge-baskets to catch fish. The owner of the pan would take a proportion of the catch.

In deeper pans, where reeds and grass grew, or in lagoons off the river or large pans where the fish had been retained by reed fences, fish are stabbed by crowds of men and boys, using special fish spears. The owner of the fishery, again, would announce the date of the fishing, and at a signal the crowd would plunge into the water, stabbing into the mud. This communal stabbing depends for its success on a large crowd; if few people attempt such a battue, fish can avoid them. On these occasions, which, as Gluckman said, are occasions of great excitement enjoyed by all, fishing may begin at ten in the morning, and at about one o'clock the owners of the fishery would go round claiming their share of the catch. At one pan, some 600 men and boys caught about 3,000 fish, and the owners claimed about 800. A good shallow pan is an important source of wealth, from which a man could get not only much fish for his own use, but also fish for trading.

Where shallow pans have much grass, they may be fished by women who use hoes to cut the grass; then, turning the grass about, they remove the fish, of which, again, the owner of the pan will claim a share. Poison may also be used to clear such pans of fish.

A final method used in the drying channels was a reed fence, put down to form an enclosure against the bank. Fish entered at one end, and on an appointed day this end was closed and the owners, with helpers to whom they would give a few fish, dragged the whole fence towards the bank until they had brought the fish into such shallow water that they could be taken by stabbing. It seems only a short step from this to the *samra* of the Mekong, with its tree-branches put into the enclosure to entice more fish to enter for shelter.

The fish caught on the Barotse plains were sold, either fresh or dried, to African middlemen, who resold to African labour at Livingstone, Bulawayo, Wankie and the Copperbelt at a good profit. Moreover, there was a considerable barter trade between the fishermen and the traders who brought provisions from the higher ground; and this trade has been stimulated by the introduction of money.

Thus, for the Lozi people of Barotseland, the annual flood brought wealth not only directly, as fish for their own consumption, but also indirectly, as produce bartered or sold.

THE KAFUE FLATS

Migrant Barotses are the principal fishermen on the great Kafue flats of Northern Rhodesia, where they are more skilled than the local fishermen. The Kafue is a tributary of the Zambezi, and seen from the air in flood, the Kafue Flats appear as a vast lake, reflecting the sky. In April they are a plain of pale green grass on which great herds of cattle graze. Drainage channels are criss-crossed by fish-fences in which non-return fishing baskets are fixed. With the high evaporation in the flooded grasslands, the alkalinity reaches the high figure of 13 c.c. of N HCl per litre.

In July the Flats are scorched and yellow in appearance and can be crossed by jeep. There are extensive lagoons well away from the main river, which are said to extend for 200 miles and on which fishing camps are made. Gill-nets are used, and these may be 40 yards long by 5 feet deep. They are set among the water weeds, which grow densely from the bottom nearly to the surface. So dense are they that they suffice to keep the nets in place without the need for poles and anchors. When the net is shot, the weeds are pushed aside with a pole to make space for the net. Seine-nets are also used, formerly made of twine extracted from lorry tyres. This is less crude than it seems, for this twine is impregnated with rubber and has a long useful life.

This is a very productive fishery, becoming up to date with the use of nylon and terylene gill-nets. It depends on the flooding of the Flats by the Kafue River, which causes a vast increase in the fish potential of the lagoons when the fish which survived the previous season's fishing are joined by those leaving the river, and both breed in the shallows. Though the majority of the fishermen are migrant Barotses, the local men provide casual assistance in addition to carrying on their traditional fishing with fish-weirs, baskets, spears and hooks.

In the Report for 1954 of the Northern Rhodesia Game and Tsetse Control Department,[140] it was estimated that some 1,200 fishermen were operating on the Kafue Flats from 114 fishing camps, and using 218 seine-nets. In 1956, the production of fish from the middle and lower Kafue fisheries areas was estimated at 3,260 short tons fresh weight, comprising 2,440 tons caught by gill-nets and 820 tons by seine-nets. This is a reversal of the tentative figures for 1955, which were 750 tons from gill-nets and 2,276 tons from seine-nets.

The report goes on to say that some reversal of the relative catches could be expected because of the different nature of the two seasons. In 1956 the late rains resulted in the river never subsiding to its normal low-water level, and this limited the use of seines owing to the usual beaches not being available. At the same time, the high-water level favoured the continued use of gill-nets in lagoons and creeks which normally dry out. This is confirmed by the fact that fewer seines and more gill-nets were licensed in 1956 than in 1955. In 1957 there was an enormous increase of fishing activity. The abnormal height and persistence of the flooding in 1956, mentioned above, stimulated activity, and there was an additional adventitious stimulus due to the closure of a road which diverted traders from the Mweru-Luapula area to the Kafue. It was estimated that some 8,000 tons of fish were caught, as compared with some 3,260 tons in 1956. There were the usual fears that overfishing was taking place, but it is doubtful if such fears are well-grounded. If the Flats have an average width of 20 miles at full flood, they will have a total area of about 5,000 square miles, and a crop of 1·6 tons per square mile (or 5·6 lb. acre) is low. This might be compared with a crop of 25 kg. per hectare, or say 22·5 lb. per acre, in the delta and flood plain of the Middle Niger.[9] Even this is considered a poor crop when compared with the flood fisheries of Cambodia, which are of the order of 45 to 135 lb. per acre. Even at the high rate of 1957, the fisheries on the Kafue Flats yield far less than the Middle Niger flood plain, and the waters of the Niger are very poor in nutrients. One might even suggest that the Kafue Flats are under-exploited.

The "bream" group of fishes (Cichlids, mainly *Tilapia*) contributes 54 to 76 per cent of most of the seine hauls on the Kafue Flats, while *Clarias* contribute 22 to 35 per cent of the seine and 42 per cent of the gill-net catches.

In experimental gill-nets used by the Northern Rhodesia Fisheries Department, the catch averaged 44·7 lb. of fish per 50-yard net set at night throughout the season at Namwala, 64·5 lb. for the three spring months in the lower Kafue, and 58·2 lb. per 50 yards of 3-inch gill-net in the same area. In 1957 the Namwala area gave 58·9 lb. of fish per 100 yards of gill-net.

The fish caught on the Kafue Flats may be sold fresh or dried. Because the fish are caught at many temporary fishing camps scattered over at least 250 miles of river, it is difficult to obtain reliable figures for the distribution of the fish. Traders come with lorries, cars and bicycles, and buy the fish for sale to Livingstone and the Copper Belt, as well as locally.

This important fishery has developed in recent years. Since it owes its importance to the annual flooding of the Kafue Flats, any stabilisation of the water-level by control works, such as for a hydro-electric scheme, must have an adverse effect on the fisheries.

THE MIDDLE NIGER

The flood fishery in the delta of the Middle Niger has been mentioned above. It is described by Blanc, Daget and d'Aubenton,[87] and by Daget.[68] At full flood, an area is available to the fisheries of some 17,000 square kilometres, and production is about 45,000 tons annually. This big crop of fish is due to the large size of the flooded area, not to a good yield per unit area. Even so, the annual crop is greater than the yield of the sea fisheries of Senegal.

Though it might be thought that the flood waters, when they return to the parent river, are rich in fish life, the whole area is not very productive. It seems that the fish only grow during the time when they are out on the flooded savannahs, and that the water, due to its inherent poverty in nutrients, may actually be carrying the maximum weight of fish. There is therefore no object in taking conservation measures to try to increase fish production; on the contrary, the fishing should be intensified so as to thin out the fish and especially those fish of little economic value. There is some evidence of under-fishing by the present native methods.

Daget gives a full account of these methods, but chiefly from the anthropological point of view. He describes how the fishery is organised and regulated by native custom, and shows that this custom takes account both of the traditional beliefs of the fishermen and of the natural climatic and geographical conditions. The native system of control has the sanction of religion; yet, while safeguarding the fishing rights of the old established communities, it allows all to take fish. Complicated but supple, it is excellently adapted to its object. Fishing takes place chiefly on the falling water, when the floods and the fish which have grown in them return to the main river.

The Alestes Fishery

One of the most important fisheries is that for the Characinid fish *Alestes leuciscus*. This is a small fish, but in season very rich in oil, and it is largely caught for the extraction of this oil which is much in demand for cooking. The fishery for this *Alestes* begins as the flood waters rise and the fish move out of the river on to the flooded savannahs. They are then small and thin, and have an unpleasant taste, because they start feeding on seeds and insects. They are caught in big triangular nets set in specially cleared pitches; fences made of clods of turf and lengths of matting may be mounted to guide the fish into the nets. A variant is to dig channels in the river bank through which the water pours out; a net is set in this artificial channel.

Most of the *Alestes* are caught on the falling water, when the fish gather into shoals for the return migration to the river. They are then well grown, have empty guts because they have finished feeding, have a good flavour and a high fat content. Even by the crude methods of fat extraction practised by the natives, as much as 27 per cent by weight of the fish may be extracted as fat.

The fishery is very productive at this stage and is carried out by the same methods as on the rising waters, but the yield varies according to the changing water-levels. The fences lead the fish into the nets and the barrages of wicker traps, which may, at this time, be placed in the passes leading from the flooded savannahs to the river, are set up to allow for the expected level of the water. Unexpectedly high water-levels, or a secondary rise after a fall, may enable fish to pass over the traps, or alternatively levels may be too low to allow them to enter.

When the *Alestes* succeed in returning to the minor bed of the river, that is, the river at low water, they form shoals which migrate upstream at lunar intervals. They are then fished from the banks by groups of men who may either be itinerant, following the shoals upstream, or sedentary in more permanent fishing villages. By native custom, no barriers may be placed across the main river channel, but they are frequently placed along the sides of the river at the mouths of bays or small secondary channels. The various fishing pitches in the river are well known; Daget lists 219 pitches in the vicinity of Diafarabé alone, along a 25 km. stretch of the river. There are hereditary and proprietary rights in these pitches.

In the river, the fishermen may work in groups for *Alestes*. Working under an expert leader, they try to surround a shoal of fish, using a kind of clap-net manipulated with both hands. They may work in association with the owner of a net, whose meshes may be too big to catch the fish, but which may help to halt the fish and concentrate them for capture. If there are a great many fishermen working in the group, the fish may be successfully chased into a blind creek, whence they may be baled out with fine-meshed nets. On steep banks, fishermen may construct platforms from which they scoop out passing fish; or two canoes, each with a large triangular net may paddle towards each other, lifting their nets simultaneously.

Various Fishing Methods

For other species of fish, there are a number of fishing methods, mostly the same as have already been described for other river fisheries. Fishing by barrages is common; they are much used in the flooded zone in channels by which fish try to regain the main river. They are not put up at any fixed time, but according to the height of the water. They may be put up where the current is strong, and the barrage may then be made of pre-fabricated fencing, made of wattles whose bases are weighted with dried mud lashed on with plaited grass. The fence may also be supported by Y-shaped stakes driven into the river-bed obliquely. The larger barriers may have a capture chamber at each end; a Niger variation of this technique is a movable door which can be used to close the capture chamber when there are many fish in it. The fish are then removed by hand-nets.

Another interesting variation on a method already described in other river fisheries is the construction of an earthen dam, at the time of rising water, to bar a passage from the river to a stream or lagoon. When the level of the river is higher than that of the stream or lagoon, a breach is suddenly made in the dam, so that water and fish are swept in. The dam is then closed again and the fish, spilled out in very shallow water, are caught by hand.

Finally, there are the individual fisheries. Harpoons are used by day and by night. By day, the fish are betrayed by their movements in the grass; by night, they are sought or attracted by flares. Rattles may also be used to attract the fish, especially catfish.

Line fishing is done both by baited barbed hooks or hooks with a sisal lure, nowadays usually laid on the bottom; or by lines of hooks on a long line staked in midwater across a channel. The fish are foul-hooked.

Many kinds of traps are used, including the plunge-basket. Large basket traps with a non-return valve are placed round the margin of lagoons, sometimes with a fence of branches to guide the fish towards the traps. Other traps are fastened to bushes.

Most of these individual methods of fishing are not very effective, and may provide little more than subsistence fishing. But an efficient individual method, the cast-net (Plate 16), has made an appearance in recent decades, and has set something of a problem. For this net upsets the traditional methods of the fishery in two ways. The less important way is that the cast-net makes a considerable splash as it falls into the water and scares the fish, which must be kept un-alarmed if the other native fishing methods are to be effective. The more important effect is that by giving the individual fisherman the power to catch large quantities of fish by himself, the elaborate tribal system of disciplined fishing may break down. So long as the fishery was controlled by the Sacrificers and the Masters of the Water, every fisherman was given the opportunity of a fair share of the collective catches and there was control of fishing effort. It is true that the powers of the pagan Sacrificers have dwindled with the spread of Islam and of French culture, but the advent and adoption of the cast-net will further shake their authority. The new method conflicts with the old; nor is this just a case of jealousy, according to Daget, for there was much sound sense in the old traditional system.

However, Blanc, Daget and d'Aubenton[87] consider that an increase of fishing effort would be desirable and suggest means of obtaining it. Pointing out that the existing native methods are unreliable and inefficient, being dependent on the water-levels which vary to the detriment of the yield, they suggest the introduction of the trammel-net and of the fyke-net with leaders. Fyke-nets are long cylinders of netting supported on a series of circular hoops of decreasing dia-meter, and with a non-return sleeve at each hoop.

As a possible substitute for the present barrages, especially since wood is becoming scarcer as the river banks become denuded of vegetation, they suggest a barrier made of netting hung on poles and forming a series of re-entrant angles alternatively facing up-stream and downstream. At each angle a sleeve of netting could be attached, ending in a fyke. The authors admit that the first cost would be high, but against this is the fact that the fishermen may find themselves forced to use this method in any case through a shortage of wood. A net which can be removed, mended and dried, might have a long useful life, which would go far to offset the high first cost.

CONFLICT OF INTERESTS

It has been shown again and again in this chapter, that the success of the very productive flood-fisheries depends wholly on the seasonal rise and fall in the river level. Any works which tend to stabilise water levels will jeopardise the existence of these fisheries. For example, it seems that the reclamation and clearing of flood-forest on the banks of the Grand Lac of Cambodia has adversely affected the fishery by causing erosion and the deposition of material, and by diminishing the good feeding grounds. The Jonglei Investigation Team, whose mission it was to study the effect on the economy of the riparian peoples of the absence of change of water levels, due to the proposed works for stabilising the waters of the Nile, were very conscious of this.

Yet only a sparsely populated land can tolerate a régime of flood. As the population increases and land hunger grows, it becomes necessary to reclaim land on which to settle an agricultural population for intensive husbandry. Though this is not inconsistent with an annual flood, which may bring down silt and renew annually the fertility of the soil (for Egypt has had this régime for thousands of years), improved rural living conditions, if nothing else, will tend to promote works which will confine the rivers to their channels, except for controlled irrigation. An equally old civilisation, that of China, has long since embanked the rivers. Vast areas of naturally irrigable land suitable for cattle-raising, will then have to go, and so must the flood-fisheries. Probably nobody would deny that far more people could be settled to produce more food, when the rivers are harnessed, than can be produced by the free-grazing and fisheries of the flood-plains. There is also the question of power-generation, which is attractive and necessary to an industrially backward country. But a price will have to be paid, and a greater or lesser loss of fish potential will be a part of it.

THE EQUATORIAL NILE PROJECT

The Jonglei Investigation Team made the most thorough study of this conflict of interests which has been recorded. Naturally, their terms of reference applied only to the flood-plains of the Upper Nile and to the Nilotic tribes living there. The Equatorial Nile Project plans to store water in the Great Lakes of Africa on the

White Nile, and in Lake Tana on the Blue Nile, and by barrages to release the stored water as required to supplement the present natural flow, for the benefit of the agriculture of Egypt. The scheme also plans to save a large part of the water at present lost by the spilling out of the Nile over its flood-plain. This will be done by clearing a canal, embanked as necessary, to carry the river across the present swamps and flood-plain.

Clearly, if the river is prevented from forming its annual flood, a vast and highly productive area of living space is denied to the fish; and this effect would be only partially balanced by other areas which would be permanently flooded and therefore a permanent source of fish. Moreover, the present fishing methods of the tribes are rudimentary and only effective in shallow waters where the fish become concentrated as the floods subside. Though it would be possible to train many of these people in more modern and more efficient fishing methods suitable to permanent deeper water, there would be the loss of individual subsistence fishing, and the fisheries would tend to become a specialist occupation producing fish for sale or barter.

The Team estimated this loss of actual fish production, on completion of the Equatorial Nile Project, at 2,962 metric tons net, and of potential fish production, if all the water at present available were efficiently exploited, at 20,280 metric tons. Among the remedies they suggested were the training of the tribesmen in efficient methods such as gill-netting, but they also made the very interesting suggestion that fish farming should be taught and encouraged, using natural lagoons and depressions as fishponds, by the addition of simple and inexpensive bunding works. Under such conditions many lagoons could be embanked to give full water control. "Fish farms adequately managed and controlled, run in conjunction with other irrigation schemes along the main canal or main river, could be operated by a small specialist proportion of the population."

They estimate, at the optimistic rate of roughly one metric ton per acre of fish produced annually, that some 300 acres of fishponds would be needed in the southern, and 2,800 acres in the central zone, to make good the loss of the present natural flood-fishery. In the author's experience, these areas would have to be doubled; for a yield of one ton per acre per annum can only be got with supplementary feeding of the fish, and this means the ready supply of a suitable cheap fodder. Feeding the fish also leads at once to a large increase in the cost of production, in the form of labour costs as well as of the fodder. An annual yield of half a ton per acre per annum is feasible using fertilisers alone. These are easily applied, reasonably cheap and easy to store.

There is hardly any doubt that the Team have suggested the right solution for the loss of fish potential, due to the reduction or abolition of a flood-fishery. There is little doubt that fish farming arose initially in China, thousands of years ago, as a result of the embanking of the rivers, and the observation of an industrious people that fish would grow very fast in the old ox-bows of the rivers, especially when means could be found to maintain the water level in them.

THE RECUPERATIVE POWER OF A FISHERY

Another point which comes out of this account of the flood-fisheries is the astounding power of recuperation of the fish. Consider the ruthless pursuit of the fish in the flood-fishery of Cambodia, not by primitive devices, but by nets of great size and barriers which are considerable engineering works. Yet for at least fifty years the fish have not only survived, but have given annually an enormous yield. Either their powers of evading fishing implements must be almost supernatural, or they must have a remarkable rate of growth and reproduction. This should be remembered when the suggestion comes up, as it so often does, that legislation is necessary to prevent the extinction of this or that fishery.

Welman,[66] describing the freshwater fisheries of Nigeria about 1939, states "the natural stock of fish in the rivers is being so heavily depleted by unrestricted methods of fishing that many species of fish of high food value will soon be in danger of extermination". It is true that it is hypothetically possible to clear out a stock of fish completely, but this does not occur in practice. The Niger still yields its harvest of fish. In the Middle Niger, though barriers, big nets and every kind of device are used against the fish, including fish battues, the advice given by Blanc, d'Aubenton and Daget[9] is rather to intensify the fishery than to reduce it.

During the author's first visit to Nigeria in 1945, his journal records, "A complete barrier had been built across the channel connecting a large lagoon with the river, and the lagoon was gradually drying out. Here, lift-nets were at work, baling out fish fry.

We spoke to a chief headman of the Nupe, who explained that his people paid a fee to the local chief for the right to fish." Again and again it was noted how all exits from the flooded land back to the river were barred by barriers fitted with fish traps. *Prima facie*, the fish should have little chance of maintaining their numbers; but in fact they do. Fishery statistics are difficult to collect, though those of the Northern Rhodesia Fisheries Department have been quoted (and how useful they are!). It is essential to any review of a fishery, that the best possible statistics should be available. Otherwise, a fishery which may not need control may be afflicted with legislation (easily evaded, it is true), and the Government led to waste resources in trying to enforce the unenforceable and unnecessary.

Further examples of the astounding recuperative power of a fishery will be found in Chapter XIV, where some swamp fisheries are described.

Chapter Twelve

THE DEEP LAKES

FISHERIES in lakes differ from those in rivers, because in lakes advantage cannot be taken of the current which is a feature of rivers, nor of a large seasonal rise and fall of level. This eliminates all the barrier and net devices which are characteristic of river fisheries, devices by which the fish are either passively swept, or enticed to migrate into suitable non-return receptacles. In fact, lake fishing is not so easy as river fishing. It generally needs more capital equipment and gives a lower yield than river fishing methods. On the other hand, river fisheries tend to be very seasonal, whereas the lake fisheries give a steadier yield all the year round.

LAKE NYASA

Lake Nyasa is the third largest of the African lakes; it is 350 miles long and about 50 miles across at its widest part. Most of the lake is more than 600 feet deep and most of the northern part is more than 1,200 feet deep. The deepest known sounding is 386 fathoms (2,316 feet). The ground on both the eastern and the western sides is high plateau, though there is a fairly wide plain between the escarpments and the lake in its southern half. In the northern half of the lake, the scarps rise sheer from the water. The contour of the lake bottom conforms with the land; the areas of greatest depth and the steepest slopes in the lake-bottom are in the northern part. On one occasion a fisheries research party at Nkata Bay laid quite a short length of net on the lake bottom at right-angles to the shore. The net had one end in 117 feet, the other in 216 feet of water, and half a mile out into the lake the depth was 450 feet.

In Plate 11, the lake at Nkata Bay is shown. The launch is anchored in 30 feet of water, a few yards from shore. To the right, the lake is already 300 feet deep.

Nearly the whole of the southern part of the lake, encompassed as it is by plains, is shallow, with much of it less than 150 feet in depth. At the north-west end of the lake, the scarps fall back, and there is a comparatively wide plain; the shore line has stretches of sandy beach and shelves gradually into deep water. Except at the southern end and at the north-western corner, the beaches are small.

Almost all kinds of fishing gear are most easily worked in shallow water. Moreover, the distribution of consumers, the potential market for fish, also tend to follow the topography. The southern part of the lake has good communications with a comparatively thickly populated area, which includes the towns of Zomba, Blantyre and Limbe, and the tobacco and tea estates. On the other hand, in the northern part of the lake, the roads must climb steeply and the towns and villages are small and scattered, while fishing is difficult because of the lack of shallow and sheltered water. In fact, everything favours the development of the fishery at the southern end of the lake.

Fish in the African Economy

Fish plays an important part in the African economy, and many of the Nyasaland Africans depend to a large extent on fish for their protective food substances, such as proteins, minerals (especially calcium), and certain vitamins. This was one of the findings of a nutrition survey of Nyasaland in 1939. But with rare exceptions, fresh fish is not available to Africans living more than about three miles from the lake shore, though a crudely cured product is eagerly bought whenever possible by people living away from the lake.

Lake Nyasa comprises about one-third of the total area of the Nyasaland Protectorate. Besides the great desirability of increasing the production and distribution of fish for nutritional purposes, it is also desirable to develop the fisheries as one of the territory's natural resources. The nutrition survey was therefore accompanied by a fishery survey, which published its report in 1942.[88] This survey was followed in 1945 by an investigation by Rosemary Lowe (Mrs. McConnell), which added further valuable information about the fishery resources of the lake. Finally, in 1953 the Northern Rhodesia-Nyasaland Joint Fisheries Research Organisation was based on the northern part of the lake at Nkata Bay. Since 1945 the Nyasaland Fisheries Department has been charged with the duty of fostering a fishery. Among its many other benefits, it has collected statistics on which some assessment of the changes in the fishery may be based. It may be said at once, that though there has been a great increase of production, the problem posed by the Nutrition Survey in 1939, namely, how to get fish to those who need it, at a price they are prepared to pay, is still with us.

Nielsen[89] has said very recently that the distribution of fish in Nyasaland is not an easy matter, for the population is widely dispersed and may be served by very poor roads which may be impassable in the rainy season. Refrigeration is being introduced, but current prices are not conducive to any costly refrigeration chain. Nielsen sums up the position by saying that while the commercial fisheries are expanding satisfactorily, there is a considerable and tragic waste of fish, especially in the rainy season, and that the continued expansion of the fishery must depend on an economic market being made available.

Changes in the Lake Level

Like other large African lakes, Nyasa is subject to both seasonal and long-term variations in level. The seasonal variation, due to differences of rainfall, inflows and evaporation, may amount to about 4 feet. There is also a long-period variation, in which the water level has been as low as 15 inches below datum between 1906 and 1915, and as high as 94 inches above datum in 1931.[88]

This rise and fall of water level has an enormous effect on agriculture and fisheries. The greater part of the land adjacent to the lake in its southern portion is low-lying and covered with bush containing many small trees. A rise of the water above its normal level means that much of the shore line will run through an area of dead trees and stumps, which make it almost impossible to work beach seines. Nor will the clearing of the stumps help very much, for further changes in the lake level may leave the cleared area either completely dry, or else too deeply submerged. At Kota-kota on the south-west side of the lake, in January 1955, the water was so low that a small wharf was high and dry, and even the water-level gauge stood sorrowfully at least 50 yards from the water. A fine smooth shelving beach, perfect for shore seining, was bare, and it was not surprising to be told that there had been a serious decline in shore seining at Kota-kota.

Apart from the physical difficulties imposed by a changing lake

29. A purse-seine on Lake Nyasa.

30. A purse-seine on Lake Nyasa, the haul.

31. Canoe with outboard engine, deep-water gill-net fishery, Lake Albert.

32. The *Chilimila* on Lake Nyasa. The end of a haul: the fish are i the bag of the net between the two canoes.

33. Dug-out canoe on Lake Nyasa.

level, there are biological effects which may have a serious bearing on the quantity and composition of the catches of fish. Lowe[73] writes: "There is probably a balance between the different species depending on the lake level. . . . These fluctuations probably have a marked effect on the fish, in addition to altering the fishing grounds, as a rising lake will drown the reed and weed beds, the main breeding grounds. The inshore species which live in the shelter of the weeds for the greater part of their life will suffer most." On the other hand, a high lake level enables fish not so dependent on weed cover to exploit new waters.

Fishing Methods

The fishing methods used in the lake itself are beach seines (already in use when Livingstone first saw the lake in 1859), open-water seines (*chilimila*), gill-nets, scoop- or hand-nets, hand lines with single hooks and set or night lines with many hooks. Of these by far the most important are the seines and the gill-nets.

In addition to these long-established African fishing methods, non-African commercial concerns have introduced the ring-net, or purse seine, which can be worked in the open water, though it does need to touch the bottom to be most effective. This gear is now being adopted by the more enterprising African operators.

The most important fish are the Tilapias, followed by *Labeo* and *Clarias*. Five species of *Tilapia* are chiefly concerned. The least important seem to be *T. melanopleura* and *T. shireana*, both species living inshore. *T. saka* and *T. squamipinnis* both live in shoals which do not range far offshore, and are the mainstay of the seine fisheries. Finally, *T. lidole* spawns in deep, clear water off steep rocky or very clean sandy shores, and lives in shoals which are usually found well offshore.

The proportions of the different species of *Tilapia* in the total production of the lake has changed with the methods used; and these in turn may have been affected by the changing composition of the stocks as these are affected by the changing lake levels. The great development of the offshore ring-net fishery may be partly the result of high lake levels, which have caused an increase in the abundance of the offshore *T. lidole*, but there has also been a great increase in the seine-net fishery on the beaches, which catch mainly *T. saka* and *T. squamipinnis*.

Ring-nets

The growth of the ring-net fishery is shown in the statistics.[116] In 1949 some 1,600 hauls were made with this gear but in 1958 over 9,000. The last may have been exceptional, but for the previous three or four years it had been between 4,000 and 7,000. Over the whole period the abundance of the offshore Tilapias, as judged by the number taken per shot of the net, has not declined. In fact, it rose from an average of 50 dozen fish in 1940 to 121 dozen in 1957. In 1958 there was a severe drop to an average of only 35 dozen per shot, but it is too early to say whether this is due to over-fishing. The fall from the peak of the previous year is too abrupt for so simple an explanation; what would be alarming would be a series of years of low or decreasing catches. Even then, however, the possible effects of changes in the lake level would first have to be discounted.

Nielsen,[89] himself one of the non-African commercial fishery operators on the lake, states that the ring-nets are usually about 200 yards long and over 20 fathoms deep, and are set from two boats, which may be 40 feet long and 11 feet in the beam. He says that the process of shooting the net may take only a few minutes but the hauling, which is done by hand, may take an hour. Most ring-net fishing is still done in the shallow south-eastern arm of the lake, but there has been some development in the south-western arm, and there is even the possibility that a ring-net fishery might be started in Domira Bay in the shallow southern part of the lake, a useful extension of the area at present fished.

The beach seine is still the mainstay of the African fisheries, and it appears that the stocks of the inshore Tilapias are maintaining themselves well, in spite of much increased catches.

Gill-nets

The general nature of the African fishery seems to be changing, and there is a tendency towards an increase in the use of the gill-net at the expense of the beach seine. There may be two chief reasons for this. First, there is increasing difficulty in getting together the large crews necessary to drag the seine; and secondly, there is the increased efficiency and availability of modern gill-nets, including nylon nets. This development has partly resulted from the vigorous policy of encouragement and assistance by the Fisheries Department.

In the southern part of the lake, the gill-net takes chiefly *Labeo*, *Bagrus* and *Clarias*. As these fish are perfectly acceptable to the African market, the increasing use of gill-nets has helped to distribute the fishing effort over a larger number of species.

Below the precipitous shores of the northern part of the lake, where beaches suitable for seining are few and small, the work of the Fisheries Research Unit and the Fisheries Department has resulted in the fostering of a deep-water gill-net fishery. The nets are shot so as to lie on the bottom, in water as deep as 180 feet, or near the limit of the oxygenated water. Experimental hauls with deep gill-nets at Nkata Bay have given reasonable yields. In one case the catch for 100 yards of net was 136 lb., of which 90 lb. were *Barbus*. This catch is not particularly good, but would make a full day's work for an African operator. A serious handicap in the use of these nets is the abundance of the crab *Potamon*. This crab does not do much damage to the fish caught in the net, but because their bodies are spiny, they tangle themselves in nets, and cannot be disentangled without tearing the net. Curiously, fibre nets are much less affected than nylon or terylene nets.

Line Fishery

Hand lining is practised, and produces substantial quantities of fish. As these are necessarily all predators, this fishery is valuable in helping to keep a balance between the predators and the non-predators. In the southern part of the lake, the long line laid on the bottom and carrying a hook every few yards, is sometimes used on a large scale, miles of lines being shot. The chief fish taken are big *Clarias*.

In the northern part of the lake, hand lining over the deeper water produces the fine large predator Cichlid *Rhampochromis*, but the fishery is not important. Small long lines laid along the rocks are more productive. At Nkata Bay the author saw an African fisherman come in with a long-line catch of 18 fish, mostly good-sized *Clarias* and *Bagrus*, taken on 68 hooks.

"Chilimila"

Another very desirable development is the increasing use of the *chilimila* or open-water seine. An improved version was designed by the Fisheries Research Team at Nkata Bay. The *chilimila* is in use in all parts of the lake but is particularly important in the northern part because of the difficulty of using other kinds of gear. The main product of the *chilimila* is the *Utaka*, a mixture of *Haplochromis* species which never exceed about 20 cm. in length, but which are in keen demand. In 1958, at eight recording stations all in the southern part of the lake, a total of some 3 million *Utaka* were recorded as landed. As *Utaka* may average about six to eight fish per pound, these fish represent a total weight of some 200 tons. Not all these were necessarily caught in the *chilimila*, for there is in use a fine-meshed seine worked from the beaches, with which *Utaka* are taken. But the Report for 1958 states that there was an increasing use of the *chilimila* during the year.

Though the *Utaka* are able to live over the deep water, since they feed largely on zooplankton, the Fishery Research Team had no reason to suggest that there are enough of them in the middle waters of the lake to give rise to a big offshore fishery. There are enough of them to give a greatly expanded fishery close to the coasts. In any case, the *chilimila*, like the purse seine, seems to be most effective when used in depths where the foot of the net touches the bottom. If the net, or a part of it, were made of very fine-meshed netting, it might be used for a fishery for the *Engraulicypris*, a small pelagic Cyprinid fish which seldom exceeds 10 cm. in length. A fishery for these small but valuable fish might be established by using the *chilimila* at night in conjunction with lights to attract the fish. The very important fishery for the *Dagaa*, a Clupeoid fish of similar pelagic habits in Lake Tanganyika, is based, as will shortly be described, on the attraction of light.

While the author was at Nkata Bay with the research team, we tried shining a light into the water while drifting on a dark night over 800 feet of water and keeping the echo-sounder working. Very soon after the light was switched on, the echo-sounder showed that small batches of fish were coming up to a depth of 12 to 20 feet below the light. We could see some of them; they appeared to be small silvery fish, very probably *Engraulicypris*, but there were some large fish as well. An attempt to secure one of these by revolver-shot was unsuccessful. The response of the fish to the light was most interesting. Within 60 seconds of the light being switched off, the fish dispersed and their traces vanished from the echo-sounder record; within 60 seconds of the light being switched on again, the traces reappeared.

The *chilimila* needs two boats or canoes to handle it (Plate 32) and if a third smaller canoe were to shine a light, such as the incandescent paraffin lamps now used on Lake Tanganyika to attract the fish, the other two canoes could shoot the *chilimila* around and under the light-boat and secure the fish. This is how *Sardinella* are caught in the Mediterranean and small anchovies at Hong Kong. In both cases, the net boats rested quietly until the man in the light-boat signalled that there were good quantities of fish under his lights. Then the net was shot round fish and light-boat, the light-boat remaining to keep the fish concentrated until the circle of the net was complete. The light-boat then rowed clear over the head-rope of the net, and began to collect more fish while the net boats completed the haul. It would be a good thing to try some such modification of the *chilimila* fishery, or a purse-seine fishery. This is one of the fisheries of Lake Nyasa which has real scope for expansion with improved nets and technique. The product, namely small fish such as *Haplochromis* and possibly *Engraulicypris*, are particularly suitable for trade, because they are easily dried, and make a compact and easily transported bagged product.

Part-time Fishermen

The great majority of the African fishermen are at present part-time fishermen, combining fishing with agriculture. Most are subsistence fishermen who only trade when they have a surplus to their own needs. Exception must be made for the fishermen of the Likoma Islands, who are specialists, particularly in the use of the *chilimila*. Their own islands are too rocky and barren to support agriculture, so they trade their fish for flour.

The lack of full-time fishermen makes the supply of fish unreliable and sets up a vicious circle in the system of distribution. The uncertainty of supply from all but a few sources discourages those dealers who might otherwise attempt to increase their clientele and to build up a regular connection by a policy of small profits and quick returns. Moreover, in spite of the findings of the Nutrition Survey of 1939, it appears that the general public is not so used to fish as to regard it as a normal essential of everyday diet. The fish-buying habit also depends on a regularly available supply. If this habit were established, the market might even be able to stand an increase in price.

The circle seems to go as follows: irregular and unreliable supplies have led to a poor market in which, even at times when fish are cheap, the turnover is slow. Because of this it is difficult to work towards a larger turnover at reduced prices. The lack of a quick turnover works back to the fisherman, who has little incentive to increase his output.

The problem will probably solve itself, for the Fisheries Department is right in doing all it can to help the Africans to build up a more efficient industry, and especially to help in the establishment of full-time and large-scale operators.

Marketing Problems

Nyasaland is not the only territory to have these marketing problems. In fact, they are almost universal in the so-called underdeveloped territories, and they all arise from the same cause. Fish produced in small lots by many operators, and distributed in small parcels, is bound to be expensive. Each person concerned must make a living, and there are many people concerned. The hawker who carries away 50 lb. of fish to sell must make enough profit from each pound to make his day's work worth while. So we have the ironical situation that in Singapore or Colombo or Lagos, fish from cold storage, caught in Britain or Canada, may be cheaper than the better quality locally produced fish, in spite of transport and refrigeration costs. In the last analysis, they are cheaper because they have been caught in great quantity by methods which give a low cost per unit of weight caught, and pass through few hands, all of which deal with a very big turnover. The only real remedy is the fostering of fishing enterprises on a much bigger scale than the individual operator or the part-time man, however great the social and financial difficulties may be.

The Nyasaland Government has helped by introducing to the fishermen better gear, and by assisting would-be larger operators with loans. Some of these have failed, mainly through lack of business sense, but some are succeeding, and these set an example. The Report of the Fisheries Dept. for 1957 quotes the case of an African fisherman who obtained a loan at the end of 1956 to capitalise his business. He was very nearly in a position to repay the whole loan by the end of 1957, though repayment was not legally due until 1966.

Development

The Nyasaland Fisheries Department does experimental fishing with new or modified types of gear, with a view to introducing the successful ones to the fishermen. It has started to introduce plank-built boats (Plate 34) in place of the present dug-out canoes (Plates 32 and 33). The latter are less crazy and unstable than they look, but even so, they are not good platforms from which to work improved fishing gear. The availability of large trees near the lake grows less and the cost of canoes rises higher. The making of dugout canoes is wasteful, for a whole tree has to be used to make one canoe. The introduction of the plank-built boat is a wise and necessary step. In experienced hands it is more stable than the canoe, has a much greater carrying capacity, and points the way to the next stage of development by its ability to take an outboard engine on its transom. Though Nyasa fishermen are no less conservative than fishermen elsewhere, there is a growing appreciation of the advantages of the boat over the canoe. Training schools for fishermen have been founded.

In 1954, the first truly commercial enterprises by Africans were begun. If progress seems slow, it has to be remembered that the ten years since fishery development really began are a very short span in the history of a country, and that it will take a generation to convert the peasant subsistence-level fishery into a commerical business able to serve the whole community. In comparison, forty years of devoted work by the Agricultural Officers all over Africa still find the great majority of peasant cultivators labouring with their hoes as they have done for centuries past.

LAKE TANGANYIKA

Like Lake Nyasa, Lake Tanganyika is in the Rift Valley. It is somewhat larger than Nyasa, being about 400 miles long by about 55 miles at its widest. It is flanked on all sides by high land and there is no extensive shallow area corresponding to the southern portion of Lake Nyasa. It is also a very deep lake. Most of the lake is more than 750 feet deep and about half of it is more than 2,000 feet deep. The deepest known sounding is 1,470 metres, about 4,700 feet. In numerous places there are shallow sandy bays, and the lake bottom has a gentle slope, but together they form only a small proportion of the surface of the lake.

Politically, three Governments are concerned with the lake: the Congo to the west, Tanganyika Territory to the east, and Northern Rhodesia to the south.

The Belgians made an expedition of hydrological and biological research on Lake Tanganyika in 1946-7, the valuable results of which are still being published. The expedition made a thorough study of the lake, and Poll[90] has published an account of the fishing methods in use by the Africans.

Fishing Methods

Hook and Line

Hook and line fishing is not very popular because there are so many small fish of little value which devour the bait. Nevertheless, hand lines are used. They may be baited with cassava paste, and may take very large fish. Poll cites the occasion when he saw a *Heterobranchus* weighing 30 kg. taken in this way. Other big fish which may be caught are the *Alestes macrophthalmus* and the *Chrysichthys brachynema*.

Hand lining in deeper water, using several hooks on the same line baited with small fish, may give large quantities of fair-sized fish. This fishing may be carried on in depths down to 50 metres, and is successful in catching species of fish which cannot be taken in nets because they live in rocky areas.

Long-lines or night-lines are laid on the lake bottom and may have few or many hooks according to the fish expected. For the big *Lates*, a few very big hooks are used, and the fish taken may weigh 30 kg. Bigger *Lates* than this have been caught by European sport fishermen at Albertville, up to 40 kg. or more.

Smaller and more numerous hooks are used on the night-lines set for the *Boulengerochromis microlepis*, the biggest Cichlid fish in the lake. For the big Silurid fish, such as *Chrysichthys* and *Auchenoglanis*, a different type of hook is used. It is well illustrated by Poll (loc. cit.; as indeed is the whole article, with splendid photographs). It is almost circular in shape. It is baited with a piece of fish or with cassava paste, and the fish are caught through the lip while browsing on the bottom. I have only seen this type of hook once elsewhere; and that was in Aden and the Eastern Aden Protectorate, where very big hooks of this shape are used for the capture of sharks, while smaller hooks are used for the capture of tuna. It may be that here again is shown the influence of the Arab traders and slave raiders.

A unique type of line fishing is used for catching the freshwater "mackerel" of the lake, *Luciolates stappersii*. The habits of these fish very closely resemble those of the true marine mackerel, and they are caught by skittering or whiffing a triple hook over the surface. The hooks are unbaited, but are furnished with a lure of white cotton. To help in the skittering movement, the short line which carries the hook and lure is attached to the end of a thin whippy rod, which may be bifurcated or even trifurcated, so as to carry two or three hooks each with its lure. The fishery is very seasonal, and takes place only just before dawn or at sunset.

Trolling is also known, using both fish bait and spoons. It is used by dhow traffic while on passage, and also from fishing canoes sailing slowly. The principal fish caught is the *Boulengerochromis* mentioned above under night-lines. It is a first-quality fish. Tiger-fish (*Hydrocyon*) and *Lates* may also be taken. As this is a favourite form of fishing by European sport fishermen, especially on the British side of the lake, it is possibly an imitation by the African fishermen.

Gill-nets

Gill-nets are much used. They are of large mesh and may be 100 to 200 metres long by 2 to 4 metres deep. They are laid on the bottom, in depths of as much as 50 metres, in the evening. They must be lifted promptly at dawn, since with the return of daylight the fish caught will, according to Poll's description, redouble their efforts to escape. Gill-nets are very productive, though they have a high first cost and will last only about six months. As the net has a large mesh, it takes only fish of large size, and as it is not dragged over the bottom, it can be used on rough ground. The best pitches for their use are naturally the mouths of narrow bays, or across the mouth of a small estuary.

An interesting offshoot of the gill-net is described by Poll (loc. cit.). A series of a dozen or so floats each have a weighted line attached to them which may be as long as 50 metres. At intervals of several metres along the weighted lines are attached pieces of gill-netting of large mesh, each piece about 1 metre square. At the intersection of the large meshes are fastened lures of thread. Large predatory fish such as the *Boulengerochromis* or *Lates* rush at the lures and are entangled in the loose meshes. The several floats are attached to one another by a line.

Beach Seines

Seine-nets are also much used, and one seen in use at Ujiji was notable because the hauling lines were furnished with bunches of grass, which made the lines act as scarers to drive the fish into the path of the net. The seines described by Poll are of several types, all but one of which are beach seines. They can only be used where the bottom is free of snags. Sunrise and sunset are the most favoured times for seine fishing, but only the hottest time of the day is unfavourable. The seine may also be used on dark nights, generally with good results. The seines may have no bag or pocket, the fish being simply enclosed in the net; or the seine may have one or several pockets. The fish taken are a sample of those present, subject to the mesh size, and include many small fish.

Poll describes a net which seems from his description very like the *chilimila* of Lake Nyasa. It is used in the northern part of Lake Tanganyika, but whereas the *chilimila* needs two canoes, the open water seine mentioned by Poll is used from one canoe in the manner of a marine purse seine. A float carrying one of the hauling ropes is thrown into the water, and the canoe then makes a circle, paying out the net and the other hauling rope, back to the float, which is picked up. Both ropes are then hauled and the net lifted into the canoe. Poll did not see any good catches made. A similar net may be used in conjunction with a bamboo plunger to frighten the fish into the net.

A Curious Net

A curious form of dragged net was shown to Poll in Edith Bay. It was a long rectangle of large-meshed netting supported at the narrow ends by a short pole. A stone is attached to the middle of one of these poles and a rope is attached to the middle of the other. The fisherman holds this rope in his hand, and lowers the net, weighted by the stone on the other pole, to the lake bottom. He then paddles slowly forward, and when the net alarms a fish, chiefly the *Dinotopterus*, the fish, flushed out of the sand or mud, makes a dash upwards, and is gilled. *Synodontis* may be caught in the same way. Poll remarks that this device, so simple and original, is based on a good appreciation of the habits of certain Silurid fish.

Traps

Traps are not much used in Tanganyika. The deep and rocky shores generally found round the lake do not favour their use. But Poll (loc. cit.) describes, and the author has seen, very large triple traps, in the form of a trefoil around a central vestibule opening upwards. No bait seems to be used and the traps may be set as deep as 75 metres, marked by a very large float. The fish chiefly caught is the *Dinotopterus*.

The Belgian expedition did a fine programme of exploratory fishing in the lake, using trawls, gill-nets and lines. They found that there were no fish on the bottom at depths greater than about 160 metres, but that at that depth there was a remarkable benthic fish fauna. As most of the lake is deeper than 200 metres, it follows that there are no new resources to be tapped in the deep water.

Summing up the results of the fishery survey, Poll remarks that Tanganyika has excellent fish of great food-value, but that of the large number of species present in the lake, only some scores are interesting from the fishery point of view, and these include big species more or less abundant and small species which are very abundant. Only a few of the most valuable species are offered for sale on the markets; the rest are used by the Africans, presumably sold or bartered among themselves. So the big fish are more frequently seen on the markets than the others, and an estimate of some 12 to 25 metric tons of fish annually sold on the markets at Albertville does not reflect the real importance of the African fishery.

Poll goes into the very interesting and important matter of the possibility of an industrial fishery on Lake Tanganyika, either an industrialisation of the existing methods of fishing or the establishment of a highly capitalised trawling industry.

In regard to the first possibility, industrialisation would probably harm the interests of the African fishermen, who already everywhere exploit to a certain extent the local possibilities.

Regarding the possibility of a modern trawl fishery, Poll points out that the Belgian mission used these nets for the first time in Lake Tanganyika. Though some useful catches were made, the several hundreds of kilogrammes of fish were taken at the cost of heavy loss and damage to the gear. At least down to the depths corresponding to the lower limit of fish life, the lake bottom is rocky. Further, where there are smooth bottoms due to silt brought down by the rivers, it was found that the rivers had also brought down trunks and branches of trees. Finally, most of the trawl catches were small fish of little commercial value.

Poll reaches the same conclusion as those given for Lake Nyasa. Since it is important to increase the production of fish, which would give a less local and more abundant distribution, it is best to help the existing native fishery by providing better nets and boats and upgrading the industry generally.

Dominance of the Dagaa

There is one fishery, however, which is at present unique to Tanganyika, and that is the fishery for the *Dagaa*, chiefly the freshwater Clupeoid *Stolothrissa tanganicae*, but mixed with the more inshore Clupeoid *Limnothrissa miodon*. This fish is truly pelagic, feeding on the zooplankton, and following the zooplankton in a diurnal vertical migration. By day, the zooplankton may descend to depths between 50 and 125 metres, and the *Dagaa* are at a similar depth by day. At night, however, the zooplankton comes rapidly to the surface and becomes concentrated at about 10 metres down. From there, it can easily be lured to the surface by shining a bright light, and the same is true of the *Dagaa*. The fishery is based on the fact that this fish will congregate under a bright light (Plates 35, 36 and 37).

There may be a vertical migration to the surface on dull days when the sunlight is diffuse, and Poll gives a graphic description of the appearance of a shoal of *Dagaa*. Towards the end of an afternoon, when his ship was stopped in mid-lake for a hydrographic station, he saw, at about five o'clock, the water change colour. Thousands of little fish were passing at the surface and he alerted the crew: "There are the *Dagaa*." But their swarm was soon followed by bigger silvery shapes, those of the *Luciolates stappersii*, a fish of mackerel-like habits which feeds on the *Dagaa*. Finally, at the edge of the bank of fish could be seen the big shapes of the *Lates*, the wolves of Tanganyika, taking their toll of the *Luciolates*.

The African fishery for *Luciolates*, by whiffing, described earlier, takes place at dawn and dusk twilight; as these fish are the predators of the *Dagaa*, it seems that the latter come to the surface waters very soon after the light fails.

A Trip on a Dagaa Canoe

The fishery for *Dagaa* takes place on moonless nights. When there is moonlight, the fish will not concentrate under a light. The following account of a trip on a canoe out for *Dagaa*, is abstracted from the author's diary for July, 1946:

"Fuel was piled in the canoe, while the fire was lit on the beach. When the fire was burning well, it was transferred to the canoe. The fire on the canoe is held at the end of a short bowsprit, in a brazier made of iron spikes driven into the bowsprit, with a floor made of flattened tins. The iron spikes act as the firebars, the tray as the grate.

"As we pushed off, the fire was liberally heaped with billets, and burned with a bright and almost smokeless flame.

"We anchored about half a mile out, the flames roared, and the hot cinders hissed into the water. To prevent the bowsprit from burning, the bowman kept splashing water over it.

"Small fish soon began to accumulate under the fire, and the bowman started to sweep them out with his net.

"Fishing was poor, and at 22.00 hr. we decided to go in. We carried a crew of four, the bowman-cum-netsman, the steersman and two others who did not seem to have any particular function on this trip. Perhaps with a good catch they would help with the net; in any case, they had to bale, for the canoe was very leaky, and we ended up with nearly a foot of water in it.

"As soon as the word came to go home, a new spirit animated the crew. They paddled with great vigour, singing a shanty, with rhythmic knocking of the sides of the canoe with their paddles. One man kept up a monotonous burden, while the others sang what seemed to be the same lines over and over again, now and then breaking out into a falsetto. I was told that their paddling shanty went as follows:

> Throw down your load, throw down your load,
>   Oh Kabwe,
> The rock is singing,
> Kakangwe has been proved worthless,
> Mandevu has been caught with his witchcraft."

Inconsequent words, these; yet not more so than:

> Sally she's a Badian beauty,
> Way, hay, roll and go. . . .

The scoop-net used has a frame of bamboo to which the net, which has a bag, is fastened. The net may be made of mosquito netting, or of fine meshed netting with about a $\frac{1}{4}$-inch bar. No doubt the latter is used when the fish are in the larger sizes. When the canoe is lying head to wind in a breeze, sparks from the fire fly down the wind and burn holes in the net.

Wood Fires and Pressure Lamps

As many as four head-loads of wood were used by one canoe in a full night's work. The best wood was considered to be that of *Pterocarpus chrysothrix*, but that of *Diplorhynchus mossambicensis* was used as a substitute. When it is remembered that there were some hundreds of canoes out each suitable night, the consumption of wood was substantial and was causing some concern to the Forestry Officers. It was a lovely sight at night to see the dark water of the lake twinkling far and near with lights; I was reminded, at the time, of the sea off Yarmouth in the herring season, with the sea lit up like an esplanade with the drifters' lights.

About 1951, the Fisheries Officer on Lake Tanganyika began to experiment with acetylene flares and oil pressure lamps. By 1953, a large number of the fishermen in the northern part of the lake were using lamps, and now the use of lamps is universal. They are probably more efficient in attracting the fish than the old fires.

Potential of the Dagaa Fishery

The canoes leak and they are also poor sea-boats, so that the *Dagaa* fishery is confined to the coastal waters, 2 to 5 km. from shore. But the Belgian survey showed that the fish are found far out into the lake; in fact, probably over the whole lake, for the appearance of the shoal by daylight, described by Poll, was in mid-lake. It seems that the fishery could be much expanded if the dug-out canoes were supplemented by boats able to stand rougher weather. Unfortunately, the weather can change very suddenly on the lake, and there can be high winds and a short steep swell. Poll quotes a tragedy, when a large number of fishermen were drowned when they were caught in a sudden wind too far out in the lake to make shelter in time.

When one considers how small is the present fishing effort for

Dagaa, and how great are the areas at present unfished, it is clear that here is a resource which can be further developed.

Kufferath[27] made a number of estimates, based on the chemical constituents of the lake, of the potential fish production. They varied widely, according to the factor used, from a possible 1,600 kg. of fish per hectare, as calculated from the variation of sulphur with depth, to 50 kg. per hectare as calculated from the content of nitrogen. On the latter minimum basis, Kufferath estimated that at 50 kg. per hectare, and assuming some 20 per cent of the stock is removed annually, Lake Tanganyika could produce some 30,000 metric tons of fish a year, with especial reference to the *Dagaa*. More recently, Capart and Kufferath[41] have come to the conclusion that the lake could certainly produce 35 kg. per hectare, or 100,000 metric tons for the whole lake. They were strengthened in this belief by echo-sounder traces, which showed that the population of fish is denser than they had thought. Moreover, Marlier[119] has recently shown that the *Stolothrissa* has a short life-history, attaining a length of 6 cm. in six months, at which size it is mature, and the females can produce 30,000 eggs each. So a much higher rate of cropping than the 20 per cent of the stock originally postulated by Kufferath is feasible.

Congo Fishery Developments

The Congo has been developing the *Dagaa* fisheries. Collart[91] states that this fishery is exploited by 80 per cent of the fishermen. He confirms that the fishery is possible only on calm and moonless nights. During the day, these fish are found deep down in the water, between about 50 and 100 metres below the surface. At night, whether there is a moon or not, the fish rise to the upper 30 metres, and lie especially between 4 and 15 metres below the surface. These diurnal vertical migrations are probably caused by the need of the *Dagaa* to follow the plankton on which they feed, and in Lake Tanganyika, as in the sea, the plankton makes notable vertical migrations, apparently in response to the light.

The function of the bright lights used by the fishermen is to attract the fish to the surface, to bring them within the reach of the scoop-net. On nights of bright moonlight, the artificial light of the fishermen is ineffective in doing this, so, says Collart, the men have to take a week of rest during the full-moon periods.

The Purse Seine

The introduction of the purse seine on to Lake Tanganyika has been described by Collart.[91] It is a European enterprise, for the capital costs of the fleet of vessels and of the nets, as well as the business experience required, puts this method at present beyond the reach of the Africans. The Belgians put no difficulty in the way of European enterprise on the lake.

Each outfit consists of a large boat, described as a decked whaler of 7 to 12 metres length, with a crew of fifteen men under the command of the skipper, and two or three smaller boats each carrying a paraffin lamp of about 2,000 to 8,000 candle-power.

The small boats shine their lamps until there is a good concentration of fish; then the mother-ship lays the purse seine around the boat and the fish. The boat slides over the headrope of the net, and the fish are left encircled. A purse seiner at work is shown in Plate 38.

These purse seines are each 200 metres long and 30 to 45 metres deep, with a mesh of 6 mm. bar. The nets may be made wholly of nylon. The net has a set of rings on the footrope, through which a strong rope, called the pursing-line, passes. When the net has been shot in a circle around the shoal of fish, the pursing-line is hauled in, usually mechanically. This draws together the footrope of the net, forming a purse, and the escape of the fish by diving away is prevented. The whole net is then shortened by pulling in the ends, until the fish are concentrated in a small bight of the net, from which they are bailed out with scoop-nets.

As might be expected, these outfits make very big catches. One night's work can easily give 5 to 6 metric tons of fish. According to Collart[120] about 60 per cent by weight of the purse-seine catches are *Dagaa*, and about 20 per cent are their predators, namely, about 22-25 per cent *Lates* and 17-18 per cent *Luciolates*. These large fish are usually put into cold store, to be held for sale during the full-moon period when there is little fish on the market. The *Dagaa* caught by the industrial fishery are either dried in special sheds, or may be sold fresh.

The Lift-net

Collart[120] describes the introduction of the lift-net, to give rise to a profitable fishery for a small outlay of capital. He had noticed

34. Planked boat being introduced on Lake Nyasa.

Dug-out canoe on Lake ganyika, with wood to attract fish, and p-net.

36. Canoe with pressure lamps, Lake Tanganyika.

37. A lift-net, Lake Tanganyika.

38. Purse-seiner fishing *Dagaa* on Lake Tanganyika.

that echo-sounder traces of *Dagaa* attracted to the surface by a bright light showed that the fish formed a column beneath the light. So, he argued, a very long conical net drawn up rapidly from below might catch the whole column. In effect, the net is suspended beneath a catamaran, between the two hulls of which the light is shone. When there are signs that a good quantity of fish has been attracted to the light, the lift-net is hauled quickly to the surface and the fish are taken (Plate 37).

A comparison of the effectiveness of the three methods of catching *Dagaa* by the use of lights to bring the fish to the surface, is given by the Service des Eaux et Forêts.[121] The traditional method, using the hand scoop-net, will give only about 7·5 tons per annum per boat. The lift-net, however, will give an average of about 5 tons of fish per month of 20 days. But the purse seine will give easily 5 to 6 tons per night.

Statistics

With the replacement of the feeble traditional methods of fishing with these newer and more effective methods, it is not surprising that there has been a most spectacular increase in the yield of fish from Lake Tanganyika by the Congo fishermen. Below are given the total production of all kinds of fish on the Congo shores of the lake.

Table I

Production of Fish in Lake Tanganyika, in the
Congo and Ruanda-Urundi.[121]

Year	Production in tons
1950	3,100
1951	3,674
1952	5,246
1953	5,659
1954	9,314
1955	11,370
1956	12,961
1957	19,448
1958	33,319

The only statistics available for fish production on the Tanganyika Territory shores are the quantities of dried *Dagaa* which are routed

NTIF

through Kigoma. The production has been rising. The quantities railed from Kigoma averaged about 1,460 tons in the three years 1947-9, and about 1,936 tons in 1955-7. In 1957, indeed, production at Kigoma was 2,260 tons. To this may be added about 200 tons exported from minor ports farther to the south, and 1,000 tons landed in the Northern Rhodesian ports. These figures add up to about 3,500 tons of dried fish, equivalent to about 14,000 tons of fresh fish.

Taking together the Congo and British production in 1957, the total was of the order of 33,000 tons. In 1958, it may well have exceeded 50,000 tons.

The production of about 1,000 tons of *Dagaa* in the Northern Rhodesian ports, in 1957, illustrates the effect of indirect measures in stimulating a fishery. The exports of *Dagaa* at Sumbu, at the southern end of the lake, rose from 148 tons in 1956 to 862 tons in 1957. "It was the construction of a road bringing the trader down to the waterside that gave the fishermen the incentive to increase production."

As on the Congo side, concentration on the valuable *Dagaa* fishery has tended to some neglect of the other fisheries, but from time to time there are reports of new ventures in smoking and drying seine-caught fish. A useful modification of the beach-seining technique was tried by the Fishery Officer in Tanganyika. Knowing that the *Dagaa* are attracted to light, and that where the *Dagaa* are concentrated the larger fish will gather to feed on them, he used a 300 c.p. pressure-lamp, fitted with a reflector, from a canoe which was taken out up to two miles from shore. When *Dagaa* and other small fish were seen to be collecting under the light, the canoe was slowly paddled shoreward until within range of the beach seine, which was quietly laid astern of it by another canoe. Greatly increased catches were made in this way.

The Fisheries Division of the Northern Rhodesian Government is successfully trying out a modified form of the *chilimila* of Lake Nyasa at the southern end of Lake Tanganyika.

LAKE KIVU

Lake Kivu also lies in the Rift Valley of Africa, between Lake Tanganyika and Lake Albert. It has an area of 1,042 square miles and has an average depth of some 700 metres. Damas, who investigated this lake,[30] pointed out the peculiar stratification of the water, which causes a complete absence of oxygen in all but the upper 60 to 100 metres (see Chapter II). He considered that Lake Kivu is a veritable desert, whose pure and transparent waters contained scarcely any plankton. The only signs of fish life were to be found on the bottom of bays or at the mouth of affluent rivers and streams.

Poverty in Fish Species

Hulot[29] confirmed that 95 per cent of the superficies of the lake. and 99 per cent of its volume, are not inhabited by fish at all, for neither the echo-sounder nor explosive charges had shown the presence of fish. Below a depth of about 60 to 100 metres the presence of methane and sulphuretted hydrogen make aerobic life impossible. Lake Kivu is remarkably poor in fish species. Hulot lists only some fourteen species taken by him in the fishery survey of 1952-4, and of these, no fewer than seven are *Haplochromis* species of little or no commercial value, though important, in a negative sense, as predators of the young stages of the more valuable species. The latter include only two species of *Barbus*, a *Barilius*, *Clarias* and *Tilapia nilotica*.

The reason for this extreme poverty in species is to be found in the recent geological history of the lake. At one time it emptied in a northerly direction into Lake Edward, but at a later period there was a volcanic convulsion which partially or completely sterilised the lake and caused it to flow southwards to Lake Tanganyika, as it still does. Volcanic activity is still taking place; recently there was an eruption of one of the volcanoes of the Virunga Range which poured a great quantity of red-hot lava into the lake.

The recolonisation of the lake after its sterilisation, and diversion towards the south, was by fish such as *Protopterus*, *Clarias* and *Heterobranchus*, which have accessory air-breathing apparatus, by fish having special parental care, such as *Tilapia* and *Haplochromis* and by fish still actually living in the rivers, such as *Barbus* and *Barilius*.

Fish Potential

Damas commented on the scarcity of fish life, and attributed the rarity of fishing villages on the lake shore to this cause. Capart and Kufferath[41] found, on the other hand, that the lake was very rich in plankton, and they took a much more optimistic view of the fish-producing potential. They accounted for the findings of Damas by his lack of an echo-sounder to find out the real quantity of fish present, and for his failing to find much plankton in the clear water by pointing out that he did not investigate the lake at night, when the abundant plankton ascends to the surface. They consider the potentialities of the lake to be great. On their visit in 1952-4, their echo-sounder revealed, by day, the presence of numerous shoals of fish at depths of 5 to 30 metres. These fish were found, by direct observation, to be *Tilapia*, *Barbus* and small Cichlid fish, probably *Haplochromis*. By dynamiting, they concluded that the fish population might attain to 500 to 1000 kg. per hectare in the coastal zone down to 30 metres. They confirmed the total absence of fish in the deeper water, and the absence of a truly pelagic fish in the lake. These findings led them to make experimental settings of gill-nets, which gave encouraging results from the start. They concluded that nylon gill-nets would be an economical proposition for the lakeside African fishermen, and demonstrations and propaganda were started among them to help them to form a peasant-scale fishery.

The calculations of Capart and Kufferath suggested that, even in its present state, the lake might produce 600 to 800 metric tons of fish annually, principally *Tilapia*, *Barbus* and *Clarias*. Each day, some 500 gill-nets could be fished, with an average of 4 to 5 kg. of fish per net per day. This would be a vast improvement on the figures for production in 1952 and 1955, which they estimated to be of the order of 20 to 25 metric tons respectively, a confirmation of Damas's finding that the African fishery of his day was a poor affair. But the statistics show[121] that production of fish in Lake Kivu has been rising steadily from 303 tons in 1950 to 841 tons in 1957.

Capart and Kufferath suggested two measures which might increase the production to the huge figure of 35,000 metric tons a year. One measure is the introduction of a true plankton-eating fish, able to make use of the dense plankton which is present, though only near the surface at night. Hulot[29] recommended an attempt to introduce the *Dagaa* from Lake Tanganyika. Le Service des Eaux et Forêts[121] reports that in February 1959 and the following months, more than 30,000 young *Dagaa* were successfully transplanted from Lake Tanganyika to Lake Kivu, with a loss of only 50 per cent. As these fish are small and delicate, this is a fine result. It is still to be seen whether they will multiply there.

Other possible fish to introduce to Lake Kivu, to fill vacant ecological niches, might be *Labeo* and *Citharinus*, a plant-eating fish such as *Tilapia melanopleura*, and a surface feeding insect-eater such as *Alestes*.

The other measure suggested by Capart and Kufferath is much more fundamental. It is to pump up to the surface the deoxygenated water from the bottom of the lake, which contains vast stores of nutrient salts. There would at once follow a great development of plankton, which would, especially in conjunction with plankton-feeding fish, give an enormous increase in fish production. This pumping could be associated with the recovery of the dissolved methane gas, which Damas noticed effervescing in his water-samples from the deep water of the lake, and which is present in a volume estimated at some 50 milliard cubic metres.

There would be some difficulties, of course. For one thing, the deep water remains deep because it is heavier than the surface water. This is partly due to the content of dissolved salts and partly because it is cooler than the surface water. It might be necessary to run the pumped water into shallow ponds to warm it before returning it to the lake. Otherwise, it might slide back into the depths from which it came, with little benefit to the surface waters. It will be remembered that the nutrient salts brought down to Lake Tanganyika by the Ruzizi River are largely lost because the waters of the river are cooler than the surface waters of the lake, so that the river tends to slide down into the depths. Beauchamp in that case[28] recommended that the Ruzizi waters might be held in some way so that they might be warmed before entering the lake.

Chapter Thirteen

THE SHALLOW LAKES

In shallow lakes there is usually no great volume of deoxygenated water unsuited to fish life, for even where the water is deep enough for a thermocline to form, the large area, relative to depth, of a shallow lake ensures mixing by wind action. Therefore fishing is usually possible over the whole area of the lake. Nevertheless, preference is usually given to such fishing gear as the beach seines, because the escape of the fish caught is prevented by the fact that the net is hauled up on to the land. Further, the operation of this type of gear is continually under supervision, whereas set gears such as gill-nets and traps are vulnerable to theft.

PULICAT LAKE, MADRAS STATE

Pulicat Lake, in the Madras State of India, supplies much of the fish to the important city of Madras. A description of its fisheries has been given by Chacko, Abraham and Andal.[92] The lake has an area of about 178 square miles and a depth over most of its area of only about six feet. It is connected with the sea by a narrow channel, where there is deep water, but the lake is in a large catchment area and there is extensive flooding in the rainy season when the water of the lake is almost fresh. The fish, as might be expected, are mainly derived from the sea, and are euryhaline species such as the mullets, and *Lates calcarifer*, the most valuable of the fish. There is a very large yield of prawns as well. Catches are considerable. At three landing points only, where it was possible to get statistics, a total of over 2,500 tons may be landed annually.

Fishing Methods

Several kinds of gear are used. There is the drag-net or beach seine, called the *Bodivala*. It is in two sections, each 720 feet long and 12 to

15 feet deep. The headrope is buoyed with floats at intervals of about 2 feet, but this net is peculiar in not having weights on the footrope. Two boats each carry one section of the net, join the sections and lay them off the shore. The net is then dragged to the bank. It is a very large net, but in Malaya, such big nets fished by migrant fishermen from this very coast of India, are a familiar sight. The catch is mainly prawns, clupeoids, mullet and crabs.

The *Kondavalai* is another peculiar net used in Madras. It may be 65 feet long and only about 24 inches high. It has neither floats nor weights, but has sticks all along it at intervals, which very effectively keep the net open. It is used by two men in shallow water, who drag it to the shore like a seine. It may also be used in connection with a fish drive. In the latter case, the net is set in a semicircle, and the fish are driven into it with a scare-line made of rope garnished with strips of Palmyra palm leaves.

The stake-net, or *Kattuvalai*, is another unusual net. It consists of two lines of nets hung from poles driven into the lake bottom. The front row of stakes is short and reaches only a foot or so above the surface of the water at high tide (there is a rise of only about 1 foot in the lake). The hinder row of stakes is set about $1\frac{1}{2}$ to 2 feet behind, and emerges about 3 to 4 feet from the water. The net attached to the shorter front stakes acts as a screen barring the passage of the fish, which must therefore try to jump over it. The second net is hung by its upper edge from the projecting ends of the longer stakes a few inches above water-level, the final arrangement making a slack longitudinal pocket of net between the two lines of stakes. The whole length of the net is about 100 fathoms. The nets are usually set in the evening and the catches collected next morning. The catch is mullets, prawns and miscellaneous clupeoids. From the description given by the authors, the *Kattuvalai* is designed to take advantage of the jumping habits of many fish and even prawns.

Another type of set-net is the *Siruvalai*. This is a strongly made bag-net of small mesh, provided with a pocket-like codend. Thirty to forty wooden floats are attached to the headrope, but there are no weights on the footrope. The circumference of the mouth of the net is about 75 feet. "The net is operated in about 4 feet of water by five men from a boat. Two men set the net by securing the two extremities of the mouth with stakes driven into the bottom. Two others move towards the bottom of the net with a scare-line. As soon as the scare-line reaches the net, all the four men close the mouth of the net; the fifth man brings the boat near and the contents of the net are emptied into it."[92]

The *Kalavalai* is similar to the *Siruvalai*, but has a larger mesh. It is used at night for the capture of soles and prawns from the deeper water.

The *Koduvavalai* is the net used for the capture of the *Lates calcarifer*, the most valuable fish. It is 12 feet long and 35 inches deep, and like the *Kondavalai* is spread by sticks. The mesh is big, about 5 to $5\frac{1}{2}$ inches from knot to knot, and the net is made from comparatively thick cotton rope which is soft and pliable and about $\frac{3}{10}$ inch in diameter. Many of these nets may be set together in a huge semicircle, in about $2\frac{1}{2}$ feet of water, and the fish are driven into the nets by two men in each of a number of boats making the maximum amount of uproar.

Mullet are caught in large numbers by the only type of gill-net used, which has a mesh of about $\frac{3}{8}$ inch, is 50 fathoms long, and has floats but again no sinkers. Cast-nets, and the rod and line, are also used.

Fishing with torchlights is done on dark nights. The torches are burnt on the fishing craft, and when fish are seen blinded and bemused by the glare, or possibly attracted by the light, they are scooped up with baskets. If the fish is a big one, it may be clubbed or speared.

This author has seen a net very similar to the *Kondavalai* in the shallow Jaffna Lagoon in Ceylon. A large canoe containing about eleven men was poled about in the shallow water. Then eight of the crew jumped into the water, here about 4 feet deep, with a net which they stretched out in the water, while two other canoes each with two men poled away downwind for about 50 yards. These canoes then poled vigorously back upwind, towing between them a rope on which split yellow palm leaves were plentifully tied. This line ripped along the surface with a mighty splash, like a shoal of fish surfacing. The canoes towed this scare-line up to the netsmen, who held the net well above the water-level. Fish could be seen flying through the air and hitting the net. The catches were mullet, bream, big sardinellas and small carangids. There is said to be some danger of injury to the fishermen from the needle-fish or gar-fish, *Hemirhamphus*, which has the habit, when pursued, of skittering along the surface at high speed, balancing on its tail. It was said that a man was killed in this lagoon by being pierced through the throat by one of these fish.

LAKE GEORGE, UGANDA

This lake has an area of about 104 square miles and lies in the Great Rift Valley in Uganda. It is connected through the Kazinga Channel with Lake Edward, and through Lake Edward with Lake Albert by way of the Semliki River. Worthington[93] found the lake to be very shallow, with an even bottom at $2\frac{1}{2}$ to 3 metres, the bottom deposits being mud. The water is always very turbid and green in colour, due chiefly to the dense growth of plant plankton, especially the blue-green alga *Microcystis flos-aquae*. The water is very alkaline.

Fishing Methods

Worthington (loc. cit.) found that the most important species of fish in the lake were *Tilapia nilotica* and the lung-fish *Protopterus*, with *Mormyrus*, *Labeo*, *Clarias* and *Bagrus*. By far the most important is the *Tilapia*. Worthington found a small and primitive fishery run by Africans. They used plunge-baskets in connection with a fish-drive by three or four men, who might take forty-five fish in an hour. They also used a long rope with numerous banana stalks and leaves attached to it. This rope was taken into about 4 feet of water and then dragged around in a circle until the two ends met. The circle was then narrowed until it was only about 15 feet across. The fish enclosed seemed unable or unwilling to escape, and were easily captured with the plunge-baskets.

Yet another method used on the lake was the short reed fence made by sticking papyrus stems into the mud at intervals of about 3 inches. Each fence was in the shape of a V, so as to guide fish which were moving up and down the shore into wickerwork non-return basket-traps.

In addition, in Worthington's time, there was a small fishery run by a European at Fort Portal. He employed some sixteen fishermen, working gill-nets from two canoes. They set their nets by day and underran them at intervals to remove the fish. This fishery had apparently been in progress for a year or two before Worthington's visit in July, 1931, and as many as 100 fish might be caught per day.

The Closure of the Lake

Since Worthington's day the lake has made spasmodic appearances in the Annual Reports of the Game Department of the Uganda

Protectorate. In the Report for 1934 it is recorded that Lake George was closed to fishing in order to act as a breeding sanctuary for the stocking of Lake Edward. It was assumed that there would be a movement of fish from Lake George through the Kazinga Channel to replenish the stocks in Lake Edward. But in the Report for 1936 eight fishing permits were issued on the Lake George shore and in the 1939 Report it was said that the fishing in the lake had reverted to local effort and that the numerous unauthorised fishermen who were steadily increasing in recent years had been removed.

During the Second World War, poaching on an extensive scale took place in Lake George, the worst offenders being immigrants who came in the certainty of heavy catches, and who were tough customers. At the end of 1943 there was a sudden and unauthorised incursion into the Lake George region of numerous fishermen intent on developing a commercial fishery. It took a long time to restore the situation to normal. "As Lake George acts as a most important reservoir for the economic fisheries at Katunguru and Katwe, it cannot be too strongly or too frequently emphasised that undue interference with the fish stocks in Lake George will sooner or later react adversely on the industries in the Kazinga Channel and Lake Edward."[141]

In the pre-war years Lake George was virtually closed to fishing, though it was known that this closure was being more or less evaded. In 1948, when the closure was still in force, it was admitted that organised poaching on an immense scale was taking place, since catches on Lake George were incredibly high.

The Uganda Fish Marketing Corporation

In 1949 there was a change in policy and it was decided to open the lake to commercial fishing. A legal notice was published which provided for the control and regulation of the fishing industry in Lake George. The fishery was to become a controlled monopoly run by a corporation, financed to a large degree by the Uganda Government, with the name of the Uganda Fish Marketing Corporation, TUFMAC for short. A depot was established at Kasenyi, on the northern shore of the lake, with an initial capacity based on an average catch of 10 tons of wet fish per day. In Plate 39 is shown the landing at Kasenyi, and in Plate 40 the fish being removed in a trailer to the factory.

The lake was thrown open to fishing in 1950 by five lakeside fishing villages, each being permitted ten canoes operating three 5-inch gill-nets. By the end of the year, some three million Tilapias of the high average weight of nearly 2 lb., and weighing some 2,900 tons, had been landed and sold to TUFMAC. It is admitted that many more fish were landed and disposed of illegally by fishermen and poachers.

The fish were processed into dried salted fish (Plate 41), and 695 tons, valued at £45,000, had been sold to the Congo, as well as 65 tons sold locally. The fishermen earned about £31,400 for their catches.

It may here be said that one of the chief difficulties facing TUFMAC has been the effect of these high earnings on the incentive to fish by the African fishermen. "It seems clear that canoe owners, who in some cases are grossing £1,000 per annum, are not urgently interested in earning more than they are doing at present; and if for any reason unable to fish are sufficiently well off to bear the consequent loss of income." The fishing effort showed wide variations as between the several villages on the lake. In an attempt to increase supplies, ten additional fishing licences were granted in 1955. This resulted in heavier landings at first, but the effort was not sustained.

In short, the industry depends on the fishing effort of the Africans, and this is, unfortunately, very variable. To the factory, with its heavy overhead expenses, time is money; to the fishermen, whose wants are few, time means little once they have earned, as they all have, large sums of money. There can be few fisheries in the world where more easy money is to be had. The total fishing effort has never exceeded 70 per cent of the possible; in 1955 the shortfall of the factory below its requirements was directly due to poor fishing effort. There was no indication that the stocks of fish were any less. When TUFMAC started to catch fish themselves, to supplement the supplies, there was much resentment on the part of the Africans. Now, TUFMAC has twenty canoes for hire, in addition to the African fishermen's own canoes.

The question of incentive goes far beyond the scope of this book, and far wider than the fishermen of Lake George. Precisely the same difficulty faces other industries which depend for their raw material on the labour of simple people. The case is known of a costly fish-meal plant set up in South-west Africa, which relied on the fishing of African fishermen for the raw material for process-ing. The same thing happened; after a few months of good earnings, the effort fell off and the factory was short of material. At the lonely island of Tristan da Cunha, the successful establishment of a crawfish industry has been made difficult because the few wants of the islanders are easily satisfied, so that the incentive to earn more is not there.

But this is not the whole story, for the widespread theft of fish from Lake George is admitted in the reports. Many of the poor catches could be ascribed to illegal landings at night, for sale mainly to the people living inland in the hills where there is an insatiable demand for fish. The illegal sale of fish cannot be wondered at, for TUFMAC could not afford to pay more than 30 cents per fish, whereas at Katunguru, only twenty miles away, they were fetching 50 cents apiece. It can be safely guessed that the bigger fish would be disposed of in this way, so that some of the catch delivered to TUFMAC would have a higher than normal proportion of smaller fish.

This was proved in 1959, when the fishermen were free to sell their fish where they wished. The average weight of all *Tilapia* caught in 1959 in Lake George was 1·34 lb., but of the fish caught in Lake George which were sold to the smoke-houses on Lake Edward, it was 1·5 lb.

Many years ago, a wise and experienced Governor told the author that many development schemes then only beginning, would fall short of accomplishment for this lack of incentive. He thought that development schemes should be associated in some way with an advertising campaign by firms offering consumer goods, so that desires were created for a wide range of products which would raise the standard of living and give the incentive to earn the money to buy the goods desired. When every African desires a car and his wife a refrigerator, production will mount.

Since 1953 the corporation has changed its products. The market for salt-dried fish in the Congo has again become more difficult, partly because of a temporary fall in purchasing power due to bad cotton seasons, and partly of the growing importation into the Congo of large quantities of processed fish from other sources, such as Eritrea, Angola and even the Canary Islands, at prices competitive with those of TUFMAC. There is always a market for smoked fish but the large quantity of firewood needed would prevent the expansion of this line of produce. So the firm turned to a high-class trade in frozen fillets of *Tilapia* (Plate 42), and, by a happy chance, the development of the copper mines at Kilembe nearby brought much business to the airstrip at Kasenyi. As the planes flew in with equipment for the mines and returned with a light load, the unused payload was available to TUFMAC at reasonable rates. In 1954, over 7 tons of frozen fillets were flown out from the airstrip at Kasenyi every week (Plate 44). In February, 1954, the fishing was impressive in its modernity in so remote a part of Africa. The following is an extract from the author's journal:

"When we landed at Kasenyi, a TUFMAC lorry was waiting to load over a ton of frozen fillets. A freight plane had already taken away 3 tons this morning, and therefore 4 tons in one day. The fillets are about 27 per cent of the whole fish. The fillets are placed for two hours in a blast-freezer, and attractively wrapped in cellophane paper, packed in cardboard cartons, and then stored in a cold room. I saw the fish being landed, fine large fish. There are large amounts of offal, and now they have ordered a fish-meal plant and can sell to Kenya and Tanganyika farmers. They also split and salt, and smoke, for the Congo, but this is now only about 20 per cent of the whole business. There are few signs of overfishing. After an initial fall in mean weight of the fish from 2 to 1·5 lb., the average weight seems to have steadied. Marking experiments show that the fish do not migrate much. Some parts of the lake are not exploited at all."

The development of the filleting trade was desirable in itself because in the days when the main market for the fish was in the Congo, only 15 per cent of TUFMAC sales reached local markets and 85 per cent was exported. In 1954, 50 per cent of sales were of the East African territories. In that year, too, the more profitable and economical use of the raw materials resulted in an increase of 11 per cent in sales turnover without any increase in selling price.

The setting up of a fish-meal plant in 1955 allowed the conversion of the very large amounts of fish scrap to fish meal; it also became possible to make into fish meal the less popular varieties of fish brought in by the fishermen. In 1956 about 200 tons of fish meal were produced, worth £11,400, which was sold chiefly to farmers in Kenya for cattle feed (Plate 43).

The statistics of the fishery are given on page 190:

Table IV

The Results of Fishing in Lake George, Uganda.
(From the Annual Reports of the Uganda Game and
Fisheries Department)

Year	No. of fishing days	Total weight of Tilapia, '000 lb.	Total number of Tilapia, '000	Av. wt. of Tilapia, lb.	Other kinds of fish, '000 lb.
1950	262	6014	3007	1·98	533
1951	305	5271	2906	1·81	874
1952	326	4608	2764	1·68	907
1953	305	5648	3290	1·73	2865
1954	305	6179	3688	1·68	1184
1955	315	4182	3141	1·47	1218
1956	289	4429	3332	1·32	2071
1957	—	4548	3790	1·24	1247
1959	—	4696	3504	1·34	1449

Decline in Mean Weight of the Tilapia

Serious concern is felt over the continued decline in the average weight of the *Tilapia*. This fell from nearly 2 lb. in 1950 to about $1\frac{1}{2}$ lb. in 1952, and remained around that figure until 1954, when the decrease was resumed.

A decline in the average weight when intensive exploitation first began was to be expected. Every effort had been made to prevent fishing in the lake for many years, and the population of Tilapias could be expected to contain a very high proportion of old and large fish. The first years of fishing would remove these, leaving a faster-growing stock of younger and smaller fish. Ultimately a balance would be struck between the rate of removal of the fish and their rate of regeneration, and the average weight would then become steady. But this balance has not been reached yet, and the consequences of a further fall in average weight would increase the difficulties of the factory in two ways.

First, in accordance with the age-old custom, the fish are bought by the piece and not by weight. The firm were obliged to grant an increase in the price paid to the fishermen in 1956, and since in the meantime the average weight of the fish had fallen, there was a considerable increase in the first costs.

Secondly, it is well known that the smaller the fish, the less the edible meat. A very big *Tilapia mossambica* weighing 4·8 lb. can give two fillets weighing 2·2 lb., or 46 per cent. On the other hand fish of an average weight of 1·1 lb. give 24 per cent of fillets. The figure of 27 per cent for TUFMAC agrees with these figures well, for a fish of 1·5 lb.; all Tilapias have much the same shape.

Therefore, if the average weight of the *Tilapia* were to fall to 1·1 lb., the firm would need 1,125 tons of raw material to make 270 tons of fillets, instead of the 1,000 tons of fish of 1·5 average weight. More fish will be needed to produce the same weight of fillets, and this might result in a further fall in the average weight. There might be the risk of a vicious circle here.

In 1958 some forty-six outboard engines were in use, which was eighteen more than in the previous year. Moreover, by the end of the year, all the nets in use were of nylon, which has a considerably higher catching power than the flax nets previously used. These two factors may have played some part in the unprecedented heavy catches of fish which occurred in July and August 1957. The quantity offered to the TUFMAC factory was so great as to be much in excess of the plant's capacity. Therefore, the Government of Uganda decided to end the monopoly buying of fish on Lake George, which was originally designed to ensure sufficient supplies to the factory. At the same time the control of TUFMAC was transferred to a private company.

These interruptions caused the total amount of fish to show only a slight rise over 1956, as Table IV shows. But this table includes, for the year 1957, fish sold to other markets as well as to TUFMAC. The average weight of the *Tilapia* shows a further decline, in 1957 to 1·24 lb., but in 1959 it was 1·34. So the mean weight of the fish has not declined since 1956, and it seems that a balance has now been struck between the rate of removal of the fish and the rate of recovery of the stock.

The Report of the Uganda Game and Fisheries Department for 1958[123] stated that the catches of fish from Lake George started to rise again in January 1958, and by March were of the order of 430,000 fish per month, or more than 30 per cent higher than the monthly average for any previous year. It would seem that over-fishing has not yet appeared in this very productive lake: perhaps the removal of the buying monopoly has also provided an increased incentive to fish. The total weight of *Tilapia* caught in the lake was the greatest since 1954.

In September 1957, there was a very heavy mortality of fish in Lake George following a violent storm. It was suggested that the reason was deoxygenation caused by the stirring up of the bottom muds and the mixing of the oxygenated and deoxygenated layers. There was, however, no effect on the commercial catches, which on the contrary, improved to the highest total ever recorded. It seems likely that the same stirring of the lake bottom may have released nutrient salts as well, for there was a heavy bloom of blue-green algae a day or two after the storm.

LAKE ALBERT

Fishing Methods

Worthington[94] made the first fishing survey of Lake Albert in 1928. He found the fisheries in a very primitive state, except in the shallow southern part of the lake, where a Belgian enterprise had introduced gill-nets, set at night and staked or anchored to the bottom. These gill-nets had a mesh of 8 cm., made of very stout twine; they were tended by a large fleet of canoes and a motor launch. The catches were chiefly the *Citharinus*, but *Bagrus* and *Lates* were also caught in considerable numbers. As much as one ton of fish was caught per day, which was dried and transported to the Kilomoto mines in the Congo.

The only other imported method of fishing was the beach seine, and not more than twelve of these were in use in 1928. Hauls might take from a few up to several hundred fish, in order of abundance roughly as follows: *Hydrocyon*, *Alestes*, *Labeo*, *Tilapia* and *Lates*. Apart from one seine used at Butiaba to supply fresh fish to the small European market, the rest of these seines were owned and operated by Swahili and Bunyoro Africans. Plates 21 and 22 show a beach seine on Lake Albert.

The indigenous fishing methods which Worthington saw in use were harpooning, especially in the lagoons; plunge-baskets, chiefly for *Tilapia* in the rivers in spate; trapping in the narrow channels between the main lake and the lagoons; and hand-line fishing for *Clarias*, *Tilapia* and other species.

On the more southerly parts of the lake, hand lines were fished to catch *Lates*; and at Panyamur, on the north-west corner of the lake, there was an active group of fishermen employing true long lines,

39. TUFMAC landing at Kasenyi, Lake George.

eshly caught *Tilapia* being removed by trailer, Lake George.

41. Split and salted fish being sun-dried, Lake George.

42. Filleting tables, TUFMAC, Lake George.

43. Fish-meal plant,
TUFMAC, Lake George.

44. Deep-frozen *Tilapia* fillets being loaded
on to a Dakota at Kasenyi, Lake George.

each carrying ten very large hooks of iron, for the capture of the big *Lates*. The hooks were baited with small fish, chiefly small catfish which were caught in traps set in the reeds. The rate of capture might be as high as one fish per ten hooks set, and as the *Lates* are large fish, this was a good result.

Early Days

The poor and scanty amount of fishing was due to the small and scattered human population. Big stretches of the shoreline had had to be cleared of their population because of sleeping sickness, which had already wiped out a large section of the population. Where there were settlements of fishermen, they were in small groups near lagoons and in sheltered bays behind sand spits, where fish were plentiful. The nearness of trade routes had a considerable influence. Thus, fishing was more active at Butiaba than elsewhere, because this port has good road communications.

Worthington estimated that the total fishing population was small, with seldom more than fifty fishermen at each fishing village. It was one of the objects of Worthington's report to show that "fish are present in sufficient quantities to warrant a considerable extension of the fisheries by the introduction of European fishing gear". In the thirty years since Worthington wrote, this is just what has happened, and the story will be given below.

There was little development in the years from 1933 to 1939. There were a series of attempts to build up a commercial fishery, and to organise the marketing of the fish. They failed for various reasons, chiefly because of marketing difficulties. One such venture, that of Lake Albert Resources Ltd., left some valuable statistics of catches in 1933. The most important fish caught were the *Citharinus*, taken in large-meshed gill-nets. They formed 80 per cent of the catch, with a minimum of two and a maximum of 400 caught in any one day.

Development

But the war changed all this. The Congo became a big buyer of salted fish for their mine-workers and other labour, and offered high prices. These at once had a stimulating effect on the fishery. It was estimated that the fisheries of Lake Albert increased by 500 per cent between 1939 and 1949, and that this had been an all-round expansion, due to an increase in the number of fishermen participating, the weight of fish landed, and the value of fish exported.

When the war ended, the fisheries were described as flourishing, and the exports to the Congo were mounting. Immigrant Buganda, attracted by high prices, fished 5-inch gill-nets laid on the bottom of the lake in deep water. The catch was mainly *Synodontis*, a fat Siluroid fish which cures well by smoking. But when there was a fall in the price offered for cured fish, most of these immigrants left.

By the end of 1945, a few wealthy African capitalist fishermen were operating, each owning a fleet of canoes and employing numbers of fishermen to work for them. Production on the lake was estimated at about 400 tons per month, of which three-quarters were caught in Congo waters, and 90 per cent of which were consumed in the Congo.

A Belgian seining venture was started in 1947. It may here be said, in parenthesis, that the Belgian Congo authorities encouraged European nationals to undertake fishing, whereas, on the Uganda side, fishing is reserved for the Africans.

In 1950 for the first time, the fishing canoes on the Uganda side were registered. This action was taken to put a stop to Congo fishermen coming into Uganda waters, where they were using seine-nets of great size, up to 800 metres in length.

In the report for 1947,[124] there is a description of such a fishery, but this time on the Congo side, at the south end of the lake. The seine was 900 yards long by 15 to 18 feet deep. It was made of tyre cords, and had a 5-inch mesh, except in the bag, which was strongly made of sisal with a 2-inch mesh. The object of this was to hold the *Lates* caught, as these are powerful and heavy fish, up to 200 lb. or more in weight.

The net was being fished six times in the twenty-four hours and, to cover expenses, had to catch fresh fish at the rate of 1½ tons per day. The weight of fish usable for salt-drying was said to be only 15 per cent for *Lates*, but up to 40 per cent for *Tilapia* and *Citharinus*.

In 1948, a scarcity of *Citharinus* was reported, which was significantly described as a periodical complaint. The report[125] said that the shortage might be due to adverse weather conditions on the normal fishing grounds. But the *Citharinus* was described as a species having extraordinary recuperative powers. At that time it was said to comprise 50 per cent of the catches, as compared with 80 per cent in 1933.

After the registration of the canoes in 1950, the maximum length of a seine-net was fixed by decree at 250 yards.

An Expanding Fishery

In 1953, a Fisheries Officer was permanently stationed on the lake, and he gave an up-to-date account of the fishery as it was in that year. In a lake of some 100 miles by 25 miles, with an area of some 2,500 square miles, about 1,300 square miles were Uganda waters and the rest Congo waters. The lake was said to have a much greater variety of fish, as well as a larger number of fishing methods, than any other water in Uganda. Of these many methods, only seining, gill-netting and long-lining were of any importance.

In spite of the light fishing load, reported as being borne by only 130 square miles out of the total 1,300 square miles available, there had been statements that the lake was being over-fished, or that fishing had reached its maximum. Only at the extreme northern end of the lake was there anything like an intensive fishery. Here, no fewer than 462 out of the 568 licensed canoes were based. The attractiveness of this region is due to the narrowness and shallowness of the lake there, which allows the whole area to be exploited, to the sheltered nature of the water and above all to the fact that it is within easy canoe distance of the lucrative and traditional market for dried fish at Mahagi Port in Congo territory. It is this part of the lake which was also fished by illegal operators from the Congo, who used seines as long as 900-1000 yards.

During 1952, the 50 square miles of lake included in this shallow northern portion yielded some 1,674 tons of wet fish. The only species which seems to have suffered from this intensive exploitation was the *Citharinus*, which, in this report, was said to have a low recovery rate.

Decline in Citharinus

Some account of the decline in abundance of *Citharinus*, reported about the years 1949-53, is given by Hulot.[29] He gives a graph showing the variations in the level of Lake Albert from 1936 to 1951, and shows that, in the three years 1944, 1945, and 1946, the lake had a low level throughout, never exceeding about 60 cm. above datum. In 1937 and 1938, the water level was high, at about 160 to 170 cm. above datum, and again in 1942 it rose to about 190 cm. The difference between the low water levels and the high water levels

is only some 120-140 cm., say 4 to 5 feet; yet at the shallow northern
and southern ends of the lake, this would suffice to flood large
areas of shallow swamp. In a low water cycle, these shallower
parts would not be flooded. Hulot's observations seemed to show
that the *Citharinus*, like some of the Indian carps, need a rise of
water, covering a large area of shallow ground, for the stimulus to
spawn, and for the safe development of the young. In the years when
this rise was lacking, the spawning may have been interfered with,
resulting in a dearth of the adult fish in subsequent years. In fact the
Belgian Fisheries Mission which visited Lake Albert in 1952-3
succeeded in capturing only a few specimens, in view of the pro-
gressive decline noted since 1947. But the Uganda statistics show
that, in 1953, *Citharinus* still accounted for 35 per cent by weight
of the fish caught in 9-inch gill-nets, and 14 per cent in the 8-inch
gill-nets. The low water levels did not seem to have affected the other
species, such as *Tilapia*, the young of which also seek the shallows
to grow. Hulot has, however, pointed out an important possible
connection between lake levels and the composition of the fish
population; this composition might well be expected to vary with
the changing conditions which favour now one, now another, of the
species. Not enough attention has been paid to this factor in any lake,
and now that a good series of statistics is becoming available, it is
to be hoped that lake levels will be considered when there is a
reported scarcity of a fish, before the scarcity is inevitably put down
to overfishing.

The report for 1954 shows graphically the very close correlation
between rainfall and catches. During rainy months, the catch is
higher, and vice versa.

Statistics for 1954 indicate that *Citharinus* showed a substantial
rise in the catches by seines in that year, though the species comprised only 10 per cent by weight of the fish caught in 9-inch gill-nets
and only 12 per cent in 8-inch gill-nets. In 1955 *Citharinus* accounted
for 21 per cent of the catches of 9-inch gill-nets and 13·5 in 8-inch
gill-nets. Clearly, the species has not recovered to the point where
it comprised 80 per cent of the catch, but it is far from negligible in
the catches.

Areas Unfished

In 1953, some 568 canoes were registered, and the fish production of
the Uganda side of the lake was estimated at about 3000 tons, of

which 2100 tons were salt-dried for the Congo market, 400 were consumed locally, and 500 were despatched to the nearest Uganda markets.

The rickety dug-out canoe was beginning to be replaced by the much more seaworthy Sesse canoes imported from Lake Victoria. The southern part of the lake was almost unfished. There were only about 120 canoes scattered at various villages along a coastline of some 100 miles. Long strips of coast were closed, in any case, to the fishermen because of the danger of sleeping sickness or because of inaccessibility. Not more than 80 square miles received any sustained fishing in this big area of the lake. No attention whatever was paid to the deeper offshore waters. In the circumstances, it may be agreed that, in 1953, there was no sign whatever that Lake Albert was being heavily fished.

Statistics

Since 1953, the production of the lake has been estimated as follows, in terms of wet weight:

Table V

Estimated Production of Fish in the Uganda Waters of Lake Albert, as Wet Weight. (From the Annual Reports of the Uganda Game and Fisheries Department).

Year	Tons
1952	3000
1953	3000
1954	3500
1955	4245
1956	7766
1957	10,348

The increase is due to a number of factors. Nylon nets are replacing fabric nets, and while nylon nets undoubtedly have a greater fishing power than fabric nets, they are also far more durable and so allow of more fishing time. There has been an increase in the proportion of the more seaworthy improved Sesse canoes, more and more of which are of an improved kind being built at Kabalega. Many of these are fitted with outboard engines. The rise in 1955 was ascribed to these factors, and to the stimulus given by high prices in the Congo, as well as to a considerable increase in the local sales of fresh fish.

The further great increase shown in 1956 was due to several factors; one was a large increase in the landings of *Alestes* and *Hydrocyon* by small-meshed gill-nets. This may be another example of a "pulse" in the fish-population, which may later be followed by a fall, just as the population of *Citharinus* rose and fell. The establishment of a market, with good landing facilities, at Panyimur at the north end of the lake greatly simplified marketing, and so stimulated fishing effort and production. Again, the increase was in part due to the construction of an all-weather road to Bulisa, where fishing became active. There was also an increase in the hitherto neglected southern part of the lake, where several beaches were opened to seining for the first time. But the development of the fisheries in the southern part of the lake awaits the construction of better access roads down the escarpment to the lake shore.

Development has also been taking place on the Congo side, and an account has been given by Capart and Kufferath.[41] They estimated production in 1951 at 2,513 metric tons, in 1953, by inference, at about 5,000 tons, and in 1955 at 9,667 tons. They advised their Government that a limit of 10,000 tons should be imposed for the crop in the Congo waters of the lake. They found that most of the fishing was taking place in shallow water, and that some localities have been exploited to the extent of 100 kg. per hectare annually without any sign of impoverishment.

Reserve Fish Potential

Taking the Uganda and Congo figures together for the year 1955, the lake gave a crop of about 13,900 tons. Over an area of about 2,500 square miles, this amounts to 5·6 tons per square mile. On the Uganda side, this was reckoned at about 19·7 lb. per acre, and for the whole lake, Congo and Uganda together, the figure is about the same, namely, about 19·5 lb. per acre. This is a low average figure, as might be expected from the small part of the lake which is exploited at all. Locally, a much higher rate of cropping must be taking place.

At the moment, Lake Albert can be considered as a reservoir of fish hardly tapped as yet, which awaits good road communications and the stimulus of assured markets for full development.

Deep-water Fishing

The deeper waters of the lake, in particular, are wholly undeveloped, and these comprise by far the greater part of the whole. Earlier reconnaissances by both Uganda and the Congo fisheries officers had shown, by the echo-sounder, that substantial stocks of fish are present in this deep water. Some account is given in the Uganda reports for 1956 and 1957 of exploratory fishing in depths down to 150 feet (about 25 fathoms). Though the deepest known sounding is about 250 feet, most of the lake bottom has depths of 100 to 180 feet.

So far, only gill-nets have been used, suitably modified for use in deep water. They were laid on the bottom, on the indications of good echo-sounder traces, in the evening, and lifted in the morning. Two sizes of mesh were used in these gill-nets, 8 inch and 5 inch. The preliminary analyses of the catches revealed fairly dense stocks of fish, catchable by gill-nets, at least as deep as 150 feet. The average catch per net per night with 9-inch gill-nets was 70 lb., chiefly *Lates*; with 5-inch gill-nets, 43 lb., chiefly *Synodontis*, but also some *Lates*. These were better results than the average inshore catches by Africans, which were respectively 56 lb., and 24 lb. for the same length of net. The *Synodontis* are disliked by the Congo fishermen, becase their long spines foul the meshes, and make them dangerous to handle; but they are fat and smoke well.

In 1957 a new nylon net 1000 yards long was used. On the first haul a total of 2,090 lb. of fish were taken. The average catch per setting, per 100 yards of net, shot at random without the benefit of the echo-sounder, was 65 lb. for the 8-inch net and 63 lb. for the 5-inch net. In the 8-inch net 67 per cent of the fish were *Lates*, while in the 5-inch net there were 68 per cent of *Synodontis* and 25 per cent of *Lates*.

The results were watched with interest by the local fishermen, and seven outboard canoes were soon operating from Butiaba, fishing with 2000 yards of 8-inch gill-net apiece in 150 feet of water. Good catches were reported and the fishermen were described as enthusiastic (Plate 31).

In view of the uncertainty of the Congo market for dried fish, it is agreeable to read that the market for fish is being developed in Uganda. Four motor vans and many bicycles were carrying fresh fish to inland centres in Bunyoro, where the demand increases as the people become more accustomed to eating fresh fish. There was also a steady supply of salt-dried fish to some of the Uganda markets.

LAKE RUKWA

Lake Rukwa is a shallow lake lying in the western branch of the Rift Valley between Lakes Tanganyika and Nyasa, at an altitude of 2,690 feet. There is no outlet from the lake, which is a closed drainage system.

The lake is about 90 miles long and is divided into two parts, a main southerly lake about 30 miles long by 15 miles wide, which is fairly permanent, and a large shallow extension, about 60 miles long and 25 miles wide, which varies very much in size and dries out altogether at times. The whole lake is extremely shallow, having a maximum depth of about 5 or 6 metres, but mostly about 3 to 4 metres. The lake was first surveyed from the fishery point of view by Ricardo.[95] She says that the water of the lake is remarkable in that it is grey in colour and so turbid that a white disc disappears from view only 3 inches below the surface. So shallow a lake is stirred to the bottom by the wind, which probably accounts for the grey suspension, and the water is very alkaline. A further account of Lake Rukwa was given by Swynnerton.[50]

Abundance of Fish

Probably on account of turbidity, which cuts out the light, plant life is scarce in Rukwa. There are few higher plants and little phyto-plankton, but zooplankton is very abundant, including *Diaptomus*, *Cyclops*, *Hyalodaphnia* and Rotifers.

The larger fauna are abundant in individuals, but there is not a large number of different species. Fish, especially the local and endemic species of Tilapia, *T. rukwaensis*, are present in enormous quantities.

There was an African fishery, almost entirely carried on by clap-nets (Plate 45), and a European fishery, first started in 1931, which failed after a few months but which was restarted in 1936. This enterprise used large seines 400 feet long and 15 feet deep. At the end of the dry season the catches were rather small, but during the rains, when the fish were said to come close inshore to feed, catches were heavy, as many as 2000 fish per haul. The catches were mostly *Tilapia*, but there were usually several large *Clarias Hydrocyon*, and occasionally *Mormyrus*.

The fish were scaled, headed, split open, gutted and laid out to dry for four or five days. In the rainy season they were smoke-dried. They were packed in baskets and pressed in a baler for transport to the Lupa Goldfields.

Lake Rukwa is obviously very productive. During the years 1944 to 1948 inclusive, the average number of *Tilapia* marketed annually was 1½ million and their average total weight just short of 800 tons. This is exclusive of fish caught by Africans in other parts of the lake and sold separately or used for their own subsistence. As Lake Rukwa has a normal area of about 360 square miles, this crop works out at some 1·6 tons per square mile or 5·6 pounds per acre. Only one small part of the lake was fished and only one species was included in the figures. About 36 tons of *Clarias* were used, and good quantities of *Clarias* and *Synodontis* were consumed as subsistence by the Africans, or cured by them for sale. Big stocks of fish, such as *Schilbe*, *Labeo*, *Mormyrus*, *Gnathonemus* and *Hydrocyon*, were not used at all.

Probably this great potential productiveness led to the exploitation of the lake by Europeans, for exploitation would need more capital and more business experience than were at that time possessed by the local Africans.

Difficulties of Development

All attempts to exploit the wealth of the lake have been dogged by the twin banes of changes in the lake level and difficulty over marketing.

No comments were passed on the level of the lake during the writer's visit of 1946, but there had been poor rains during the few years before 1948 when the lake was described as having the lowest level in living memory. In 1949 the rains failed almost completely, and the result was a disastrous shrinkage of this very shallow lake from an estimated normal area of about 360 square miles to only 150 square miles in October. By the end of December 1949, the lake was estimated to be 80 per cent dry.

All life in the lake was adversely affected. On the freshly-exposed lake bed there was a luxuriant growth of reeds; there was a heavy mortality among the herds of hippopotamus. The fish which were left in the shrunken area of shallow water were an easy prey for vast flocks of fish-eating birds, especially pelicans. The commercial fishing continued, but was made very difficult because boats and gear had to be handled across great areas of unstable mud-flats. In view of the importance of saving what fish were left, and to maintain a source of fish for the subsistence of the local Africans, all commercial fishing was stopped in October. Of the three European concessionaires fishing at the beginning of the year, two had stopped before June.

It might have been thought that the obvious tendency of the fish to become concentrated in what water was left, would have resulted in big catches in the seine-nets. This was indeed the case with *Synodontis*, of which over a million were caught in September and October, 1949. But the catches of *Tilapia* never rose above the normal monthly average. This is notable, even after allowing for the greater physical difficulties of fishing. It might well be that the toll of birds, crocodiles (of which there were a great many in the lake) and other predators, in the straitened and shallow water areas left, had already thinned the survivors out. But during 1949, until the closure of fishing in October, and with only one of the European concessionaires at work for most of the year, about a million *Tilapias* were marketed by the African and European fisheries combined.

It is interesting and instructive to follow the consequences of the drought. In the first place it may explain why Lake Rukwa has comparatively few species of fish. Such a drought as this, leading to the almost total disappearance of the lake, must have happened many times before. Only fish able to survive, either by having accessory air breathing organs or by being able to bury themselves in the mud, or fish able to survive in the remnants of the affluent streams and rivers, would remain alive to recolonise the lake when it refilled.

Secondly, the stocks of the most important species, *Tilapia rukwaensis*, must have been reduced to a very low level, such as could not have been brought about by the most drastic and sustained overfishing it is possible to imagine. There were fears that this species might have been wiped out, for clearly conditions in the water area left would be abnormal, due not only to a scarcity of oxygen, but to a concentration of salts due to evaporation, which would produce very alkaline conditions.

Good rains fell in 1949-50 and the lake began to refill; but there was no commercial fishing there for the first time in many years. Seining would in any case have been difficult or impossible because of the dense growth of reed-beds, in some places a mile wide. The new rise of the water in 1950 drowned much of this vegetation, but it still remained an almost insuperable obstacle to fishing, even had a commercial fishery been permitted. The Africans did well with their traditional methods, since some 306 canoe-days produced 5,692 *Clarias* of an average weight of 1½ lb.

Experimental fishing showed that some *Tilapia* had survived, for though the adult fish seen were few, and none were caught, fry and young were plentiful.

By the end of 1951, the lake had made a remarkable recovery. It then held a satisfactory amount of water, and trial fishing showed that, on the whole, the fish fauna had regained its original character. Fish which were considered to be intolerant of a low oxygen content, and which therefore might be expected to have succumbed during the drought, reappeared in some abundance. Possibly a few may have survived in the streams. *Tilapia* were abundant at all stages from fry to breeding adults, but they were, as yet, smaller in size than before the drought, with an average weight of about 12 ounces, as compared with 18 ounces. *Clarias* were everywhere abundant, as also were *Schilbe*, *Labeo* and *Hydrocyon*, species which are neglected in the fishery.

The commercial fishery was reopened in 1953, with one European concessionaire. The physical difficulties due to the vegetation were still there, but the submerged reed-beds were beginning to break up through wave action and rotting. There were so many Africans fishing on their own account that the concessionaire had great difficulty in recruiting labour for his own fishery. He had to buy most of his fish from the Africans. Even so, he handled over a million *Tilapia*, weighing about 300 tons, and 48,000 lb. of *Clarias*. There were indications that the average weight of *Tilapia* was returning to the pre-drought average.

In 1953 a million *Tilapia* were marketed, and in 1954 another million; but in 1955 and 1956 the new commercial effort died out, chiefly due to marketing difficulties. Before going on to this second bane of Lake Rukwa, it is important to stress the quick recovery of the fish stocks in general, and of *Tilapia* in particular, from the catastrophe of 1949. Two years only of renewed water in the lake sufficed for the fish stocks to build up again to nearly their former level. This is yet another illustration of the extraordinary recuperative power of the tropical fisheries, and shows up in a strange light the restrictions imposed on the pre-drought fishery, in the form of mesh regulations and a close season. If these were designed to protect the fish, they were shown by Nature to have been a waste of time and of fish potential. These restrictions were imposed in spite of the known fact that only a small fraction of the lake was fished at all.

Marketing

Marketing of the fish was not difficult in the heyday of the Lupa Goldfields and the fishery had its best days then. But these goldfields had become worked out even by 1946. They died out altogether as a market for fish for the African labour employed there, in about 1950. The next best available markets were Chunya and Mbeya, and the Central Railway, reached at Itigi. But attempts to sell fresh fish in Mbeya failed because of the high cost of transport and lack of refrigeration.

In 1953, the then European concessionaire accumulated considerable stocks of surplus smoked fish, which he was unable to market, because his price was not competitive, due to high business overheads and the high cost of transport to any large market, such as to the Central Railway.

There was a brief flash of hope in 1954, when large quantities of smoked fish were sent by road to the Rhodesian Copperbelt; but the orders were not repeated in 1955, and in 1956 the commercial exploitation came once more to an end.

These marketing difficulties did not affect the small-scale African trade in dried and smoked fish. Hawkers collected the product in small lots and no complaints were heard except that the fishermen grumbled at the price offered. The African fisherman has few overhead expenses, and the hawker, by coming to him, solves the problem of transport. To the large-scale operator the isolation of Lake Rukwa, coupled with rising costs of transport and overheads, with which the price of fish does not keep pace, is a drag on development which will be changed only by a great economic development in southwestern Tanganyika.

LAKE VICTORIA

This great lake has an area of some 26,000 square miles and a total length of coastline of some 3000 statute miles, including the islands, which form about 3·7 per cent of the area of the lake.

Original African Fishing Methods

The fisheries of Lake Victoria were first fully described by Graham.[96] Apart from fishing devices in use in the rivers, there were fixed gears in the lake itself, long reed fences ending in a series of non-return compartments from which the fish are removed. Movable fences, worked something like a seine-net, were also used; and another version was the *usambo*, which was essentially a line of conical baskets lashed together in a row and dragged up to the shore like any seine.

Another interesting gear on the same principle was the *ngogo*, a long fence made of papyrus stalks, which floated on the surface, and was shot in a complete circle (Plate 46). The circle was then folded on itself so as to become progressively smaller until the fish could be dipped out with a basket. As the *ngogo* floated on the surface it seems likely that the small fish caught, which include the small pelagic fish *Engraulicypris*, may be attracted to the shelter of the papyrus matting. If so, the *ngogo* has many parallels elsewhere.

Other devices included fish spears, and fish baskets. All these fishing devices of an earlier day are being replaced by introduced European methods, except the long-line, which, using modern materials it is true, holds its own as an important implement.

Before going further into the modern fishing gear, a word should be said about the indigenous fish traps and fish-fences. An investigation was made by the Lake Victoria Fisheries Service into the performance of these implements in Lake Victoria. The table on page 206 is taken from their Report for 1951.

These gears are obviously effective, and each type accounted for over 3000 of the valuable and controversial *Tilapia esculenta*. As these traps are described as too numerous to estimate, in the Kavirondo Gulf alone, plainly they must take a great weight of fish. Even if there were only a hundred of them, their catch, at the rate of the sample traps given above, would amount to 300,000 fish or about 20 per cent of the total catch of this species in the Kavirondo Gulf. Unluckily, these traps are so numerous and so scattered that no actual data for their total catch is available. But they cannot be ignored when the overfishing question in the Kavirondo Gulf is discussed.

It will be seen that the catches of all fish become great in April, May, and in some cases, in June. These are the months of heavy

The Shallow Lakes

Table VI

Statistics of the Catch of Fish by a *Kek* on Lake Victoria.
(From Report, Lake Victoria Fisheries Service, 1951.)

Month	Baskets ex-amined	T. escu-lenta	T. vari-abilis	Clarias	Schli-be	Labeo	Proto-pterus	Syno-dontis	Alettes
Numbers of									
1950									
Nov.	529	80	30	12	17	—	6	2	—
Dec.	320	42	7	1	2	—	1	—	—
1951									
Jan.	192	28	28	14	—	—	6	—	—
Feb.	148	192	22	10	—	—	6	—	—
Mar.	216	117	8	16	77	145	4	24	4
April	1,202	967	3	220	8,488	19,077	2	2,358	12,519
May	310	578	7	33	345	976	3	21	461
June	216	203	2	24	69	55	3	8	20
July	96	414	103	—	2	1	2	1	—
August	227	136	15	—	260	21	1	—	—
Sept.	193	186	7	—	104	—	—	—	—
Oct.	175	204	28	—	85	5	—	—	—
Totals	3,824	3,147	260	330	9,449	20,280	34	2,414	13,004

Table VII

Statistics of the Catch of Fish by an *Osageru* on Lake
Victoria. (Lake Victoria Fisheries Service, 1951).

Month	No. of baskets examined	Numbers of T. esculenta	Numbers of T. variabilis	No. of days recorded
1950				
November	170	204	25	17
December	342	427	7	16
1951				
January	500	606	—	25
February	340	888	2	17
March	352	510	101	22
April	400	901	39	20
May	420	1,026	72	21
June	234	179	11	24
July	150	91	2	26
August	168	61	28	23
September	No observations			
October	175	204	27	22
Totals	3,251	5,097	314	233

rain, when the rivers would be running in spate. The *Labeo* and *Alestes* then have a definite spawning run up-river, and this is very clearly shown in the catches of the *kek*. But it is interesting to see that the *Tilapia esculenta* catches rise to a similar maximum at this time, not only in the *kek*, but also in the *osageru*.

Long-line fishing, one of the original African fishing methods, is of much greater importance, especially in the Uganda waters of the lake, than is generally realised. The gill-nets and beach seines are used where all can see them, but long-lining is done in the more remote and inaccessible grounds, and in two distinct types of water.

First, it is used in deep water off rocky islands; and secondly, in shallow water with a muddy bottom, often among papyrus and water-lily fringing swamps, or in water bounded by them.

Most fish are taken by the first method, the species being usually *Bagrus* and *Clarias*, with a few *Barbus* and *Protopterus*. The long-line catches big fish; the average weights are about 10 lb. for *Bagrus*, 5 lb. for *Clarias*, and 19 lb. for *Protopterus*. There may be as many as seven fish caught per 100 hooks at times; at others the average may be as low as two. With such large fish it is easy to make paying catches and the fish are always in demand.

The second type of long-line catches chiefly *Protopterus* and *Clarias*, but the number caught per 100 hooks is lower.

The long-lines are seldom laid actually on the bottom. They are buoyed at intervals, to keep as many of the hooks as possible clear of the mud. Since all the fish taken on long-lines are predators, their use is to be encouraged as likely to lead to a more balanced catch of fish from the lake. Nylon lines and modern hooks are now widely used; and when power-driven craft become more frequent, long-lining may assume a new importance as one means of tapping the deeper coastal waters.

Introduced Fishing Methods

The two introduced methods of fishing are the gill-net and the seine. Of these the gill-net is by far the more important. This net was first introduced before the 1914-18 war, but was used in rapidly increasing numbers during the post-1918 boom years, between 1925 and 1930. At first they were used only in the Kavirondo Gulf, because at Kisumu on the Gulf is the railway line to Nairobi, the biggest and most reliable market. Moreover, the Kavirondo Gulf seems especially suited to the growth of *Tilapia esculenta,* the "Lake Fish" *par excellence.*

When first used on unfished stocks (or stocks fished only by indigenous methods, which, however, are far from ineffective), very high catches were made per standard length of gill-net. At the time of Graham's visit in 1927, the average catches had fallen to about nine fish per net. But the number of nets in use continued to rise, for there was a very profitable fishery. It has been estimated that in 1954-5 some 250 miles of nets were being set nightly in the Kavirondo Gulf.

It is not to be wondered at that the catch per net declined further until it reached about two fish per net. Very roughly, the number of fish taken per net tended to vary inversely with the number of nets set. For many years this average was about two fish per net, sometimes a little more, sometimes a little less. For many years this average has persisted. It seems that the stock of *Tilapia* is about in balance with the high fishing effort. If there has been some tendency towards a further decline in the last two or three years, the great increase in the amount of illegal seining in the Gulf must be taken into account. The time of the Fishery Officer at Kisumu is largely occupied in trying to control these nets; fines and confiscations totalling as much as £3000 in one year were imposed. No fewer than forty-one illegal seines were seized in one raid on two beaches only. The seines may be fastened end to end to make huge nets which may be dragged in from ¾ mile out in the lake. Catches must be heavy to make men risk fines and confiscation again and again.

The quantity of fish taken in this way cannot be known; but if their numbers were to be added to the numbers taken legally and recorded, and to the numbers taken in the indigenous traps, it is likely that the observed decline in the catch per net in the last two or three years could be explained.

Overfishing

The Kavirondo Gulf, as the Lake Victoria Fisheries Service report for 1954-5 ruefully says, is always in the news. The cry of overfishing is seldom silent. But what is meant by overfishing? It cannot mean the extinction of the fishery; the recovery of Lake Rukwa shows that. If it means a diminution in the catch per net, that is,

45. Scoop- or clap-nets in use on Lake Rukwa, Tanganyika.

46. A *Ngogo* in use on Lake Victoria.

47. Plank-built boats on Lake Nakivali, Uganda.

48. A modern fishing village on Lake Nakivali, Uganda.

49. Lake Kariba.

50. Kariba Dam.

51. *Salvinia* on Lake Kariba.

less economical fishing, a remedy would be somehow to stop the use of the seine-nets, and in any case to reduce the number of gill-nets allowed in the Gulf. The catch per net would rise, and be followed a year or so later by a rise in the total number of fish and the total weight of fish taken. But as at least 4000 fishermen earn the greater part of their living in fishing in the Gulf, that might not be politically feasible. Unless and until that can be done the present situation will persist. If the price of fish goes up, more nets will come into use and the catch per net will fall; if the price of fish falls, fewer nets will be used and the catch per net will rise.

The present low catch per net may result in many of the fishermen leaving the Gulf to fish outside, and there are indications that this is happening.

Elsewhere on the lake, especially in the Uganda waters, the catch per net has fallen in the last four years, and this seems to have become more marked since the ban on the use of gill-nets having a mesh of less than 5 inches was lifted. But the years from 1952 to 1956 were years of falling lake level, and this might have had some effect on the catches of *Tilapia* three or four years later. The notable fluctuations in the fisheries of the African lakes must make it desirable to wait for a longer series of statistics before a convincing case can be made out for a real decline in the *Tilapia* fisheries.

Other Kinds of Fish

Unfortunately it is difficult to market, in the fresh state, fish other than the *Tilapia*, for the lake abounds in good food-fish of other species. Small-meshed gill-nets take great quantities of *Labeo victorianus* and other fish, but the lack of communications prevents fresh fish from being sent away from many good fishing areas, and the fishermen have no incentive to work when they cannot realise their catch.

The Kagera River in Uganda is now one of the exceptions; there is a very rich fishery for *Tilapia, Barbus, Labeo, Schilbe, Synodontis, Bagrus, Clarias* and *Protopterus*. On an average, some 25,000 5-inch gill-nets, 75,000 3-inch gill-nets, and 150,000 hooks, set on long-lines, are employed annually there, together with a number of seine-nets. Catches have been as high as 400 tons. This production could have been much higher if there had been better access to markets. In 1958 this was at last provided in the form of an all-weather road linking the main fish-landing place with the main road system of Uganda. It can now be confidently expected that the Kagera River area will become one of the biggest producers of fish on the lake.

Seine-nets

The use of the seine-net is second in importance to the gill-net. In 1953 it was estimated that there were 1,000 seine-nets in use on the lake. In 1955-6, 100 seines were licensed in the Uganda waters and 508 in the Tanganyika waters of the lake. The meshes of seines are usually small, of a little more than 1-inch bar, but in Uganda bigger meshes are used because of the muddy nature of the bottom. The seines are usually 250 yards long. Very large hauls of *Tilapia* may be made by seines, but perhaps the biggest hauls are of the small *Haplochromis*, of which 4,000 may be taken in one shot. Seining is a profitable method of fishing, but it does need a certain amount of capital and at least eight to twelve persons to operate it.

Fishing Craft and Nets

In recent years there have been notable improvements in the fishing craft used. There had been no major alterations in the design or build of these craft for at least fifty years, since an Arab introduced the *karua*, a small dhow about 31 feet in length with a large lateen sail. They are used only in the Kavirondo Gulf and are very fast in a breeze. Most of the craft used for fishing are the so-called Sesse canoes of Uganda, large canoes, but very frail. In Tanganyika a few dug-out canoes still survive, but most of the Tanganyika fishermen use an improved version of the Sesse canoe by adding internal frames; this version is now being used all round the lake.

As early as 1953 it was reported that the fishermen were keen to install power, and indeed some Uganda fishermen had already bought outboard engines to fit into their strengthened and modified Sesse canoes. By 1958, it could be said that canoes without an outboard engine were becoming rare and had difficulty in finding crews. Little progress has yet been made in the introduction of genuine powered fishing craft; but the atmosphere is favourable, and there may be considerable developments in the next decade.

Nylon and terylene nets were slow to be adopted. The fishermen were sceptical of them as recently as 1952, but it was soon found that though their first cost is higher they caught a greater weight of fish, of greater value, during their working life, than the flax nets used previously. Most of the nets in use are now of synthetic materials.

Production

The total production of fish in Lake Victoria was estimated in 1958 at 70,418 tons, valued at about £4,364,000. This is a respectable total, a substantial figure in the economy of any country. It may be compared with the 45,000 metric tons produced annually in the delta of the Middle Niger, and with the fishery in the Lake District of Indonesian Borneo, estimated at 17,500 metric tons. It cannot yet compare with the 100,000 metric tons of the Grand Lac of Cambodia.

Reckoned over the whole area of the lake, which is about 26,000 square miles, the annual crop is of a very low order, only about 7 lb. of fish per acre. Only the coastal waters are at present fished, so that the crop per unit area fished must be somewhat higher. In the Kavirondo Gulf it is much higher. The Gulf has an area of about 250 square miles and produces an annual crop of about 3000 tons. This works out at about 42 lb. per acre, again not a particularly high figure by comparison with some of the Uganda lakes. It is rather better than Lake Albert as a whole, though not nearly so good as the shallow northern end of Lake Albert (page 195).

No account has yet been published on the effect of changing lake levels on the fisheries, though it was recorded that in one year high lake levels submerged many of the seining beaches. Such changes of lake level must also affect the abundance of fish. Certainly, fish are described as being difficult to catch during the rains; so much so that most of the fishermen do not fish at all then. On Lake Albert, on the other hand, the best fishing is during the rains.

Deep-water Survey

Looking ahead to the next decade or two, when powered fishing craft may be operating in some numbers on the lake, a deep-water fishery survey has been started. It has already been said that at present only the coastal waters are being fished and that little fishing takes place in water deeper than about 90 feet. That may be partly because the present fishing canoes cannot work at such depths, nor so far from the coast. In the Uganda survey, the trawl was chiefly used. Very little fish was found in the deeper water, though in the preliminary summary of the survey, the depths are not separated, and blank or poor hauls were made in shallow as well as in deeper water.

A similar survey, done on a smaller scale, in Tanganyika waters, used gill-nets as well as the trawl. Fish appeared to be more plentiful in the deeper water here, and there are a number of records from depths of 135 to 306 feet where the catch was from 10 to 40 lb. The full results of the survey must be awaited, but it is already clear that the really deep waters of the lake do contain some fish. One would like to see sunk gill-nets used in large fleets, and not only trawling, which never seems very successful in fresh water. The difference between the results in Uganda and Tanganyika may have been due to the seiche movement well known in the lake (see Chapter III); the Uganda waters may have been without oxygen in the depths, while, in Tanganyika waters, mixing may have taken place, thus carrying oxygenated water to the bottom layers.

One very interesting and probably important finding of the survey is that the small silvery pelagic fish *Engraulicypris* is very much more plentiful than had been previously realised. They were revealed by their traces in the echo-sounder, and confirmed by hauls with a midwater trawl. As these fish resemble in size and habits the very important *Dagaa* of Lake Tanganyika, the way may be open to a similar fishery in Lake Victoria.

THE LAKE DISTRICT OF INDONESIAN BORNEO

Vaas describes the fisheries in the Lake District along the River Kapuas in West Borneo.[44] The nature of these lakes has already been described on page 55. The bulk of the fish catch consists of the predatory fish such as the Siluridae and Ophiocephalidae, and *Notopterus*. These fish are taken on hooks, and owing to the difficulty in obtaining hooks during and after the last war, the predators increased in numbers to the detriment of the fishery as a whole. Vaas shows that, in any case, in confined waters the predators must get the upper hand in a mixed population of fish. He quotes the case of a deep depression in a river bed isolated during the dry season, which was cleared by derris poisoning. The water was found to contain 177 predatory fish of a total weight of 50 kg., and only 38 vegetarian fish weighing 16 kg.

During the rainy season, there are vast areas of flooded land around the margins of the lakes in which the non-predators grow and breed. But when the lakes shrink back into their dry-season basins and the area of water becomes narrow, the predators take their toll. The fish fauna then gives the impression of a preponderance of predators, which is easily borne out by an analysis of the catches and the exports. There thus seems to be some seasonal alternation of predators and non-predators. The same was true of the Zambezi before the creation of Lake Kariba. Since the lake formed, the proportion of predators has fallen.

The fishing methods used in these lakes are, first, hooks for the predators. Spears and lances, often used at night from canoes equipped with a lamp, are also used against the big predatory fish. For all kinds of fish, fykes are put up made of bamboo matting, which may be as long as 30 metres and 15 metres high. These fykes seem to resemble the *osageru* of Lake Victoria; like them, they are designed to shepherd the fish into non-return enclosures or traps set in gaps in the fykes. Cast-nets are widely used; and nets may be used instead of baskets in connection with the fykes mentioned above. There is no mention, in Vaas's account, of gill-nets in these lakes.

THE FISHERY IN THE GRAND LAC OF CAMBODIA

At the time of low water, there is a fishery in the open waters of the Grand Lac in Cambodia, using very large but shallow nets. These may be as much as 8000 metres long, though only 2 metres deep. In water as shallow as this, obviously no purse-seine could be used, nor can ordinary seines be used because there is no land on to which they could be drawn. The solution found in the Grand Lac is to shoot two nets in a wide circle, so that they overlap each other and enclose the fish between them. The outfit to work these nets may be very elaborate. There may be two net-carrying boats which lay the nets. Then there are two boats, each with a turnbuckle worked by eight men pushing capstan bars. Finally, there is a boat which carries lengths of split-cane fencing and poles.

When the two net-laying boats have finished laying their nets in two overlapping semicircles, the ends are taken over by the capstan boats, and the nets are wound in on the capstan, hour after hour,

until the area enclosed by the nets becomes very small. A rectangle
of posts supporting an enclosure of split-cane fencing is then made
by the boat carrying the materials; the enclosure may lead into a
chambre de capture by way of a non-return gate. The fish enclosed
by the nets are manœuvred into the fenced enclosure, and thence
driven into the *chambre de capture* by men wading. The frantic mass
of fish, which may weigh several tons in one shot, may try to escape
by jumping, and injuries to the fishermen are not uncommon.

Small-scale independent fishermen and their families may come
close to the gear during the last stages of a haul, and spread nets
vertically above the water to catch fish which succeed in jumping
clear. This, by the way, seems to be an almost universal custom;
namely the tacit right of outsiders to salvage fish escaping from
another's fishing. In Uganda, Ghana and Malaya seines may be shot
around the bag of a big seine just before the big seine is hauled out
of the water. The fish which manage to escape the big seine then
become the perquisite of the small operators.

Chapter Fourteen

THE SWAMP FISHERIES

THE main character of a swamp is that it is more or less filled with vegetation, and may often, as in the South American and African swamps investigated by Carter, be deficient in oxygen. Other swamps have more or less large areas of open water, where fish not specially adapted to a low oxygen content can live. In fact, there is every gradation from a lake with large fringing reed beds, to the swamp where most of the water surface is covered.

THE RAWA BONOROWO

The Rawa Bonorowo near the south coast of Java could be referred to as a seasonally inundated prairie, or as a marsh. Vaas and Schuurman[97] state that it is the last remains of a bay which in recent times has been gradually filled with volcanic soil brought down by the rivers. In the years 1820-30, the Rawa was described as a large brackish marshy area bounded by a river on each side. One of these rivers communicated with the sea, and during the last half-century, canals have been dug through the range of dunes which separate the Rawa from the sea, with the object of trying to improve the drainage. But these have soon silted up, and the swamp is a large flat area of poor drainage, where water accumulates in the wet season to form a marsh of about 20 sq. km. In the dry season, the Rawa shrinks to one square kilometre, or, as in 1940, may dry out completely.

When the water level in the Rawa falls below that of the sea outside the dunes, a dam is built across the River Wawar, which drains the swamp. This is to protect the paddy land from the harmful effects of salt water. But some sea-water may enter, and the fish fauna usually includes some brackish-water species.

Villages have been built on slightly elevated areas in the swamp, or on artificially made mounds, to house the people who till the rice fields. The borrow-pits for these raised mounds, and the drainage canals, are very important in the fishery economy of the Rawa Bonorowo, for in them the water remains when the rest of the marsh may be dry, and in this water the survivors of the intensive fishery in the shallow waters of the marsh live to repopulate the area in the next wet season.

During the period of low water, there is a very dense vegetation, and this was studied in a small area of open water. At the margins there were grasses and sedges; next a zone of *Ipomaea reptans* and *Lophotocarpus guyanensis*. Still closer to the centre was a very wide zone of water hyacinth which completely covered the surface of the water from shore to shore in many places. Finally, in the centre were the true aquatics, such as *Hydrilla, Limnophila, Utricularia* and *Najas*. It is interesting to note, for comparison with Carter's findings in the swamps of Uganda, that under the dense beds of water hyacinth there was a low oxygen content and a high level of carbon dioxide.

When the Rawa refills in the rainy season, the water flowing in will have drained through numerous paddy fields and have received the sewage of the villages standing round the lake. As has already been said, the area of the Rawa at high water is twenty times as great as at low water; a very large area is therefore inundated in which the mineralisation and liberation of nutrient materials can affect the production of the Rawa.

The Fish

The rather poor oxygen conditions in the marsh favour the dominance, in the wild fish fauna, of those of the family Labyrinthici, which have accessory air-breathing organs. In fact, the Sepat java and the *Anabas testudineus*, both small Labyrinthine fish, between them accounted for some 42·5 per cent of the catches. They were chiefly caught with the cast-net. But 39 per cent of the catches consisted of shrimps or prawns, taken with scoop-nets attached to a handle and pushed about in the vegetation. The little Labyrinthine fish *Rasbora argytaenia*, which never exceeds a length of about 5 cm., made up a further 8 per cent of the fish; they are caught with the shrimps in the scoop-nets.

All the rest of the fish, including the introduced species *Puntius javanicus, Trichogaster pectoralis* and *Osteochilus hasselti*, accounted for only about 10·5 per cent of the catches. The common carp, also introduced, does not appear in the list of fish caught. It would seem, therefore, that in this marsh only fish with an accessory air-breathing organ and able to flourish in conditions of poor oxygen concentration, contribute significantly to the yield of the fishery.

Fishing Gear

It is significant that drag-nets are not used, for the vegetation would obviously not allow a clear haul. Beside the scoop-net and the cast-net, a gill-net is used, in which the principal catch is the Climbing Perch, *Anabas*, and the plunge-basket, used in the shallow water for mud fish, obviously *Clarias*. The basket trap is used, usually in conjunction with a fence. Finally, there are hook and line, and one fisherman may use twenty to twenty-five lines at a time. It is easy to conclude that the catch by hook and line will be mainly *Anabas*, *Ophiocephalus*, *Clarias* and probably eels.

The Annual Recovery

When the water starts to rise after the beginning of the dry season, the surviving fish spawn. They must be few in number, for not only are they heavily and very thoroughly fished while the water level is falling, as well as in the small area of water left in the dry season, but the dry-season area is itself only one-twentieth of the wet-season area. When the Rawa dries out completely, as happened in September 1940, only the fish which remained in the drainage canals and borrow-pits can have survived. In fact, Vaas and Schuurman noted that, at the end of December 1940, there was a considerable area of open water without any fish. Yet in March 1941 all the usual species were found to be present. It seems that, in this Rawa, most of the fish which form the population at high water, and which are the object of the fishery when the water is falling, are the same season's young, and that only a handful of fish which survive over the dry period suffice to maintain the population of fish and supply the fishery. Since this is so, the capture of the surplus would seem to be an economical exploitation, but the importance of the deeper points of the marsh as places of refuge when the marsh dries up needs no emphasis. The astonishing reproductive power and very rapid rate of growth of the young fish are also illustrated in this fishery, as they are in the flood-fisheries described in Chapter VI.

THE BAHI SWAMP

The remarkable fishery in the Bahi Swamp of Tanganyika is of the same character as that of the Rawa Bonorowo, in as much as the swamp dries up more or less completely each year, so that the supply of fish must be annually replenished from a small stock of survivors.

The Bahi Swamp is situated in a depression in the central part of Tanganyika, into which a number of rivers drain, and to which there is no outlet. It is an area of low average rainfall of the order of 15 to 40 inches a year, and with great annual variations. In July 1946, the rains had been much below average and the swamp was quite dry. In more normal years, the rain falls in the months from November to May, and the swamp does not dry until September.

Bahi is a station on the central railway which runs across Tanganyika from Dar-es-Salaam to Kigoma on Lake Tanganyika, and it is the centre of the fishery, when one exists, from which the dried fish, surplus to local requirements, is sent away by rail.

A Dry Fishery

"At Bahi village we managed to find two men with a knowledge of the fishing places, and we took them with us, and motored for 16 miles over the flattest country imaginable, with sparse trees, and a sandy soil, but with big areas of dried mud. Over these we travelled at high speed, and I had the unusual experience of motoring over a fishery at 50 miles per hour. We came on beds of withered reeds and rushes, around which were a few low bunded areas where crops had been grown in the receding floods. Then there were big areas of dried mud pitted with the hoof-marks of cattle which had been driven to the receding water. It was impossible to drive further over these rutted areas, so we stepped out into the fierce heat, where the air was windless except for the numerous little dust-devils which came spinning over the parched ground, and made us clutch at our hats and shield our eyes. To the south of us lay a belt of green rushes, full of cattle, and beyond this again lay the great bare flat mud-pan which is the last of all the swamp area to dry out, and where most of the fishing takes place as the water recedes." (Abstract from the author's notes.)

The area inundated depends on the amount of rain in the surrounding catchment area. As this varies so much from year to year, so the yield of the fishery must vary. In 1919, and again in 1946, there was very little rain and no fishery.

The Seasonal Fishery

The following is an account of this extraordinary fishery, as the author was given it on the spot by the administrative officers, and by fishermen, through interpreters.

Only one kind of fish is caught, the mudfish or catfish *Clarias*. It grows to a length of about 18 inches, and is scaleless and slimy to the touch so that they cannot be caught by hand. There are spines on the gill-covers, and four barbels on the snout.

Fishing Methods

The fishery starts in the rivers, when the river bed fills up with water. Here, fish-weirs, in the gaps of which traps are placed, are chiefly used. The traps are the usual wickerwork basket with a non-return valve, about 5 feet long and 28 inches in diameter, tapering to a flattened end, which is unlaced to extract the fish. Here the catch may be very heavy, one man taking as much as 500 fish per day. However, the price paid for the fish, and the method of smoking, soon to be described, suggest that the fish are small. Nets are also used in the rivers, and single hooks, baited with meat, chicken or fish guts.

The fishermen believe that the fish are carried down the rivers by the floods. The orthodox belief is, that the fish fall from the heavens with the rain, but the fishermen have seen birds digging the fish from the mud and are ready to believe that they do bury themselves in the mud when the water dries up. The fish are said to be fatter and in better condition at the beginning than at the end of the season.

Later in the season, the rivers flood the swamp to a greater or lesser extent each year, according to the amount of rainfall. The fishery in this temporary marsh begins when the water starts to recede and shrink into channels and pools. Weirs up to 300 yards in length may be put up, with traps set in the gaps (Plate 12). Simple seines are also used. They are rectangular nets with the headline and footrope mounted on lines rove through the meshes but not hitched to them. About 25 feet of net is set into about 17 feet on the ropes. The mouth is kept open by two poles about 3 feet long, passed through beckets and held by hand, or hauled by ropes made from baobab fibre. There are papyrus floats on the headline and stones on the foot-rope. Apparently the net is pulled forward in such a way that the footrope is in advance of the headrope, and the loose setting of the net on the ropes ensures a bunt in the net to retain the fish caught. The meshes were very irregular, as one might expect with a home-spun twine, making a home-made net; but it appeared to have a $\frac{3}{4}$-inch bar, single twine.

Nowadays modern nets are coming into use, brought by immigrant fishermen from other lakes. About 300 to 400 fishermen may take part in the fishery, mostly migrants, but with many local people, who take up fishing in the season as an addition to their usual herding of cattle.

Marketing

The fishermen form regular camps on the site of the fishery. The fish are smoke-cured on the spot. A matting tray is used, but to economise the smoke, the tray of fish stands, not on poles over the fire, but on an oven of mud and wattle enclosed on three sides and with the fire on the fourth side. Consequently the fish must be very hot-smoked, cooked in fact, as the fishermen themselves call it. The fish, for the purpose of smoking, are bent into a circle, with the tail hitched on to one of the spines on the gill-cover. The smoked fish are said to last as long as three months with re-smoking. They are packed in wicker baskets, each holding about 20 lb. of fish. They are sold on the markets or to Indian traders who despatch it down the railway to other markets.

The fishery is expected to be good if the level of the Bubu River, the most important of the rivers which empty into the swamp, rises to a height of six feet or more at the railway bridge east of Bahi Station. The fishermen said that they had never known the swamp to remain wet throughout the year, so as to give an all-the-year-round fishery. The statistics of the fish despatched from Bahi Station show that the catches roughly coincide with the rainy season, the best catches being about March to May, towards the end of the rains when the level of the water would be falling.

The fishermen were positive that only this one species of fish is caught. The Tilapia is well known to them as *Ngege*, but they have never seen this species caught in the Bahi Swamp.

Statistics

Statistics of fish sold on the markets and despatched by train suggest that about 75 per cent of the fish are exported by rail. This figure is confirmed in the Report of the Department of Agriculture of Tanganyika for 1956 which records that 1956 was a good year for the Bahi Depression fishery, for 120 tons of smoked catfish were railed during the year, and at least another 20 per cent distributed by lorry and head-load. This represents at least 450 tons of fresh fish when allowance is made for the loss of weight during smoke-drying.

The statistics show how variable is the yield of this fishery, in rough consonance with the variation in the rainfall, with which it is even more closely associated than most freshwater fisheries. Below are given the recorded quantities of smoked fish railed from Bahi Station in each year since 1941:

Table VIII

The Weight of Smoked Fish Railed from Bahi Station.

Year	Quantity (tons)	Rainfall (in.)
1941	37	21
1942	126	39
1943	321	18
1944	22	21
1945	168	24
1946	nil	17
1956	120	30

The Annual Recovery

The problem of how the fish taken in this fishery manage to recruit their numbers is even more difficult to understand than in the case of the Rawa Bonorowo, for the latter only dries right out in very exceptional years, while the Bahi Swamp, on the word of the local people, dries out in most years. In 1946 the author noted in his journal (from which the description of the fishery given above is taken) that ". . . fields of withered maize, and, in front of each shamba, a small patch of pumpkins, green in spite of the drought.

Water-holes, mostly either dry, or with mud on the bottom, show the gradual fall of the water-table."

Probably large numbers of fish are washed down with the flood of the Bubu River. But this would hardly account for such a big fishery over so large an area. It seems likely that the fishermen's own explanation is correct, and that enough fish may survive in the damper places to produce a fresh generation of fish each year. The *Clarias* is elsewhere known to be able to survive for some time in mud (pages 92 and 234).

No doubt, at some time in the future, check-dams will be constructed across the rivers flowing down into the Bahi Depression, to give a reserve of water to tide that thirsty land over the months of drought, and that is bound to affect the fishery in the swamp. For in years of poor rainfall the water coming down will be largely retained in the dams, and only in years of really good rainfall will there be the great overspill needed to flood the swamp and start the fishery. On the other hand, if the Africans are right in their belief that many of the fish are swept down the rivers into the swamp, there might be good fishing in the check-dams, as some compensation for the loss of the swamp fishery.

THE MALAGARASI SWAMP

This swamp has a very different character from that of either of the swamps so far described, for it is permanent and has large lagoons of open water. It is situated in mid-Tanganyika, to the north of the main railway line, and drains to Lake Tanganyika by the river of the same name.

Water Gipsies

Macquarie[98] gives some description of the upper part of this swamp and of its inhabitants, as he saw them in 1938. The principal fish caught were *Tilapia*, similar to those common in Lake Victoria, though of a smaller average size. The name of the tribe was Wanahoza, and they resented as an insult the name of Wakiko which was commonly given them.

This tribe are all fishermen and spend most of their lives afloat. They fish over a wide area each year, visiting practically all the lagoons and navigable waters east of Uvinza and north of the central railway. The Mtamba, near Buzongwe, is a long stretch of water (possibly the River Igombe) from 1 mile to 2 miles wide when Macquarie visited it, but it was said to extend much farther after a good rainy season. A lagoon, Mkwassi, which he passed next day on safari, was about 3 miles long and a mile broad, and there were the remains of many little grass shelters on the shore. This was the site of one of the fishing camps of the Wanahoza which was annually visited.

Macquarie was told that downstream, before the water joined the Malagarasi River, there was an open area of water called Katamaguru, and most of the Wanahoza were settled along its shores. They move about with all their belongings in canoes, and when on passage build no shelters ashore. That is why Macquarie called them the water-gipsies of the Malagarasi. But when fishing a large stretch of water, they had to have shelters for curing and storing the fish.

The fish are gutted and smoked over a pit in which the fire is lit, in the manner so common, for example, in Uganda (Plate 25).

Generally, each family did its own fishing. At the time of Macquarie's visit, the fishing was being done mostly with spears, but that may have been seasonal. Spears were especially effective for the capture of the big Silurids, which could be clearly seen on the bottom. The great clearness of the water of this swamp is one of its most remarkable features. The Wanahoza also showed Macquarie nets which he described as splash-nets, well made of bark twine, and he concluded that they were used for some kind of fish which moved in shoals periodically. This splash-net is almost certain to be a gill net into which the fish are driven by splashing, as is also the case at the present time.

The fishermen to whom he spoke had sold in advance the season's catch on contract to a Swahili trader.

A Little-exploited Fishery Resource

The Fishery Officer of Tanganyika Territory first reported on these swamps in the Annual Report of the Department of Agriculture for 1949.[127] He says that the vast area of rivers, swamp and seasonally flooded grassland known as the Malagarasi Swamp had been but little explored, especially from the fisheries viewpoint. He estimated the available water surface at from about 700 square miles for the permanent swamps to 3,600 square miles for permanent and seasonal swamps combined. Preliminary investigations indicated a rich and varied fish fauna which was then almost unexploited. This failure to exploit was due to two causes, first the very sparse population of the swamp area itself, and secondly, the lack of communications to any market. One part of the swamp is close to the central railway line and an important commercial fishery has developed, exporting its produce by rail. Smoked *Tilapia* in bales were being shipped by train at Malagarasi Station in 1946. This commercial fishery, in contrast to the largely subsistence fishery which had previously prevailed, arose about 1943, when a large demand and high prices in the Congo brought traders up the line from Kigoma and Ujiji buying fish. Though this trade was stopped by the Belgian authorities in 1944, because of the poor quality of the cure, the industry was sufficiently well established to market its products along the central railway line, and has since had no difficulty in disposing of its entire output within Tanganyika itself,

The Present Fishery

The fishery at Katare was conducted entirely with gill-nets at that time made by the fishermen themselves out of khaki sewing cotton. The net is used in two ways. By day the nets are set and the fish, almost wholly *Tilapia*, are driven into them by splashing and beating the water. At night the nets may be set again, but the catches at night are not *Tilapia*, but a great variety of other species such as members of the Characidae, Citharinidae, Mormyridae and Clariidae.

The *Tilapia* are of two species, *T. nilotica* and *T. karomo*. The ratio of the species seems to be about four of the former to one of the latter. Measurements of samples of both species show that the *T. nilotica* has a mean length of 17·5 cm. and *T. karomo* about 19 cm. This confirms Macquarie's note that the fish he bought in the swamp were similar to, but smaller than, those on Lake Victoria.

The Report of 1950[128] describes a steady expansion of the fisheries, though it is difficult to assess the quantities produced because they are distributed by so many buyers on foot and by road, as well as by the railway. The railway alone carried 116 tons of smoked fish, equivalent to some 350 tons of fresh fish. Experimental fishing confirmed that there were dense populations of fish which were virtually unexploited. The most productive method, gill-netting, was still liable to interference from crocodiles, but the demand for crocodile skins had led to so much hunting that the risk of damage was being considerably reduced.

The Economy of the Swamp

Heavy and prolonged rains in the 1951-2 rainy season made the Malagarasi Swamp a wilderness of submerged vegetation till well into the dry season, and the fish, especially the *Tilapia*, were widely dispersed in the big flooded area. The difficulties of the fishermen were increased by the flooding of their camps and the breakdown of communications. But as the water subsided, there was very heavy fishing, though once again it was not possible to estimate the amount. There is here one of the richest unexploited fish stocks in Africa; unexploited because of the unhealthy nature of the area and the difficulty of getting the fish away to markets. An investigation of the fish was made by two officers from the Jinja Laboratory of the East African Fisheries Research Organisation. Many species of fish new to science were found. The crystal clearness of the water of these swamps has already been noted; Miss Lowe (now Mrs. McConnell) stated that she was able to watch the fish on the bed of the swamp as though they were in an aquarium. The reason why the swamp is so abundant in fish life, in spite of this clearness, which is due to an almost complete absence of plankton, is because of the presence of two species of fish which are able to feed on the water-lily and its seeds, and on other plant material. They pass out a partially digested mass which forms the main food of other species of fish, especially the *Tilapia*.

Gill-nets of all mesh sizes gave rich results. When set overnight they took few or no *Tilapia*, while making good catches of other species. Even nets with a mesh as small as 2 inches were tried in the swamp areas on an experimental scale. They were found to make heavy catches of the smaller species of fish not caught by other means, yet they took scarcely any immature *Tilapia*. For instance, in a total of over 860 fish taken with these small-meshed nets, there were only twelve young Tilapias, but the catch included many commercially valuable species such as *Distichodus* and *Schilbe*, which are compctititors and predators on *Tilapia*.

Unlike other swamps, the Malagarasi supports a dense population of fish, all of which are in good condition. This is in contrast with, for example, the lily-swamps of Lake Kioga, which are relatively very unproductive. The reason is believed to be the presence of fish able to eat and at least partially digest vegetable matter, which is so plentiful in a permanent swamp, and so to make available to other fish, such as the valuable Tilapias, a fine flocculent and nutritious detritus, which seems to be an effective substitute for plant plankton. It is not easy to understand why there is no phytoplankton in this swamp. Possibly the dense growth of submerged plants takes up the nutrients available. In some of the ponds at Malacca this phenomenon was noticed; fertilisers which in most ponds gave rise to a well-developed plankton, with very turbid water, in one or two of the ponds nourished a dense stand of *Chara* or *Enhydrias*, and the water remained crystal clear. In this case there was competition between the submerged plants and the plankton, with the former getting the upper hand in exceptional cases.

Aquatic insects and molluscs are also uncommon in the Malagarasi Swamp, so that species of fish which are usually insect eaters, such as *Schilbe*, feed on small fish, chiefly Haplochromids, in this environment.

The Malagarasi Swamp differs from the stagnant swamps investigated by Carter[6] in that there is a considerable flow of water which provides a suitable environment for fishes without special adaptations for air-breathing. Nevertheless there must be, even in such a swamp, large areas of deoxygenation which must be subtracted from the total area in regard to fish-production.

THE BANGWEULU SWAMP

The previous paragraph applies especially to the great Bangweulu Swamp where it has been shown that there are such extensive zones of deoxygenated water which, following on the influx of new water by rainfall, may be flushed out of the vegetation into the lagoons and channels. The fish may then have to migrate out of these areas or be killed if they fail to do so.

Bangweulu Swamps, which are probably one of the largest in the world with an area, even at low water, of about 1,500 square miles, first attracted the attention of the world through the death among them of David Livingstone, after a terrible struggle, in the wet season. It is a journey not lightly to be undertaken even today. Yet that intrepid explorer and keen observer noted, in almost the last entries in his journal before his final and fatal collapse, the nature of the fishing industry of the swamp. His description holds good to this day. He wrote: "The great number of fish caught by the weirs, baskets and nets now, as the water declines, is prodigious. The fish feel their element becoming insufficient for comfort, and return from one bouga to another towards the lake; the narrower parts are duly prepared by weirs to take advantage of their necessities; the sun heat seems to oppress them and forces them to flee."[99]

That was written nearly a century ago; the same fishing methods are in use today. Yet in the years between 1948 and 1957, the swamps gave a fish crop of between one and two million pounds of fish annually. As these were dried fish, the quantity is equivalent to about 1,500 to 3,000 tons of fresh fish, with some tendency to rise over the period.

Description of the Swamp

Accounts of the Bangweulu Swamps and their fisheries have been published by Ricardo[95] and Brelsford.[100] The latter is specially valuable because the sociological and tribal customs which affect the fishery are set out in detail.

Brelsford describes the swamp as a flat mass of green swamp grasses and reeds, dotted with countless lily lagoons and intersected by many open or semi-open channels.

The author has flown over the swamps many times and his journals describe them as "an immense area of lake and swamp as far as the eye can see; open water, very shallow and of every shape and size, connected by irregular leats, with here and there a better-defined river, very winding between beds of reeds. Drier tongues of ground carried a few trees and huts. Close up to the edge of the swamp there was dense reed with papyrus clumps, and water tracks for canoes. Barriers half a mile long were frequent near the shores, and also near the sparse villages on the higher ground marked by bushes. But farther out there were big patches of open water grown with water-lilies. The big leats had weedy bottoms, but some clear sandy patches as well. I saw no traps in this type of water." And again: "I saw some fine fish-weirs in Bangweulu at least two miles long. A small island separated two weirs; all the weirs over which we flew seemed to face about north-east."

Changes in Water-level

Brelsford (loc. cit.) describes the seasons and changes of level of the water in the swamp. The dry season is roughly from May to October, and the rains fall during the period from November to April. But even after the rains have stopped the rivers continue to pour their waters into the Bangweulu basin for a month or more at a fast rate, so that May and June are the times of highest water in the swamp. During July and August there is a gradual fall in the water level which becomes more rapid in the months from September to November. The annual range is of the order of 4 feet, but, in so flat an area this rise suffices to flood the vast plains to the south and east of the permanent swamp.

There are also long-period variations in the water-level. Brelsford gives some evidence that there have been three high-level periods in the last seventy years, namely, round about 1875, 1910 and 1943; and periods of low water about 1895 to 1905, about 1920, and in the 1930s.

Effect of Changes in Water-level

Both the seasonal and the long-term variations of water-level have a profound effect on the life of the swamps and of their inhabitants. Long-term low water-levels mean that large areas of the rich swamp soil are available for cultivation, while the fish are more easily caught because of the comparatively smaller area of water in which they live. So these may be the years of plenty, with abundant ground crops and grain, though perhaps with less fish to export because so many more of the people are attending to their gardens. On the other hand the periods of high water are hard years because the gardens are under water, leaving only a few small patches barely able to support a family or two. In high-water periods, in fact, dry land has to be artificially made by building mounds of soil, so that a poor cassava crop can be grown just above water-level. It is in times like these that the fish-wealth of the swamp-dwellers comes to their aid; for there is always a sure market for their fish by barter or for cash against grain. But low-water levels also affect communications, and even today there have been marketing difficulties at times of low water when the channels may be too shallow for water transport, while the exposed mud makes foot travel extremely arduous.

The seasonal changes in water-level also have a great effect on the swamp-dwellers. As the water recedes from their houses, life in the villages becomes easier though travel by canoe may become more difficult. The effect on fishing is no less marked. At the time of rising and high water, from December to April, the water area is so much increased that fish are not easy to catch by nets in large quantities. During this period fishing is mainly for subsistence, but as soon as the rains stop and the water-level starts to fall, the fishing parties begin to go out, though in July and August the winds are high and the weather cold. That is also the main planting time, so short trips only are made to catch fish for subsistence and to exchange for fishing materials or meal.

The time for falling water between August and November is the time of the greatest catches by the weirs, as Livingstone noted so long ago. The falling water-level also has the effect of concentrating the fish in the more permanent lagoons and channels, thus making them easier to catch.

Fishing Methods

Weirs

The uniformity of the topography of the Bangweulu Swamp, as Brelsford points out, does not suit those fishing methods that depend on a big fall in water-level, or upon the presence of big rivers, large stretches of open water, or currents and spates. So the fishing methods are few in number, but they are so well adapted to the peculiar conditions that it seems doubtful if they could be bettered, though there could perhaps be some improvement in the materials of which the gear is made.

The weirs already mentioned are of two kinds. There are the long earth dams made on the edge of the flood plains, which are conspicuous from the air. These earth dams have gaps in them through which the water pours when the water-level rises. Fish are swept in with the rising water, but they are so few in number that though traps may sometimes be set in the gaps, the catch on the rising waters is small. At the highest water-level the water pours in, not only through the gaps, but often over the top of the dam, and a great area landward of the dam is flooded. Here the fish which have been swept in, grow and multiply. When the water-level falls the water pours out again through the gaps into which basket traps with non-return valves are fitted. The catch may be exceedingly heavy, for the device seems to be almost wholly efficient. But because the dams are on the edge of the swamp area, the season of fishing is short, say during the first fall in the water-level, in April and May.

Brelsford tells how the same method was used by the labourers whom he employed on the clearance of the swamp channels. Brelsford had arranged for the spoil from the clearance to be bunded on either bank so that a current might be created which would help to keep the channel scoured. But as soon as there was a small head of water between the canal and the swamp the labourers made breaches in the bunds and put fish traps in the gaps.

The second kind of weir is built in permanent waters. It is made of sticks and brushwood driven into the mud bottom and packed with a mass of grasses and tough reeds. These weirs are set across every open channel with the slightest indication of a current. The gap or gaps in the weir are closed when the weir is not fishing by a gate made of plaited reeds, but when the weir is fishing these are replaced by non-return basket traps tightly wedged into the gaps.

These weirs across channels are troublesome to water transport, for though canoes can pass over the gaps, larger launches cannot. The enforcement of a 3-foot gap in the weirs to allow of the passage of transport was naturally very unpopular because the whole working principle of the fish-weir depends on the most complete barrier possible to the movement of fish except through the special gaps in which the fish traps are set.

Mintesa

The weirs are especially effective in the capture of the small *mintesa* (*Gnathonemus* sp.). Full-grown at 9 inches, it is a popular fish as it contains much fat. Large shoals move upstream and there is an ingenious modification of the basket trap by which these upstream migrants are caught. The traps are set in pairs, one of each pair being placed in the gap in the weir with its mouth facing downstream but with the non-return valve removed and the blind end of the trap closed. The fish enter these traps but find they cannot pass through. They then turn back and on the turn the current sweeps them down into the second of the pair of traps, which has its valve in position but faces upstream. There may be as many as thirteen pairs of baskets in a weir 45 yards long during the *mintesa* season.

It is believed, with some reason, that the *mintesa* and other fish move freely only during moonless nights, so during nights of bright moonlight the traps may be removed. The catches of *mintesa* in these traps during the season may be colossal.

Tilapias

Weirs may be placed where there are only slight currents and where the water is deepest, for the capture of members of the Cichlid family, especially the Tilapias. Single baskets facing the current may be used in these weirs,

There are many variations in the setting of traps and weirs. They may be placed at the end of the dry season across backwaters which are rapidly drying out, and in order to give the illusion that the gap in the weir is a shady channel, the top of the gap may be thatched with grass covered with earth. This thatch also serves the purpose of catching those desperate fish which try to leap over the gap in the fence. One particular fence watched by Brelsford caught an average of twenty fish per basket each day for six days, after which the backwater was practically dry.

Clarias

When the water begins to rise about November, a different type of basket trap is used. It is in the form of a long, narrow cone about 4 to 6 inches wide at the mouth, but sometimes over 6 feet long. This kind of trap catches the catfish *Clarias*, which in Bangweulu may reach a length of over 3 feet when fully grown. Once such a long, narrow fish enters the trap, it has no room to turn round to escape. This device resembles the bamboo tube traps set in the lagoons of Nigeria for another species of Catfish.

Proprietary Rights

There is a peculiar custom with regard to the fishing weirs. There is one owner, who is descended from the original builder. "He invites whom he likes to repair the weir and to fish with him, and if it is a big enclosure he will call in friends as well as his family" (Brelsford, loc. cit.). The largest weirs, chiefly the earth dams on the flood plains at the edge of the swamp, will sometimes take as many as twenty men to work them. People who have no weirs and are not invited by owners, sometimes go to the chief and ask his help in getting a place. The chief enquires who is short-handed and can sometimes find a place for them, but the chief cannot tell an owner whom he has to take nor can he deprive a man of his weir so long as he wants to go on using it. For it is believed that the ancestral spirits that aid the weir would not help any but the rightful owner, and the chiefs respect this belief. This is an interesting case of proprietary rights in a fishery.

The Commercial Fishery

The second important method of fishing in the Bangweulu Swamps is net fishing from fishing camps, as contrasted with the lesser all-the-year-round net fishing for subsistence and small barter. The usual procedure is to drive the fish into nets set in creeks and lagoons, many nets often being joined together to give a big catching area. Once the nets are set and held in position by reeds driven into the mud, the fishermen move off in their canoes to form a semicircle facing the nets. Then the line of canoes moves slowly towards the nets, striking the water with poles and paddles to frighten the fish into the nets where they gill themselves. Several such drives may be made in the same area if the catches are good, but fishing usually stops in the early afternoon, when the catch is taken back to camp for drying or smoking, and the nets are cleaned and put up to dry.

The nets are of different mesh sizes, related to the fish sought, and may each be 40 yards long. They used to be made of local material; the strongest fibres came from the roots of a creeper and a net made of this fibre might last as long as eighteen months. The creepers, and the root of a tree which made nets slightly less durable, had to be imported from the mainland in exchange for fish. During the last war nets were made from cords stripped from the inner lining of old motor-car and lorry tyres, and because these fibres are coated with rubber, they made the best and strongest nets of all. Nowadays, ready manufactured nets of flax or nylon are generally used.

Fishing Camps

Brelsford writes that there is no typical group of net fishermen as compared with weir fishing, for there are no proprietary rights in net fishing and any kind of combination of relatives or strangers may be found in a fishing camp, as long as there are at least six to ten men so that a large area may be covered with the nets.

On going to the fishing grounds the men take as much cassava meal as the canoes will hold. In addition, they must carry the nets, the brushwood frameworks for the grass-thatched huts to be built for shelter and for the framework of the fish-drying racks. They also have to take firewood for cooking and for smoking the fish when the weather is unfavourable for sun-drying. The canoes leave for the fishing quite full of the necessities of life for weeks or even months of camping in the heart of the swamp.

Food is shared in the camp, and turns are taken at providing it. Each man keeps the fish caught in his nets and has his own drying rack in the fishing camp, which may be only a firmer patch of floating sudd. Each man may carry his own fish away for marketing, or he may sell on the spot to travelling buyers who tour the swamp during the season. These may, in turn, be agents for larger distributing firms, or they may be individual hawkers who buy and carry on bicycles to the markets in the Rhodesian and the Congo Copperbelt towns, as much as 150 lb. of fish at a time. Nowadays, there is a brisk lorry traffic in dried fish to the Copperbelt.

More recently there has arisen a trade in fresh fish, the buying launches carrying ice in which the fish are packed. As early as 1941, some 25 tons of fresh fish per month were being thus collected and distributed by one firm to the mining towns of Mufulira and Luanshya.

Fishing, Tribute and Licensing

There is no hereditary or long-term tenure of net-fishing grounds, and hundreds of stranger fishermen may visit the swamps for the netting. At the close of the season each man should, by custom, send tribute in fish to the local chief. The fishing grounds have always been regarded as being open to anyone so long as the tribute was paid, though a chief might turn out a stranger who had fished the previous season but had left without paying tribute.

At the present time, with the imposition of a licensing system, the connection between fishing and tribute has broken down. The break was so sudden in so long-established a custom, that some explanation is called for. The reason, in Brelsford's view, is that fishing has rather quickly changed its character from a tribal affair in which the chief could claim "first-fruits", to an important export industry, and a chief has not the same claim on cash. But the end of tribute, even though a few faithfuls may still make a voluntary offering, has apparently meant some diminution in the authority of the chiefs, since the payment of tribute was an acknowledgement of his territorial rights.

Minor Fishing Methods

Among minor fishing methods are the combined fish drives by women using wide-mouthed fishing baskets about 3½ feet long and 18 inches deep. The basket is used like a push-net, and is held by the flat upper margin and pushed forward so that the flat lower edge is well below the surface. As one such basket by itself would not catch much fish, a group of women work in a line with their baskets touching. At any time of day a few women will band together to fish. All shallow pools are free of any kind of tenure or fishing rights.

The catch consists mainly of small fish, which are used, subsistence-fashion, as a daily relish with the cereal food. Brelsford writes that a man has a good deal to say to his wife if she does not fish well enough to get relish every day. This is in contrast to the men's fishing, which is mostly for sale or barter.

Long-line or night-line fishing is important because the method provides the largest kinds of fish, such as the Tiger-fish and big *Clarias* and *Heterobranchus*. Sometimes the ugly but valuable Bagrid fish *Auchenoglanis* is taken on baited lines.

The long-lines are thin ropes sometimes 50 yards long, with a hook baited with entrails or meat every 3 feet along its length. It is usually subsidiary to net and weir fishing, and is used at the same time where there are open channels or lagoons close to a fishing camp. The rope with its hooks is stretched across such an open piece of water just below the surface, with the baited hooks dangling down. Each end of the rope is attached to a pole stuck in the mud, or to reeds on either side of the channel. It may be used by day or by night.

Spearing is a fishing method of opportunity, when a man in a canoe on passage may see a fish and transfix it with his spear. But spears may also be used to harvest the fish in enclosed pools.

Finally, in parts of the swamp which dry out, catfish may burrow into the mud. Their position is located by stamping on the hard-baked mud surface, and the fish, which may be as much as 3 feet down, are dug out with hoes.

The Recorded Fishery

From 1943 onwards, the history of the fisheries of the Bangweulu swamps can be followed in the annual reports of the Northern Rhodesian Game and Tsetse Department, which is responsible for the fisheries.

The first report for 1943[129] states that the importance of the fisheries, which provide an incomparable cash crop for the Africans and a wealthy industry in which thousands participate, had scarcely been appreciated. Fish Control Regulations had been introduced in 1943, including the licensing of the fishermen referred to above. It was found that the fishing industry, which had been wholly developed by African enterprise, was gradually expanding; and in 1945, for example, was quick to take advantage of the new private road transport services for the speedy movement of fish to the Copperbelt.

In the years 1948 to 1950, an attempt was made to deal with the fish weirs in the interests of fish conservation, but the native authorities were unwilling to disturb the traditional rights in weir fishing. They may have had some justification for their attitude, for as quotations have shown, the fish-weir, with its apparently destructive effect on the fish stocks, has been in recorded use for nearly a century, and has been in almost certain use for ages before that. In this book there are repeated examples of the astonishing recuperative power of tropical inland fisheries. There would seem to be little cause for alarm at a method of fishing that has not, over a very long run of years, adversely affected a production of fish which has always been high enough to bring wealth to thousands, and is now, with statistics available, shown to be high, and if anything, increasing.

Statistics

The statistics, in the form of the weight of dried fish exported from Bangweulu, are given below, as they have been abstracted from the annual reports.[129]

As an average of the last five years recorded, the Bangweulu produced some 742 tons of dried fish, equivalent to about 2,226 tons of fresh fish. Allowing for the daily consumption of thousands of people in the swamp and exports through minor channels, the total production cannot have been less than 3000 tons, and may have been much more.

Table IX

Export of Dried Fish from the Bangweulu Swamp.
(Extracted from the Annual Reports of the Northern Rhodesia Game and Tsetse Department.)

Year	Tons of dried fish exported
1948	523
1949	701
1950	458
1951	*Not available*
1952	820
1953	564
1954	917
1955	692
1956	685
1957	850

As the swamp has an area at low water which Brelsford estimates at about 1,500 square miles, the rate of fish production is about 2 tons per square mile, or 7 lb. of fish per acre per annum. This is a very low rate of cropping, and might be considered even lower if the yield on the basis of the swamp at high-water level were used. So far from there being any danger of overfishing at such a rate of cropping, one might think that the swamp is under-fished. But in a swamp, as Carter originally showed, there are more or less large areas which are deoxygenated and therefore unsuitable for the life of fish not in possession of special modifications for breathing atmospheric air. Though the big catfish, which have such organs, are an important part of the catch in the swamp, the area of swamp suitable for the life of the remaining fish must be considerably smaller than the total area. It can be confidently expected that the Research Station which is based at Samfya on Lake Bangweulu, will in time give some estimate of the total of this great area of swamp which is liveable by normal fish at any given time.

Variations in Production

The variations shown in the production of the swamp are susceptible to explanations given in the Reports from which they have been taken. The year 1949, for example, was a year of very low water-level, and therefore vast catches were made in the early part of the year, though the low level disorganised water-transport and made the marketing of the fish a matter of some anxiety. In the interests of fish conservation the fishery was stopped, except for local subsistence, as from November. Unfortunately, the exports are given by calendar years, so that they include both fish from the end of one season and the fish from most of the next season.

The year 1953 was also a year of exceptionally low water, but this time there was not an exceptionally large production of fish. This may be because there was at that time some political unrest which upset the industry. The point to make is that these years of low water-level, during which the fish might be considered exceptionally vulnerable to fishing, did not result in any diminution in the supplies of fish in the subsequent years. The fish crop in 1956 was affected by the number of men who were employed in clearing the channels in the swamps, and therefore not available to fishing.

The recorded fluctuations in the annual crop of fish seem to have explanations which are independent of the state of the fish stocks.

Chapter Fifteen

LAKE AND DAM STOCKING; FISH TRANSPLANTATION

AN extremely important aspect of fishery development is the stocking of artificial bodies of water, or the transplantation to natural bodies of water of fish able to make better use of the primary production than the native fish. Examples of both will be given in this chapter. Among the more spectacular are the transplantations of *Tilapia zillii* to Lake Victoria (page 61), and that of the *Dagaa*, *Stolothrissa tanganikae* to Lake Kivu (page 180).

The building of dams and reservoirs of all sizes is increasing in tropical countries. In some cases, as for instance in Ceylon, it may be a case of bringing again into use the massive irrigation system of reservoirs of an earlier century.

Some of the dams are for the generation of hydroelectric power, but as these are often deep, and often also situated in high and hilly land, they are not always very good subjects for the creation of fisheries. Some are to supply drinking water for the human populations, and in these it may not be desirable to create a fishery by stocking with fish. But there are many and extensive dams for the purpose of water conservation in semi-arid countries or for irrigation, and great numbers of farm dams, village ponds, ponds for watering stock, all of which could make a substantial local contribution to the feeding of the people.

THE RAWA PENING, JAVA

The first example will be the Rawa Pening, in central Java. This is a large lake formed in recent times by volcanic action. A good description of it is given by Vaas and Schuurman.[97] The original aspect of the plains now occupied by the Rawa must have been that of a tropical forest. When the lake was formed, the submerged trees and vegetation decayed to give peat. The surface of the lake began to shrink through the growth of vegetation, and a marsh was formed. In the second half of the nineteenth century, the villagers of the lake shore used to dig out the peat and partially decayed trees, selling them for fuel. Methane gas production in the soil sometimes made the plastic peaty bottom rise to form small islands of peat, which might be 50 square metres in size, or more.

In 1916 a dam was built by the Irrigation Department in the river through which the lake discharged, to build up the water-level so as to use the lake as a reservoir. This dam was raised in 1938-9 to increase the capacity.

In 1931 the lake had become very badly choked with vegetation. No less than 8 km.^{2} of the total area of 17·7 km.^{2} at high water, or 9 km.^{2} at low water, were completely covered either with floating masses of grass or with the water hyacinth, *Eichhornia crassipes* Solms. The marshy character of the Rawa increased as a result of this growth, until the whole area was threatened with extinction as an irrigation reservoir. In these circumstances, no important fishery could exist, and in this large body of water only about 200 fishermen found a living, catching a yearly crop of about 6,500 kg. of small swamp fish.

Swamp Clearance

The fishery authorities at the time saw that a total removal of the choked mass of vegetation was the only way in which to save the Rawa as an irrigation reservoir and to create a more important fishery. The work was carried out between 1932 and 1939. The floating masses of water hyacinth mixed with grasses were sawn into squares of about 7 square metres with special saws as used in Europe for the same purpose, and sent drifting away downstream. Rooted water hyacinth was cut loose, dragged to the bank, dried and burnt. The work of clearing was delayed and made more difficult by the enormous masses of peat which came floating to the surface in newly cleaned areas; methane was released in such quantities that the water seemed to be boiling. But gradually grass began to grow in the cleared areas and genuine aquatic submerged vegetation. On the shallow cleaned shores, the cultivation of rice began. The lake was stocked with great numbers of the young of three introduced species of fish, namely, the common carp, *Puntius javanicus* and *Trichogaster pectoralis*. At first, no doubt, fishing was prohibited in order to allow the new fish to become established, but in 1934 fishing was again allowed. The catch in that year was some 18,000 kg. but it rose to 90,000 kg. in 1936, and to 200,000 kg. in 1940. This is a fantastic improvement on the meagre 6,500 kg. of the unimproved Rawa. But the benefit of the clearance went much further. The Rawa again became an important reservoir for irrigation with a long life assured; the health of the population improved because malaria decreased; and, finally, new areas were opened up for rice production. The total cost of clearance was about 88,000 Dutch florins, mainly for labour.

Of the fish stocks, the common carp were not a success, and the catches in 1957 were mainly shrimps, *Puntius*, *Trichogaster* and *Tilapia*, among the introduced fish, and *Ophiocephalus* among the original fauna (Vaas *in lit.*).

LAKE TEMPÉ, CELEBES

An outstandingly successful case of transplantation is the Tempé Lake in South Celebes. This lake has a large seasonal change of level, having an area of some 9,455 hectares at low-water level, in October-November, when the average depth is only 1 metre, and is then divided into three separated bodies of water. At high-water level, it is one lake of an area of some 20,000 hectares. At low water, parts of the surrounding land are cultivated with maize and pulses, while in other parts there is the natural vegetation. At high water, all this vegetation is mineralised, giving very rich feeding conditions for fish.

The original fish fauna consisted of the usual group of swamp fishes, such as the Snake-heads, *Ophiocephalus*, the so-called Climbing Perch, *Anabas*, and the smaller *Glossogobius* and *Monopterus*. There were also a few euryhaline migrants from the sea.

Transplantations

This natural fish fauna contained no species able to use the very great amount of vegetable matter produced in the lake, so from 1925 the introduction of exotic species was started. The following species were introduced:

> *Helostoma temminckii*, 1925
> *Puntius javanicus*, 1937
> *Trichogaster pectoralis*, 1937

Osteochilus hasselti, 1938
Clarias batrachus, 1944
Cyprinus carpio, 1948

The introduction of the predatory *Clarias* was accidental, and of the others, the common carp, as usual, failed to establish itself in face of predators and competition. The really successful introduced species are the *Puntius javanicus*, or Tawes, and the *Trichogaster pectoralis*, or Sepat Siam. Both these are vegetable feeding fish, the *Trichogaster* feeding mainly on epiphytes and the *Puntius* directly on soft leaves and water-plants.

Before these transplantations, the produce of this lake sufficed only for subsistence fishing, but since the transplantations the production of fish has risen to the point where an important export trade has developed. The story is well illustrated in the statistics. At present, the fish crop consists of about 70 per cent *Puntius* and 20 per cent *Trichogaster*, with all the remainder contributing the remaining 10 per cent. The fishery is of the usual flood-fishery type, described in Chapter V, taking place at the falling and low-water levels.

Exports of Fish

There was no export of fish before about 1934, and the exports did not really leap up until the most successful of the transplantations, those of *Puntius* and *Trichogaster*, had been made. As shown above, these were introduced in 1937, yet by 1939, only two years later, there was this sudden increase in production resulting in a great increase in exports (Table X page 242).

The spectacular success of the transplantations is seen in the figures for exports, which increased thirteen-fold between 1934 and 1941. The outbreak of the war in the Far East at the end of 1941, with its disruption of trade and shortage of fishing gear, soon showed itself in a fall in exports to almost nothing in 1945. There was a revival in 1946, rising to very large exports in 1948 and 1949. But the troubled state of Indonesia since then has kept this trade well below its best.

LAKE LOMBOTTO, CELEBES

Another lake in the Celebes, Lake Lombotto, which is a shallow lake with a maximum depth of $4\frac{1}{2}$ metres and an area of some 4,950

Table X

Exports of Salt-dried Fish from Lake Tempé, Celebes.

Year	Exports of salt-dry fish (million kg.)
1934	0·4
1935	0·5
1936	0·4
1937	0·5
1938	0·5
1939	3·6
1940	3·9
1941	5·2
1942	1·4
1943	1·5
1944	0·4
1945	0·05
1946	2·8
1947	2·4
1948	10·5
1949	7·9
1950	1·3
1951	0·8
1952	1·3

hectares, was found to have an original fauna of only gobies and shrimps. In 1942 *Tilapia mossambica* was introduced, and in 1947 *Trichogaster* also. Attempts to introduce the common carp and *Osteochilus* failed At present the lake produces some 440,000 kg. of *Tilapia*, 400,000. kg. of *Trichogaster* and 1,300,000 kg. of shrimps.

LAKE NAKIVALI, UGANDA

Worthington[93] made the first report on this lake, which is one of a group of small lakes forming a system of open water areas in a big papyrus swamp which drains, at any rate when the water is high, into Lake Victoria. The lake has an area of about 10 square miles and has a maximum depth of 3·5 metres. Its shape is liable to alter somewhat with the detachment of large masses of floating vegetation. Worthington described the lake as not rich in variety of fish life, with the catfish or mudfish *Clarias mossambicus* as the most important fish, together with a smaller *Clarias* (*C. werneri*), and two species of *Haplochromis*. In 1931, when Worthington made his observations, the lake supported about twenty-five fishermen who fished the *Clarias* with long-lines of about fifty small hooks. They also used small basket traps for the smaller species of *Clarias*. Worthington recommended the introduction of *Tilapia* species into the lake.

Early Days

Pitman[101] visited the lake in 1933. He confirmed Worthington's belief that the lake has periodical differences of level, which are of great importance in connection with the fishery for *Clarias*. He quotes his experience at the end of 1926, when the lake had inundated the low-lying flats to the east for a considerable distance. These flats are intersected by numerous small channels, and up these travelled tens of thousands of large mudfish "to take advantage of the rich feeding to be found all over the submerged grassland. One major and two minor fishing camps were seen in which tons of huge fish were drying. Freshly caught fish were being brought in throughout the day. No skill in catching it is necessary, for dozens of scantily-clad natives jostled each other in the shallow channels, walking to and fro, some feeling with their feet for the slimy prey, others thrusting their spears at random into the muddy water . . . the extent of the catch gives some indication of the Silurid resources of this lake, and with what the (introduced) juvenile *Tilapia* will have to contend . . . apparently every undesirable in the district gravitates to the locality to take his share of the heaven-sent harvest. . . . I have rarely come across a more disreputable crowd."

Transplantation of Tilapia

Pitman stocked the lake with about eighty *Tilapia nigra* (*sic*) in 1934, and in 1937 the western extremity of the lake was netted for a week, but no *Tilapia* were caught. In 1939 some 1,800 *Tilapia* fry were transplanted from the Kazinga Channel to the lake. The *Tilapia* of the Kazinga Channel could hardly be other than *Tilapia nilotica*.

In 1940 a *Tilapia* of about $1\frac{1}{2}$ lb. was caught by one of the local fishermen and in 1941 it was evident that the *Tilapia* were well established. But it was considered advisable to wait until 1942 before permitting an organised gill-net fishery. The local fishermen were instructed in the use and repair of the standard 5-inch gill-net. The adult fish examined were all typical *Tilapia nilotica*, of an average weight of 1¼ lb.

The Modern Fishery

The number of nets licensed to fish in the lake was gradually increased to twenty-four in 1947. In 1948 some 49,000 *Tilapia* were caught and the fishery was beginning to have a considerable local importance.

In 1950 123,548 Tilapia were recorded as caught, and only eighty-two *Clarias*. The 1951[130] and 1953[131] reports of the Game and Fisheries Departments complete the story. The lake is the most productive for its size in Uganda, and the income of the fifty-four licensed fishermen reached about £20,000. In terms of food, the whole of the surrounding district was supplied with fish, and about 150 tons of smoked fish, surplus to the local requirements, were exported to the Congo. It is described as a most satisfactory fishery, apparently free from troubles, more or less self-regulating, and the less interfered with the better. Plank-built canoes are used, and are illustrated in Plate 47.

Good roads have been built to the lake to facilitate the marketing of fish, and help has been given to the fishermen to establish the cleanest and most attractive fishing settlements in Uganda. I can extend this by saying that they are the best fishermen's settlements I have seen in Africa (Plate 48). A high standard of village pride has arisen in the fishermen, who now feel that they have a permanent stake in the industry. This is indeed a far cry from the ruffians reported by Pitman in 1926 and the fishery for mudfish of 1931. It is a success story which gives an example of what can be done by the transplantation of a suitable fish to a new site.

TRANSPLANTATIONS TO LAKES VICTORIA AND KIOGA

Lake Victoria had no weed-eating fish, and this was probably a factor in the slow turnover of material in the lake, resulting in a rate of fish production below the best possible (page 50). Since about 1954, many thousands of the fry of *Tilapia zillii* have been introduced into the lake. In 1955-6 a *T. zillii* was captured in the lake which weighed nearly 2 lb. Its stomach was crammed with chewed-up vegetation. In that year a breeding population of *T. zillii* was firmly established in Entebbe Harbour. In 1956-7 this fish was appearing in the African catches and they were common in fishermen's nets in Uganda. In 1958, this fish was comprising up to 30 per cent of the catches in certain favourable localities and there seemed to be well-established populations. As this *Tilapia* does not compete for food with the indigenous species of *Tilapia*, their multiplication to the point where they will form a high and regular proportion of the yield of the lake will be sheer gain. Two other species of *Tilapia*, not native to the lake, have also been introduced. They are *T. nilotica* and *T. leucosticta*. Their habits are less interesting, from the point of view of the utilisation of the available food in the lake, than those of *T. zillii*, but *T. nilotica* showed a very rapid rate of growth.[132]

The same *T. zillii* has been introduced into the great, shallow marshy Lake Kioga, where it has established itself even more quickly than in Lake Victoria. It now forms about 10 per cent of the commercial catches in most parts of the lake, and 40 per cent locally.

When the astonishing results of stocking herbivorous fish in Lake Tempé are remembered, the stocking of *T. zillii* in Lake Victoria may prove to have been of great benefit to the feeding of the peoples of East Africa.

STOCKING OF DAMS AND RESERVOIRS

There are many brilliant examples of the stocking of dams and reservoirs with fish, resulting in the creation of new fisheries.

Lake Tjiburuj, Java

The first example will be the artificial Lake Tjiburuj in West Java. This lake came into being in 1920, when two dams were constructed in a shallow valley, impounding an area of water which is 40 hectares in area at maximum, and is drawn down to about 23 hectares at low water. The depth at maximum is about 6 metres, and at low water about 5 metres or slightly less.

The main purpose of the dam is to store water for the irrigation of about 300 hectares of paddy land. The dam is surrounded by hills, some of which are of limestone, where there are quarries and lime kilns. On the shores of the lake are many cassava-milling sheds, and all the waste products of these are thrown into the lake, to the extent of about 120 kg. per month. Moreover, all the waste products of human habitation of a number of villages, and the excrements of cattle and buffaloes, also go into the lake. The water is therefore well manured and supports a rich plankton.

Vaas and Sachlan[60] give an account of the fishery in this lake. In 1922, shortly after the lake became filled, the fishing rights were leased to the owner of a dairy farm for a period of thirty-three years. The management of the lake fisheries was undertaken on a commercial basis, on a system of manuring, regular cropping and restocking.

The fish stocked are vegetable and plankton feeders, and include the common carp, *Puntius javanicus, Osteochilus hasselti*, a plankton feeder, *Tilapia mossambica* and *Helostoma temminckii*, both either epiphyte or plankton feeders. But 60 per cent of the total catch consists of *Puntius javanicus, Osteochilus hasselti* and *Helostoma temminckii*. Stocking takes place at two-monthly intervals, with about 30,000 fingerlings of common carp, *Puntius* and *Helostoma*, of 1 to 5 cm. length.

Several of the commoner predatory fish of the Javanese lakes are absent, probably as a result of the frequent cropping and restocking. The lessee allowed the local fishermen to fish the lake daily except on Fridays and Saturdays, using a seine-net 50 metres long. They sell the fish either on the spot or in neighbouring markets, and pay the lessee 2 rupiahs per kilo landed. Angling is also permitted at a fee of 5 rupiahs per day. Half the proceeds of these licences went to the village fund.

The average daily catch of fish was about 1,200 kg., or at a rate of 500 to 600 kg. per hectare per year. In 1954, the yield of fish was some 13,000 kg. Since the lease lapsed, the lake has been run by a Fisherman's Co-operative of some 160 members.

Dam-stocking in India

Valuable work is being done in India on the stocking of dams and reservoirs, including, more recently, the transplantation of euryhaline species such as the mullets and the milkfish, *Chanos chanos*. The latter do not, of course, breed in their new habitat. As an example of dam-stocking work in India, reference is made to the paper by Chacko, Krishnamurthi and George[102] on the fisheries of the Kanigiri-Duvvur Reservoir in Madras State.

This reservoir holds a permanent supply of water received from the Pennar River and also the drainage from a catchment area of 90 square miles. It has an area of 12,465 acres, and is used for the irrigation of about 90,000 acres of land. The fish fauna is derived from the Pennar River through the supply channels, and consists of the usual fish, of which the Snake-heads (*Ophiocephalus*) are the most important from the fishery point of view. The Fisheries Department of the Madras State stocks the reservoir annually with the Indian carp *Labeo fimbriatus*.

The fishery of this reservoir is leased to a private contractor, who employs many of the fisherfolk of the surrounding villages and pays them for 50 per cent of their catches.

The fishing gear used includes drag-nets, which give a yield of about 300 lb. per day, and wall-nets (presumably gill-nets), stake nets, cast-nets, plunge baskets, basket traps, dip-nets, and hook and line.

The total production of the reservoir is about 248 tons per year, of which the major portion are Snake-heads and the stocked *Labeo*. The rate of production works out at about 84 lb. of fish per acre per annum.

The prominence of the Snake-heads in the yields of all the Far Eastern waters so far discussed is due, not only to their popularity as food fish, which gives them a high price, but also because their accessory air-breathing organ enables them to be kept alive out of water for many hours, which greatly eases the marketing problem.

Trinidad Leaseholds

A smaller example of the creation of a new source of fish by transplantation and stocking is the reservoir at Pointe-à-Pierre in Trinidad. This reservoir, of about 220 acres, is used for storing water for technical use in connection with the oil refinery of Trinidad Leaseholds. It is an attractive body of water, which is filled by pumping from the Guaracare River. It has a depth of about 30 feet at highest level and about 20 feet at lowest. The water is on the alkaline side of neutrality and the average temperature is about 83° F. In 1949 the author was asked to suggest a suitable fish for stocking, so that the dam could produce some fish for the Trinidad Leaseholds employees. The common carp had been tried but had failed to establish itself.

There were known to be some Caymans, small alligators, in the dam, and there was abundance of the predatory fish Guabine (*Hoplias malabaricus*), the same predator which flourishes in the sugar-cane fields of British Guiana and is there called the Houri. The Caymans were found to feed to a large degree on crabs rather than fish, but the presence in large quantities of the Guabine was a formidable obstacle to the establishment of an introduced species. The introduction of *Tilapia mossambica* was advised and in 1950 a consignment of these fish was sent to St. Lucia, one of the Windward Islands, from Singapore. From there, where they bred freely, some were taken to Trinidad and stocked in the reservoirs at Pointe-à-Pierre in June 1950. Mr. Knowles, the Personnel Officer to the Company, was responsible for this and he has followed up the matter, and given the history of the introduction and its results.

After the first stocking there was no news of the fish for some twenty-seven months and there was some reason for the belief that the stocking had been a failure, which would not have been surprising in view of the presence of predators with special adaptations to local conditions. But in October 1952, a boy fishing in the reservoir with rod and line caught a fine *Tilapia* weighing about 1½ lb., and Mr. Knowles at once started a fishery using fish traps of chicken-wire. The fish are of a good size for the table, and in March 1957 a sample of twenty fish had the following distribution in length and weight:

Table XI

Measurements and Weighings of *Tilapia mossambica* in the Trinidad Leaseholds Reservoirs, Pointe-à-Pierre.

Length (in.)	f.	Weight	f.
9½	1	10–11 oz.	2
10	1	12–13 oz.	4
10½	6	14–15 oz.	2
11	1	16–17 oz.	2
11½	1	18–19 oz.	2
12	2	20–21 oz.	1
12½	2	22–23 oz.	4
13	4	24–25 oz.	1
13½	1	27 oz.	1
14	1		

The samples, taken in traps, showed two length-groups, and a dissection of ten of the specimens showed that the smaller group, of lengths from 9½ to 11 inches, were all females, while those from 12 to 14 inches were all males. This is typical of the length-distribution of *Tilapia mossambica* when breeding freely. The females grow more slowly than the males.

There is a seasonal variation in the catches, but the total quantity of these very acceptable fish taken from this reservoir in a year is about 6000 lb., and there seems no reason why more should not be taken. At this rate the crop amounts to only about 29 lb. per acre per annum, a low figure when compared with other such dams.

On the other hand, the reservoir can have no fertiliser because the water is needed for technical purposes, and certainly no organic fertiliser such as sewage could possibly have access to the water. The use of nets, which might muddy the water, is also ruled out. Nevertheless, a new source of fish has been created where there was none before.

It is hard to believe that it took twenty-seven months for the fingerling Tilapias to grow to 1 lb. and more. It is more likely that, for many months, there was an unseen struggle between the introduced fish and the predators, with the Tilapias gradually gaining the upper hand in the population race, until it was suddenly discovered that a fishable stock was established. The history of the stocking of Lake Nakivali was somewhat similar. This lake also abounded with predators and it took several years before a stock of the introduced *Tilapia nilotica* established itself.

In many cases, the introduced fish fails to establish itself. Examples of this have been given earlier in this chapter. The common carp seems particularly vulnerable and failed to establish itself in any of the Indonesian lakes mentioned. It also failed in Trinidad. This is the most domesticated of all fish, and has been so for millennia. It may have lost the power, under tropical conditions of predation, to hold its own in the wild. It suffers the kind of fate which one would expect a herd of pedigree Jersey cattle to suffer if turned loose in an African game-reserve.

Beneficial Effect of Predators

Once the introduced fish has established itself, the presence of predators is certainly beneficial because they will crop down excess of young, which will always be far more in number than the water will support. They therefore leave more growing-space for the survivors, while the predators themselves salvage the excess of young of the introduced fish and turn it into edible fish if the predator species is acceptable. The effect of predation is seen when this reservoir in Trinidad is compared with an irrigation reservoir in Jamaica, where there are no natural predatory fish.

This reservoir was York Dam, on Hampden Estate. A chicken-wire fish trap, similar to those in use on the Pointe-à-Pierre reservoir, baited with a piece of meat, produced twenty-three *Tilapia mossambica* of the same stock as those used to stock the Trinidad reservoir. The distribution in length and weight of these fish was as follows:

Table XII

Measurements and Weighings of *Tilapia mossambica* from York Dam, Jamaica.

Length (cm.)		Weight (gm.)	
12	2	31–40	2
13	–	41–50	3
14	2	51–60	2
15	3	61–70	1
16	2	71–80	1
17	2	81–90	2
18	2	91–100	1
19	–	—	
20	5	131–140	6
21	2	141–150	2
22	2	151–160	1
		161–170	1

All but two of these fish were males. Probably the females were mainly brooding young and so were not feeding nor interested in the bait in the trap. It will be seen that the largest fish in this dam, as sampled by the baited trap, was only 165 gm., or under 6 oz.

The results of dam-stocking in Ghana, about to be described, show the benefit of stocking the predatory fish *Lates* along with such fish as *Tilapia*. In Jamaica itself, interesting results have followed the stocking of the predatory Tarpon in *Tilapia* ponds, and in Trinidad, the Guabine.

Dams in Tanganyika

The stocking of dams is making great progress in Africa. In Tanganyika, the case of the Kerenge Dam in Tanga Province may be quoted. It is a shallow valley drowned by the construction of a big earth dam. It is filled partly by rainfall catchment and partly from the small stream which already existed in the valley. It covers an area of about 200 acres and the melancholy stumps and boles of the drowned and dead trees stand out forlornly at the upper and shallower end of the lake. When visited shortly after its construction it had a small fishery, mainly with hook and line for the predatory fish, chiefly *Clarias*, which occur naturally in all such waters and which were probably derived from the original small stream. The dam was not put up to grow fish but to supply water to the considerable village which housed the workers on a neighbouring sisal estate, which built the dam.

The dam was stocked by the Tanganyika Fisheries Department and the report for 1955[133] states that the crop of fish was of the order of 2000 lb. per month and could probably yield more, but that fishing is planned to give the entire labour force a fish ration once a week. The report for 1956[134] states that the average of 2000 lb. of fish per month was still being maintained, the catches being made by seine-net. A nylon gill-net had been introduced in 1956, which had more than doubled the catch. Some 9,650 lb. of fish, all Tilapia of 1 lb. weight or more, were caught in sixty-one days.

The report for 1957[135] gives some information about the very successful stocking of the dams of the Williamson diamond mines, and the nearby Alamasi mine dam. The Tanganyika Fisheries Department was very closely associated with the stocking and fishing of these dams and excellent progress is reported. The mines are virtually self-supporting for fish supplies and a full-time European employee is engaged in the fishing operations. Though not all the dams were fished throughout the year and the amount of fishing has varied from month to month the catch of fish in the Williamson dams amounted to some 20,400 lb. of fish. All these are "new" fish, taken in fisheries which did not previously exist, in dams not originally made for the purpose of fish production.

Such dams are to some extent self-stocking, as in the case quoted above, with native fish either originally present in the valley now flooded by the dam or perhaps washed in with floods. Some of these fish are valuable in their own right, as is the case with the *Labeos*, locally called *ningu*. On the debit side are the predatory fish such as *Clarias* and the lung-fish *Protopterus*. The former is a valuable food fish, and its presence in a dam need not be wholly unfavourable, for it also undoubtedly helps to crop down excess fry, and so keep a balance in the dam between the size of the fish population and the food resources. But the lung-fish is more destructive because it will bite fish out of gill-nets, so damaging the net, and as it is not acceptable as food by the Tanganyika folk living beside the dams, there is no incentive to catch them.

Elsewhere, where all the predatory fish are welcomed as food, fishing, chiefly with hook and line or with night-lines of many hooks, helps to keep a balance between the predators and the introduced and indigenous non-predators.

The lakes and dams in the central Rift Valley of Tanganyika are especially interesting as examples of the benefits of stocking waters, which either had no natural stocks of fish, or lacked herbivorous and plankton-feeding fish, such as the Tilapias.

The characteristics, and the fish production, of the more important of these, are given in Table XIII below.

Table XIII

Some Waters in the Central Rift Valley of Tanganyika.

Water	pH	Titre. cc. N. H Cl.	Bicarb. Alkain.	Ca. ppm.	Na. ppm.	Area, Acres	Fish Production per Ann. Tons	per Acre lb.
Lake Babati	8·6	4·55	278	18	74	4480	400	200
L. Kitangiri	8·9	4·55	278	10	140	28000	700	54
Mianje Dam	8·65	4·30	262	46	130	800	60	168
Hombolo Dam	7·74	3·25	198	—	—	3450	225	230
L. Haubi	7·62	3·25	183	16	71	350	—	—

The figures estimated for production of fish per acre and per annum should be compared with those on page 77. These waters are far from fully exploited; Lake Kitangiri has had only two years of a commercial fishery, and is rapidly developing into a very important source of fish. Fishing on Lake Haubi only made a start in 1960.

All these waters are very alkaline, with a high soda and bicarbonate content, as the analyses show.

Lake Babati, like Lake Nakivali (page 243), had only a stock of

Clarias, until, in 1935, it was stocked with *Tilapia nigra*. In 1958, *T. nilotica* and *T. melanopleura* were added. Now, catches, chiefly of *Tilapia*, average two to three tons per day in the season.

The Mianje Mungaa Dam was built to supply water to an irrigation scheme. It was stocked with Tilapias (probably *T. pangani*). In 1952, and now supports 50 full-time fishermen. The catches are mostly *Tilapia*.

The great Hombolo Dam was made to protect the Central Railway track from flood damage. It contains self-stocked *Clarias*. In early 1959 some 5,500 *Tilapia* fingerlings were stocked, chiefly *T. pangani*, and *T. melanopleura*. Now, little more than a year later, Tilapia is one of the principal fish among the 225 tons of fish estimated to be landed annually from this dam. It supplies fresh fish to the important town of Dodoma.

Lake Haubi was stocked with Tilapias in 1958, and in 1960 commercial production was beginning.

The two dams, originally put up for other purposes, have, in fact, proved, after stocking, so productive of fish, that in retrospect, it would have been worth while to have made them for their fish production alone.

Northern Rhodesia

The Tanganyika reports speak of the lack of accurate data on the results of dam-stocking but there is a full description of the experimental fishing results in a dam in Northern Rhodesia. Mortimer[103] describes the Lundazi Dam in the Eastern Province of Northern Rhodesia. A weir was originally constructed in 1927 across the junction of the Nsuzi stream and the Lundazi River which drain into the Luangwa River, an important tributary of the Zambezi, but it was breached in 1938 and a new weir was built in 1946. When full, the dam has an area of water of about 70 to 75 acres. The maximum depth is some 28 feet and there is an annual drawdown of 6 to 8 feet.

The dam, which was first investigated in 1953, had three native and self-stocked species, namely, the inevitable *Clarias*, *Labeo annectens* and a species of *Barbus*. In 1947, the following exotic species were introduced:

Salmo gairdneri, 12 fingerlings, the Rainbow Trout,
Lepomis macrochirus, 28 fingerlings, the Bluegill Sunfish,

Tinca vulgaris, 6 fingerlings, the Tench,
Micropterus punctulatus, 12 fingerlings, the Spotted Bass.

By 1953 all these exotic fish had disappeared from the dam. But in 1947 there were also introduced the African fishes *Tilapia melanopleura* and *T. macrochir* to the extent of fifty-eight fingerlings, and the stocking was resumed in 1955 with the stocking of nineteen fingerlings of the predatory Cichlid *Serranchromis thumbergii* and *Tilapia mossambica*, both local fish.

Regular fishing of the dam was begun in January 1954, though it is believed that there was fishing by the usual African methods of basket traps in the shallower parts of the dam before that date. Gill-nets were introduced, and from 1954 to 1956 only nets of 4-inch mesh were allowed. Later, gill-nets of 2- and 3-inch mesh were used. The nets were set at night and lifted in the morning. At first, seines could not be used, because in this, as in so many other dams, drowned trees were an obstruction to any kind of dragged net. Clearance of a part of these allowed of seine-netting in 1957.

The average seine-net haul gave about 150 lb. of fish, of which the introduced Tilapias comprised 87 per cent by numbers, but rather less by weight, since a substantial part of the catch was *Clarias*, with an average weight of over 3 lb., as compared with an average weight of about $\frac{1}{2}$ lb. for the Tilapias.

The 4-inch gill-nets caught, as an average per setting per 100 yards, 35 to 36 in 1954-5, declining to about 22 in 1955-6 and to 11 in 1956-7. The total weight per annum reached its peak in 1955-6, at some 2,900 lb., dropping to 1,588 lb. in 1956-7.

The average weight of the fish caught by the 3-inch gill-nets was much below that of the 4-inch gill-nets, as would be expected, and it is unlikely that this smaller mesh will be used.

The average crop of all kinds of fish, calculated as pounds per acre per annum, varied from 18·9 lb. in 1954, when the investigations began, to some 41 lb. in 1955-6. The average over the whole five years was about 30 lb. per acre per annum. Over half the fish caught were of the introduced Tilapias, so that the yield of this dam has been substantially increased by the introduction.

Many farm dams in Northern Rhodesia are stocked with fish, and one of these is described. It was put up by a tobacco farmer to supply his house with water (Plates 52 and 53). It has an area of about 30 acres, with a maximum depth of 9 feet at the bund, and a 30-foot spillway. It has natural stocks of *Clarias* and the small *Tilapia sparrmanni*. It has been stocked with *T. melanopleura*, which have cleared the dam of weeds. The stumps of the trees originally in the flooded area still stood. Trial fishings with night-lines of twenty-five baited hooks gave ten *Clarias* weighing 32 lb. while three gill-nets of 4-inch mesh gave fish to a total weight of 55 lb. This farmer allows his African labourers unlimited fishing with hook and line and the availability of fish was an inducement to the labourers to stay on, at a time when there was a shortage of labour. The farmer himself did much sport-fishing in his dam with a spoon for the predator *Serranochromis*, which is also excellent to eat, like all the Cichlids.

Southern Rhodesia

The reports of the Northern Rhodesia Game and Tsetse Control Department, which has charge of fisheries, express disappointment at the slow rate of progress in the stocking of water-conservation dams, but this is not so in Southern Rhodesia. There, the movement is in full swing and is encouraged by the Government. A subsidy helps those who build water-conservation dams and fish stock is available for them. Wallis[104] has estimated that there are some 47,500 acres of water-conservation dams, including the great Hunyadi Poort Dam and the Mazoe Dam, and most are stocked with fish.

Dams in Kenya and Uganda

In Kenya and Uganda also there has been very active stocking of dams. The report of the Kenya Fisheries for 1957 says that a great many dams have been built in the African areas of the Nyanza Province in the last few years to provide water supplies for the people and their stock. Where dams were found to be without fish, *Tilapia* from the Provincial fishponds at Kisumu have been introduced. A serious difficulty that has been encountered in many dams is the presence of trees and bushes in the water, and the failure to remove these snags at the time when the dams were being constructed has greatly reduced the value of the fisheries in the dams. The African farmers in one district have shown great interest in a scheme for domestic fishponds. The district is very thickly populated, and over sixty ponds, varying in size from about 100 to 150 square yards, were dug and stocked with fish.

Dams in Ghana

In Ghana, the stocking of dams put up by the Department of Tsetse
Control and the Rural Water Development Board began in 1950.
These dams were primarily for water storage, but their fish potential
was early realised and they were stocked with fish by the Fisheries
Department. For example, the Rural Water Development dam at
Jirapa in the arid Northern Territories of Ghana was fished by seine
in January 1950, when the dam had an area of about 4 acres. There
were no naturally occurring fish except small *Barbus*. The following
fish were introduced:

Tilapia galilaea	968	weighing	43 lb.
„ *nilotica*	34	„	5 „
„ *zillii-melanopleura*	276	„	16 „
Labeo sp.	34	„	3 „
Citharinus sp.	45	„	5 „
Clarias sp.	56	„	9 „

In February 1951 this dam was fished by cast-net and seine. The
catches were largely *Tilapia*, of which 610 lb. were taken. Most of
them were *T. galilaea*. Thus the total weight of 55 lb. stocked one
year previously had increased by at least 550 lb., for the sampling
was light and there was no diminution in the catches in successive
hauls, such as would be expected if most of the fish in the dam had
been caught. The *Labeo* and *Citharinus* had failed to establish
themselves. The *Tilapia galilaea* and *T. nilotica* weighed ¾ lb. and the
T. zillii ½ lb.

As another example the Rural Water Development dam at
Dorimon, fourteen miles west of Wa, has an area when full of about
16 acres with a maximum depth of about 14 feet. It drains by a
small stream to the Volta but the passage of fish up from the river
is barred. Trial seining in the dam showed, again, that the only
naturally occurring fish was a small *Barbus*. Early in 1950 the dam
was stocked with 1188 *Tilapia* species, including *melanopleura*,
zillii, *galilaea* and *nilotica*, as well as smaller numbers of *Citharinus*,
Clarias, *Heterobranchus*, *Labeo* and *Leptotilapia*. The end of the
year showed the presence in the dam of good stocks of *Tilapia*, of
which 90 per cent were *zillii*. A number exceeded ½ lb. in weight.
Clarias were plentiful, but none of the other species had established
themselves.

52. A farmer's dam in Rhodesia.

53. The same. Drowned trees with roosting birds.

54. A prawn-pond on Singapore.

55. Fishing a prawn-pond. The water rur out through a fine-meshed net.

56. Fishing a sugar-cane field, British Guiana.

In 1952 instruction schemes were started to teach the local people, who were not fishermen, how to fish these and other dams. By 1957 a catch of some 28,000 lb. of fish was made by these pupils alone, and it is certain that this was only a fraction of the total. Lawra now has the most thriving fish market in the northern Territories and is the only one where fish can always be confidently expected.

By no means all dams are suitable for stocking with fish. Those that are deep, and especially those which are sheltered by high banks or by trees from the mixing action of the wind, may become de-oxygenated and so unable to support much fish life. To avoid disappointment, lakes and dams should be examined from this aspect before stocking with fish. A case in point is Lake Bunyoni in Uganda. This lake has an almost permanent stratification, with the deeper water more or less completely deoxygenated, because the lake is narrow and deep in relation to its area, so that the action of the wind fails to mix the water. Repeated stockings of this lake have failed.

Dangers to Public Health

While storage dams are of the greatest value in areas of seasonal rainfall or in arid climates, both for water conservation and as potential sources of fish, they are liable to introduce a danger to public health. This is because they may provide breeding places for Anopheline mosquitoes which carry malaria, and for the snails which carry Bilharzia. If ponds are kept clear of vegetation, the fish will deal with any mosquito larvae which may be present. Most fish will do this, but the Tilapias are especially effective. To give an example: at the Malacca Research Station, a few inches of water had been left standing in a concrete tank, and there were about fifty mosquito larvae in this water. Three small Tilapias, about 6 cm. long, were placed in the tank. One hour later there were no mosquito larvae. If the ponds are kept free of all emergent vegetation and all vegetation which overhangs the water, there will be very little laying of mosquito eggs in the pond at all. But ponds can become dangerous if they are allowed to become covered with weeds or with masses of algae in which the larval mosquitoes can develop, safely screened from the attentions of fish. The introduction of weed-eating fish such as *Tilapia zillii* and *T. melanopleura* is a strong safe-guard, but the pond surface and banks must be kept clear. Much of the benefit of water conservation will be lost, if the human populations

STIF

which rely on the conservation dams are riddled with malaria.

Though the spread of Bilharzia is in the last analysis due to the insanitary habits of people living near water and will only be checked in the next generation through the spread of education, the actual vectors of the disease, water-snails, can be checked by keeping a pond clear of vegetation. If the snails could be eliminated there would be an end to the disease. There has been considerable study of ways of getting rid of the snails. Copper sulphate is a powerful snail poison, which is being much used, but it is also a general poison which may be fatal to human beings, stock and fish. Biological means of control would be much better and so a search is being made for snail-eating fish with which to stock dams. The Lung-fish *Protopterus* has flat, crushing jaws and molluscs form a very high proportion of its food. Moreover, it is in most places regarded as a valuable food-fish. But the present lack of knowledge as to how to breed the fish easily prevents its regular use on a large scale in ponds and dams. Several small species of the *Haplochromis* group of fishes are known to be preferential mollusc feeders, and one of these, *Astatareochromis alluaudi*, has been recommended. In the Congo, striking results have been claimed for the Cichlid fish *Serranochromis macrocephala*.

This fish was brought to Ghana and an attempt made to breed it, but it failed to establish itself in its new environment. Meanwhile it was found that the common *Hemichromis bimaculatus* was an effective eater of water-snails, though its performance varied, for it seemed to be less effective as an anti-snail agent in turbid water. It has been bred and stocked, at the request of the medical authorities, in a great number of dams in Ghana.

There is a third danger from dams, and that is due to the Blackfly, *Simulium damnosum*, which not only has a very painful bite, but transmits Onchocerciasis, a disease which may give rise to blindness. The flies breed in fast-running clear water, and it was found in Ghana that there was breeding on the spillways of dams as well as in the natural streams. But very striking results were got by treating the breeding waters with a sludge of DDT in clay suspension, the count of Blackflies falling to a low level for many miles below the place of application. An account of this work, so necessary in Ghana when the people were resettled on the rivers and streams after the clearance of the tsetse fly, is to be found in the Annual Reports of the Ghana (formerly Gold Coast) Fisheries Department for 1952-5.

Chapter Sixteen

MISCELLANEOUS AND MINOR FISHERIES

THIS chapter will first deal with fisheries in impounded waters in which the fish are self-stocked but in which there are no other cultural practices.

BHERIS

In the delta of the Ganges are great areas of brackish-water lagoons, formed by the changes of course and silting of the river mouths. They have already been mentioned in connection with the fertilisation of some of them with sewage water (Chapter II).

Pillay[105] describes the fishery in one such lagoon, or Bheri. The lagoon is shut off from the river by embankments in which there are wooden sluices. Stocking begins in January-February, when the sluice gates are opened at high tides and the water allowed to flow in. At the turn of the tide the gates are shut. This process continues until April, when a large quantity of fish and prawn fry will have entered with the water from the river. From then onwards until about September, no attention is paid by the fishermen to improving the growth of the fish crop, apart from letting water into the pond as required, occasional repairs to the embankments and a watch against theft. From about May-June onwards, the ponds are fished on a small scale for the fishermen's subsistence. Whenever water is let in through the sluices, some fish, prawns and crabs are caught in traps set in wicker screens at the sluices.

Large-scale fishing begins in September, and is continued until November. As no more tidal water is required in the ponds during this period, as much water as possible is let out. The fish and prawns, which have grown well during the interval of several months since their entry into the Bheri with the incoming water, are thereby concentrated in the deeper parts of the Bheri and in the trenches left by the excavation of soil for the bunds. These deeper parts are fished with drag-nets, generally during the evening or at night, so that the catches can be sold early in the morning. Sometimes a part of the catch may be kept alive for the market in small ponds or in floating cages.

Pillay says that the Bheris, which were formerly operated by the owners, are now leased out for a period of one or two years only, at an annual rental of Rs. 40-50 per acre. As these periods of lease are so short, the lessees are naturally interested in marketing all sizes of fish that will fetch a price, and not in measures which will increase production. Formerly, it was the practice to stock the immature fish in subsidiary ponds where they might be kept alive when the main ponds were drained for fishing, so as to be ready for restocking when the Bheri was refilled. However, as the Bheris are annually restocked from the river, it seems doubtful whether this is economic. One would rather have thought that the maximum possible extraction of the fish carried naturally into the ponds would be the most economical way of fishing. Pillay also says that formerly the ponds were ploughed over when dry after the fish harvest, but that this procedure was no longer carried out. Since the productivity of the Bheri must be a function of the fertility, for the fish enter as fry and grow to marketable size there, and since fertility can be much increased by exposing the mud to the mineralising action of the air, it is to be hoped that this cultural practice will be revived. The catch of these self-stocked ponds is largely Penaeid prawns, together with brackish-water fish such as mullets and *Lates calcarifer*.

THE PRAWN PONDS OF SINGAPORE

The extensive mangrove swamps on Singapore Island are the site of a notable fishery for prawns. The trees are felled, though the stumps are usually left in the water, and an area of suitable size is bunded off with mud embankments (Plate 54). In these embankments one or more wooden sluice gates are built, operated by turnbuckles, so that they may be opened either at the top or at the bottom. The size of these ponds may vary from 1 or 2 acres to over 20 acres, the layout depending on the configuration and extent of the swamp. Between the ponds are the deep ditches from which the mud for the embankments has been taken. There are also the natural channels in the swamp. Attached to each pond or group of ponds is a caretaker's house, usually combined with a store for the fishing gear, and for the ice and boxes used for despatching the catch. The ponds are a characteristic sight, with their usually bare mud banks (for the salt will not allow much plant growth) and the jungle of ragged mangrove stumps half-submerged. The curious pyramidal mounds of the burrowing crabs, and the stench of the mangrove mud, are abiding impressions.

There is a total area of 1393·5 acres of prawn ponds in the island which employ 193 fishermen. The annual production is 326 tons. The production per acre varies widely, from 0·10 to 0·32 tons. Experimental prawn ponds were put up by the Fisheries Officer, Dr. Tham Ah Kow, to obtain accurate evidence of the performance of these ponds and to try measures to improve their productivity. They were constructed towards the end of 1954, and cover an area of about 14 acres. By the end of 1956, after rather more than a year's work, they had yielded 18,024 katties (say 24,000 lb.) of prawns and fish, sold on the open market for $19,444. As the cost of construction of the ponds was $12,840, including the ancillary buildings, it is seen that the capital was recovered in less than two years. Prawn ponds are operated on twenty days per month by the existing fisheries, but it was shown in these experimental ponds, that the number of operations per month could be reduced without reducing the catch. This indicates that the labour thus saved could be used for other subsidiary production projects such as pig-rearing, and in that case the dung from the pigsties would fertilise the ponds.

The usual organisation of this industry is for a towkay or entrepreneur, to finance the construction and upkeep of the ponds and pay the wages of caretaker and fishermen. He recoups himself usually by selling the prawns himself, though he may employ an agent. The fishermen get a commission on the production as an inducement.

Fishing

This fishery needs a considerable rise and fall of tide to be worked successfully. There must be at least 7 or 8 feet of difference between spring high and low water, and preferably more. At high tides, the wooden sluices are opened at the top, so that water rushes in, and carries with it the late mysis and early post-larval stages of the Penaeid prawns. At low spring tides, the bottom of the sluices is opened, and the water is let out through a long sleeve of tapered net of fine-meshed ramie. This sleeve is supported on a chute of wood (Plate 55). It is an impressive and unforgettable sight, to go to a prawn pond at night, and see the sluice lit up with incandescent oil lamps, and hear and see the water roaring down the chute through the net into the ditch, half empty at low spring tide. At intervals the sluice is closed, the narrow end of the sleeve of netting is untied and the prawns and the few fish are emptied into baskets. They are taken to the caretaker's house-cum-shed, and are there sorted out into the various kinds and qualities of prawns and fish. Care has to be taken to look out for sea-snakes, which are not uncommon. The sorted catch is iced in baskets, ready for the morning market.

Life-history of the Prawns

Hall[106] worked on the prawns of these ponds and found that three species are mainly concerned. These are *Metapenaeus ensis, M. mastersii* and *Penaeus indicus*, but there are also important quantities of *M. brevicornis*. The mangrove mud is fertile and grows a great deal of algae; these in turn give rise to much detritus. The *Metapenaeus ensis* and *M. brevicornis* are predominantly vegetarian, and no doubt all are vegetarian in their young stages, but at least the larger *Penaeus indicus* are definitely carnivorous, feeding on the larger crustacea, including smaller prawns. The basis of the fishery is the rapid growth of the young stages of these prawns once they have entered the pond.

The prawns breed in the open sea, but not at a uniform intensity throughout the year. *Penaeus* breeds mainly during the north-east monsoon, say between November and March, and the *Metapenaeus* species may breed twice each year* in the inter-monsoon periods. It is a fallacy, Hall concludes, that replenishment of the pond with young prawns takes place monthly at spring tides. There are three peaks of abundance of the young prawns, and the success of the Singapore prawn ponds is related to the fact that the island is situated near the breeding places of all three main species, thus assuring a good supply of young.

The initial catches of the nets are due to the sweeping down the sluice of the small juveniles which happen to be near the gates, but the main and later catches are of maturing specimens actively trying to migrate back to the sea. *Penaeus* starts to appear in this

---

* Though the species breed twice each year, the individual prawns of each species breed only once, mainly at the end of twelve months; but some individuals delay breeding until the eighteenth month.

way in the commercial catches about one month after entering the ponds, while the *Metapeneus* species appear to spend some five months in the ponds before they are taken in numbers in the commercial catches.

PRAWNS IN PADDY FIELDS

Menon[107] describes a very interesting fishery in the paddy fields of the coastal region of the Travancore-Cochin State of south India. In this part of India, only one crop of rice is taken annually, and the fields lie fallow for the rest of the year. They are naturally intersected by canals, up which come from the sea the young stages of Penaeid prawns which are bred in the deeper water off the coast. About 11,000 acres of these paddy fields are used for the raising of these young stages to marketable size.

Soon after the rice crop is harvested in October, the bunds of the paddy fields are strengthened and if necessary raised, and temporary wooden sluice gates are installed in them. Water is let into the fields through these sluices only when the tide has raised the water in the canal to its highest level. This is to ensure that the water flows in with the maximum force, since the number of young prawns entering with the water depends largely on the force and duration of the current. After about twenty-five to thirty minutes, the level of the water in the field is the same as that in the canal and the sluices are then closed. At low tide, a good proportion of the water is allowed to flow out, so as to allow more water to be let in at high tide. When water is let in at night, a lamp may be hung at the mouth of the sluice to attract more prawns.

The fishery for the marketable prawns usually starts with the neap tides four to five days before every new and full moon, and is continued for seven to eight days. A net, about 20 feet long and mounted on a wooden frame fitting into the sluice gate, is put into position when the level of water in the canal is near its lowest, so that there is the maximum head of water between the field and the canal. The sluice is then opened, and the water rushes with considerable force through the net, carrying with it some of the prawns, which collect at the narrow and closed end of the net from which they are emptied into boats moored nearby. The time taken for completing the fishing is about the same as that required for filling. If the fishing is done after dark, a light is placed at the sluice to attract the prawns in the field into the out-rushing current.

The salinity of the water in the fields may rise from 2·6 to 3·3 per cent during the dry season, and there must obviously be some period prior to the next paddy crop when the salt can be washed out of the soil.

This method of catching prawns is to a large extent a device for fishing them with the aid of the sluice and net, since the intervals between any two spring tides, when the prawns enter, and the neap tides when the prawns are flushed out through the net, is only a few days. But, says Menon, some twenty-five to thirty years ago the practice was somewhat different. After the fields had attained a high stocking rate in the way described above, the sluices were kept closed and the fields kept under water for from two to three months, thus allowing the prawns to grow. The rice stubble apparently is a good fertiliser, giving rise to a dense growth of algae, upon the detritus of which the prawns fatten. That practice came nearer to a definite culture; but, from the account of the similar prawn fishery in the mangrove swamps of Singapore, just described, it is probable that, even in the existing technique of this paddy field prawn fishery, the young prawns may remain in the fields, between entering and leaving, for some weeks, to grow substantially before making their way to the sluices.

Menon gives valuable statistics of the yields of this fishery. In terms of fresh weight of prawns, this may vary from about 700 to 1900 lb. per acre per season. The prawns are marketed in the dried condition and the rate of production per acre becomes 106 to 295 lb. of dried prawns. Practically the entire production is exported from the port of Cochin to Rangoon, Singapore and Hong Kong. In 1952 3,825 tons of dried prawns were exported, an impressive figure.

As in the case of the Bheris, the owners of the paddy fields do not, in most cases, fish the prawns themselves, but lease out the fields after the rice harvest has been gathered. They thereby derive an additional income, which in recent years has been of the order of Rs. 100-300 per acre.

FISH IN RICEFIELDS, JAVA

Ricefields are under water for many months, the length of flooding depending upon the rice variety, which is itself dependent upon the length of time during which water is available. Flooded ricefields, which often have deeper ditches in them to facilitate the drying-off of the fields for ripening the crop and for harvest, are favourable sites for the production of fish. There is a considerable natural production of fish carried into the fields with the irrigation water. Around the root-systems of the rice plants there is often a rich growth of filamentous algae; and there may be a good growth of epiphytic algae and diatoms both on the submerged rice stems, and on the surface of the soil. Often, one may see traps put into the gaps in the low bunds which surround the fields to catch fish moving out after a period of growth. Plunge-baskets are often used in the fields to catch the catfish *Clarias* which is one of the commoner fish, and a predator on other fish and insects.

Hofstede and Ardiwinata[108] give an account of fish culture in irrigated ricefields in West Java. They point out that if irrigated ricefields are to be used, not merely for the growing of rice but also for the production of fish, the following two factors are of prime importance. First, there must be a regular supply of a sufficient quantity of water throughout; and secondly, there is the effect upon rice cultivation, for example, the frequent necessity of raising the water-level, the reaction of the paddy variety and effect on the soil of long periods of inundation. Where these factors are unsuited to both the fish and the rice, the rice must clearly be considered first, since the rice crop is the main object of the cultivation and the fish can never be anything but a catch-crop.

Simple procedures of management, such as raising and strengthening the bunds to prevent leakage and to save irrigation water, tend to increase the yield of fish and prevent them from escaping.

Fish may be reared in ricefields as a second crop. It is customary in many regions to use the land for growing other crops after the paddy has been harvested. If sufficient water can be provided during a period of at least three months, then it is possible to rear fish profitably on such grounds. The paddy fields are then to be regarded as fishponds; the bunds are made higher, repairs are effected, and trenches are deepened. The production of the naturally occurring wild fish in paddy fields is estimated at some 3 kg. per hectare during a six-month period. This rate of production is very low, yet when reckoned as the production of the two million hectares of irrigated ricefields in Java, it would amount to the production of some 6000 tons of fish annually.

If farmers are prepared to take the trouble to prepare their fields for the raising of a catch-crop of fish, they usually cease the production of wild fish and concentrate more on the production of one particular fish variety which is stocked in the fields. Carp were almost exclusively raised before the war of 1939-45, but since the war, the *Tilapia mossambica* has also been cultivated. Though Soong showed that Tilapia are difficult to establish in ricefields because of the predatory fish naturally occurring there, this fish has been more successful in Java.

Usually, the ricefields are stocked with fingerling fish from 3 to 5 cm. long, and the rate of stocking depends on the fertility of the water and the soil, the amount of water available and the length of the rearing period, the aim being to raise fish for consumption purposes each weighing from 75 to 100 gm. This is a very small fish, but it appears to meet the requirements of the consumers in Java. Hofstede and Ardiwinata put the theoretical production per hectare per annum at about 300 kg.

In parts of West Java where there is enough irrigation water throughout the year, the farmers can plan the continuous use of their fields. The most frequently applied system is of three harvests in each two-year cycle. The fields are in use for paddy cultivation for a total time of fifteen months in two years, leaving three intervals of three months of fallow between each harvest and the next planting. During this flood-fallow it is possible to raise fish alternately with rice.

There is also a mixed rice and fish cultivation. The fish are reared on the paddy fields while the rice is actually growing. This system can be applied from about five days after the paddy has been transplanted until the time of draining off the water. When the water has to be reduced for the weeding of the crop, the fish can either be sold as small fish, or they can be restocked when weeding is over and the water is deepened again for a further growing period.

Hofstede and Ardiwinata (loc. cit.) give some very interesting results of a statistical survey of the production of fish and rice. This was done in a series of demonstrations arranged to encourage the rearing of fish in irrigated ricefields in areas where this form of fish culture was little known. They show that, in a period of from 40 to 60 days between the second weeding of the rice and the flowering of the paddy, seven experimental plots gave crops of fish varying from 28 to 50 kg. per hectare, with an average theoretical annual yield of about 300 kg. per hectare per annum. In these experiments carp of two varieties were used, namely, gold carp and dark-coloured carp. The latter did better, probably owing to their being less conspicuous to predators in the brownish muddy water. In all the demonstrations it was shown that the yield of rice, expressed as the weight of wet paddy immediately after harvesting, was increased by 3·7 to 7·5 per cent over unstocked control plots. This increased yield of padi is ascribed to two factors. The first is the tillage of the surface layers of the soil by the browsing and dibbling of the carp in their search for food, and the second is the manuring action of the faeces of the fish.

FISH IN RICEFIELDS, MALAYA

In Malaya, a different fish is used in the ricefields. This is the Sepat Siam, *Trichogaster pectoralis* Regan, which is not a native of Malaya but has been introduced from Siam. In ponds this fish of the Gourami family will grow to a size of nearly ½ lb., but in the shallower depths of ricefields it seldom exceeds a length of about 12 cm. and a weight of 2 or 3 oz.

The fish are not usually deliberately stocked, but are already living in the irrigation canals and enter the fields with the irrigation water. There they breed and their young grow rapidly. In one or two of the ponds at the Malacca Research Station, Sepat Siam were found to be naturally occurring. There had been ricefields near the site of the ponds.

Each group of ricefields drains towards some lowest point, and at this point a deeper sump is excavated. The sump, called a *telaga*, is usually surrounded by banana trees, both to give shade and for the sake of the fruit.

The Sepat Siam, having entered the ricefields with the irrigation water, then breed and the young grow during the growth of the rice crop. When the fields are drained for the flowering and ripening of the paddy, the fish accumulate where there is still water for them. This means that they collect in the *telaga*. The owner or lessee of the fields seldom catches these fish himself. He usually sells the fish, as they are in the *telaga*, to a merchant who catches them himself. A sloping screen is set up beside the *telaga*, and then the mixture of fish, water and mud is scooped out with buckets and filtered through the screen. Almost all the fish can be taken in this way. They are easily sun-dried, being small fish, and are exported to the Indonesian markets. The lessees claim that the sale of the fish pays the rent and the water dues, leaving the paddy as clear profit.

Soong made an examination of this fishery in the Krian district of Malaya.[109] The fertile areas for rice production in Krian are near the sea coast, where the water is neutral; here the yield of Sepat Siam was also the highest, and consistently high. It was of the order of 200-400 lb. of fish per acre per paddy season. In the inland part of the Krian paddy area, where the water is slightly acid (*p*H 6 to 6·8), the yield of rice is less, and the crop of fish is only of the order of 10 to 50 lb. per acre per season. Soong explains the difference by his finding that the fish seem to produce more eggs in the neutral area than in the acid area. He discounted the effect of abundance of food, because the fish from both areas invariably had full stomachs. Fish from the neutral area were feeding on zooplankton and blue-green algae, whilst in the acid area the fish were feeding on green algae (mostly desmids).

FISH IN SUGAR-CANE FIELDS

In British Guiana, sugar cane is grown on a great scale in the flat coastal plains. It seems to be a characteristic of sugar-cane culture here that the fields must have a period of flood-fallow, when the harvested fields stand under water for about nine months before being replanted. The fields are cambered and the trenches between the ridges are deep. As the field is flooded to the point where the tops of the ridges are covered, it follows that there may be 5 feet of water in the trenches. In view of this depth of water, and the fact that each field may be 10 acres in area and under water for many months, the potential for fish production of these fields should be great. Brown pointed this out,[80] and gave the figure of some 15,000 acres of fields under flood-fallow at any time. Moreover, the fields are served by a system of canals, both high-level canals to bring the water to the fields and to serve as communications for barge traffic and low-level canals for drainage. The total area of this canal system is estimated by Brown at some 6,000 acres (Colour Plate I).

The water is supplied either from an embanked river or from great shallow reservoirs, called conservancies. These conservancies contain many fish, including some of those shown by Carter to have accessory air-breathing organs. These fish are carried into the cane fields when they are flooded, and they are always present in the canals.

There is no reason to believe that the water and soil of the flood-fallows are particularly favourable to high fish yields. On the other hand, the area available is very great. Brown gives no data for the yields of fish, but in 1949 sample catches from a number of trenches in one field gave a figure of about 65 lb. of fish per acre. If this field was typical, there is a production of about a million pounds of fish annually in the flood-fallowed cane fields.

Brown describes the last stages of draining a flood-fallowed field as a scene of great excitement. People assemble with nets, dippers and baskets, and bail the fish from the trenches at the outflows where the lowered level has concentrated the fish from the whole 10-acre field (Plate 56).

The plantation managers do not like to allow fishing in the fields themselves, as the trampling of many people would break down the ridges. The fish are all washed out into the canals on draining and can be caught there.

As the flood-fallowed fields are practically fishponds, it has often been considered whether a regular fish culture could be done in them. Attempts are being made to stock them with other fish, especially the *Tilapia mossambica*, but so far this exotic fish has proved unable to stand up to the heavy predation that goes on in the fields. A high proportion of the fish there are predators. Moreover, there is already a rich fish fauna with special adaptations for life in swampy conditions. It seems likely that the best line of advance might be, as Brown suggested many years ago, the production of the fry of the Hassar, *Hoplosternum littorale*, both to increase the rate of stocking of the fields and to provide more fodder for the predators, of which the most common and popular is the Houri, *Erythrinus unitaeniatus*. This fish will also find plenty of food, apart from fish, in the abundance of prawns and insects which are found in the flooded fields.

SELF-STOCKING RIVER DAMS

The dams built across the tributaries of the Volta in Ghana have already been mentioned, but can be considered once more here because they are to a large degree self-stocking. Morris,[110] who was concerned in the resettlement of the river banks once the tsetse fly had been eradicated, saw the annual wastage of fish which took place when the dry season came and the tributaries dried out into isolated pools. He noticed, as did Vaas in Borneo, that the predators had very much the upper hand in these shrinking waters, to the detriment of the fish yield. He saw that this annual wastage could be checked and fish made available to the local population, if an adequate area and depth of water could be held up by placing a simple weir at the tail end of the natural pool. This he did with an earth dam, carefully levelled at the top (Plate 4). The result was that a pool, which previously shrank to a length of 240 yards and a depth of 6 to 15 inches by the end of the dry season, was held up to a length of a mile above the weir, and to a depth of 6 feet at the deepest reach.

The effect on the fish population was almost incredible. The old pool, when fished out at the end of the dry season, had yielded $13\frac{1}{2}$ lb. of fish (Plate 6), most of them belonging to the predatory species *Hydrocyon*. The valuable non-predators, *Tilapia* and *Citharinus*, only weighed 3 lb. in all, and were very small. But seine-netting and cast-netting in the lagoon held back by the new check-dam at the end of the dry season produced 3,250 lb. of fish, with the non-predators well in excess of predators (Plate 7). The size of the fish was also excellent. Buxton (quoted from the Ghana Fisheries Department reports) found that this and other similar dams were annually restocked by migration from the main river (Chapter III).

Bell-Cross[145] has confirmed this by observations on a fish-ladder in the spillway of the Mwekera Dam in Northern Rhodesia. Fish ascending the ladder were counted and weighed. Some 24 out of the 31 species of fish known to be present in the Mwekera Stream below the dam were observed moving up the ladder.

There appeared to be no relation between these upward migrations and the phase of the moon, the intensity of the light, or turbidity, but there was a good relation between the rate of water-flow and migration. This was at its most active at and shortly after an increase in the rate of flow in the spillway as a result of heavy rains. Most species of fish moved during the daylight hours.

As was found in India (page 88), there was no indication that the migration was for the purpose of spawning (except in the case of the *Barbus* species).

These findings show that a dam will tend to be self-stocking from the stream below if the spillway is passable by the fish, and that their ascent is stimulated by an increased downflow of water.

MINOR SUBSISTENCE FISHERIES

Minor fisheries for subsistence are very common and very important in tropical countries.

Soong[111] describes fishing with small lift-nets in irrigation canals in Malaya (Plate 57). The fish in these canals are those which stock the ricefields with the irrigation water, and the survivors of the rice-field fishing which return to the ditches and canals. These canals are also fished intensively with hook and line, and with cast-nets. It is common to see a man with a small cast-net walking and fishing his way along, dropping his catches into a basket.

Soong[112] describes the fishery for the *keli*, *Clarias batrachus*, in the Krian district of Malaya. This is a fish of the ricefields and ditches, which, having an accessory air-breathing apparatus, is not only able to live in the sometimes deoxygenated water of the paddy fields, but can cross over land, provided the land is moist. This explains its almost universal occurrence wherever there is water.

This fish is nocturnal and its movements are most pronounced after heavy rain. These habits are well known to the people, so when conditions are suitable there is great activity, with people setting up small traps in the drains, and baited lines. These are baited usually with earthworms, and one operator may set as many as fifty baited rods, which are stuck into the ground. He visits the lines at intervals throughout the night, and sells his catch at the dawn to passing merchants. This fish will remain alive for a long time in the minimum quantity of water and is always marketed alive. Soong writes that no less than 400 tons of *keli* were marketed from the 35,000 acres of irrigated paddy land in North Krian.

Another important and popular fish of the paddy fields and ditches of Malaya is the *aruan*, or Snake-head, *Ophiocephalus*. This is a fine fish with firm white flesh, well-flavoured, though a little bony by European standards. It has, like the *keli*, an accessory air-breathing apparatus, though of a different structure. It is a predator, feeding on fish, frogs, tadpoles and aquatic insects. It is the common-est of sights to see the lines of anglers along the banks of the canals and ditches, all after Aruan, which may grow to a weight of many pounds, or after smaller fish. Almost all this fishing is for subsistence, yet Soong says that, in addition, a substantial tonnage surplus to subsistence requirements is sold in the markets. It is one of the most popular fish in India too; there it is known as the Murrell. Because of its ability to remain alive for many hours in little water, or none, it is very easy to market.

In British Guiana there is a rich fish crop to be had from the irrigation and drainage canals, for these are replenished with fish from the sugar-cane fields. Not only the cast-net, but hand-nets and baskets are used in great numbers. Pairs of women may be seen with their "gila-gila" nets, small hand-nets, with which they move slowly along the ditches, catching mainly small prawns. Hand-nets or baskets are very commonly used elsewhere (Plates 58, 59).

The plunge basket is almost universal as a means of catching fish in flooded fields, in drying ditches, even in small slow rivers.

Thienemann[113] describes a small subsistence fishery for freshwater prawns in the Lamongan lake in Indonesia. Large batteries of small wicker traps were set in the shallow water. Taking a census of twenty-one fishermen or women, Thienemann found that they were using between them 1917 of these small traps, the largest number handled by one operator being 150, the smallest 40. In a total of ninety-four man-days they took between them some 25 kg. of prawns, together with 944 specimens of small fish, chiefly *Puntius* and *Rasbora* species. This was essentially a subsistence fishery. Prawns may be caught in brackish water by small fences and traps, sometimes with a light to attract the prawns (Plate 62). Thienemann also describes the fishing of the reed beds in these lakes by girls using their sarongs as fishing implements.

A simple lift-net for catching mangrove crabs is shown in Plate 61. When crabs have been attracted on to the net by a bait, the net is lifted.

At the Malacca Research Station, permission was given to a number of people to fish with rod and line in ponds which had not yet come into use. One elderly woman caught ninety small *Betok* (Colour Plate VI), the celebrated Climbing Perch, *Anabas*, in an afternoon. The total weight cannot have exceeded about 5 lb., but this fish is popular among Malays, because it has a round, firm body and curries well.

There are subsistence fisheries of opportunity. On one occasion the author witnessed a fishery of this kind in Rhodesia. Heavy rain had fallen as we made our journey along the main Mazabuka-Livingstone road, and in one of the small streams which pass under the road beneath a bridge there was a run of small *Barbus*. Crowds of African men and women, with any means to hand, such as baskets or even pieces of cloth, were paddling or wading along the banks and

57. A lift-net at work in an irrigation canal, Malaya.

58. Women fishing for prawns with a hand-net, Nigeria.

59. Women fishing with a small hand-net, Fiji.

60. Fishing for small *Barbus* in a spate in a stream in Rhodesia.

61. Baited lift-net for crabs, Borneo.

62. Small prawn fence and light, Java

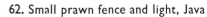

in the water, dipping out great numbers of the small silvery fish (Plate 60). These fish were only 2 or 3 inches long, and *Barbus* is a bony fish. But they were obviously very acceptable to the African passers-by; and they would be an acceptable relish when boiled up and eaten with rice or cassava porridge. They would also be a valuable source of proteins, minerals and vitamins.

In the tropics, these up-river runs, or downriver drifts, of small fish following freshets, are common. The author saw a similar transient fishery in Malaya, after a heavy rainstorm had brought a flood of water down from a large paddy-growing area. The banks of the swollen torrent passing under the road were crowded with men throwing cast-nets, using lift-nets and dip-nets and fishing with hook and line. They were joined by passers-by on the road, who came up at the double.

The last example of minor fisheries which will be given here is the bailing-out of a piece of water to secure the fish. At Jasin in the Malacca State, near a village, there was a pond connected with a small swamp. Four or five men had built a low earth dyke across the connection with the swamp and were bailing the water out of the pond with buckets into the swamp (Colour Plate V). After many hours' work they were able to catch the fish with hand-nets, plunge baskets and cast-nets. This is very common towards the end of the dry season, or where there has been a shortage of rain, so that the level of the water in small areas is low. It is widely practised in Africa and in South America, yet another of the universal fishing techniques which must go far back into the history of primitive man.

In earlier chapters of this book fisheries have been described mainly in the guise of industries, which means that the produce is bought and sold. But wherever there is water with fish in it, people will be found fishing for themselves. This may not be because they are poor, but because they must have "relish" and it is there for the taking. Naturally, most of this subsistence fishing is done by the very young or the elderly, by people not yet at work, or by those who are past active work. But the total quantity that is taken in these subsistence fisheries must be very great. At any time there must be thousands, or in the case of a big country, hundreds of thousands, of subsistence fishermen; and even if their individual catches may be a few ounces of prawns or half a dozen small fish, or even one fair-sized fish, the aggregate over a year must be very great. None of this may pass through the markets nor be recorded in any statistics. The statement that a territory has a very low consumption of fish per head is often unimpressive. The figure has probably been arrived at by dividing the total quantity of fish which has been recorded in the markets by the total population. It is likely to be a most misleading statistic since only a small fraction of the fish caught in a territory may be sold on the markets.

FUTURE TRENDS

The future may well bring big changes to the freshwater fisheries. One remedy, popularly canvassed for the future of those tropical countries in which there is a disastrous rate of population increase, is industrialisation. That will affect the inland fisheries in many ways. Apart from possible pollution of the waters and the abstraction of water for industrial use, it may mean the embanking of the rivers, so that the seasonal flooding no longer takes place. That would put a stop to some of the world's richest freshwater fisheries. Secondly, there would be a concentration of the population in the towns; this indeed is already taking place all over the world. It is a by-product of mass suggestion (unintentional, it is true), by radio, and above all by the cinema. The younger generation is becoming restive with the life of their peasant forebears, and their flight to the towns is a fact. There are areas of land untilled even where there is a need to grow more food, because the younger men are not there to till them. In the towns, the immigrants may become casuals; the problem is well known to every Chief Constable, and need not take up more space in a book on Tropical Inland Fisheries. Here, it need only be said, that the danger is recognised in many countries, and that active measures are being taken to make country life more attractive and to bring as many as possible of the benefits of town life to the villages. The concentration of population in the towns at the expense of the country can only aggravate the difficulty of finding the protein necessary for full health, inasmuch as subsistence fishing will no longer be possible for most town-dwellers, and thousands of former producers will then become consumers. On the other hand, people in employment for wages in towns represent a concentrated cash market, as, has for example, already happened in the Rhodesian Copperbelt. This should lead, as indeed it has in the Copperbelt, to an improvement in distribution and marketing, which, in turn, might give an added stimulus to the professional fishermen to improve their fishing methods and equipment.

BIBLIOGRAPHY

[1] Ruttner, F. (1940). *Fundamentals of Limnology*. Translated by D. G. Frey and F. E. J. Fry. University of Toronto Press, 1953.

[2] Eriksson, E. (1952). "The Composition of Atmospheric Precipitation". *Tellus*, Vol. LV, No. 3, 1952.

[3] Debenham, F. (1948). Report on the Water Resources of the Bechuanaland Protectorate, etc. H.M.S.O. 1948.

[4] Ruttner, F. (1931). "Hydrographische und Hydrochemische Beobachtungen auf Java, Sumatra, und Bali." *Arch. für Hydrobiol.* Supplement Bd. VIII.

[5] Marlier, G. (1954). "Recherches Hydrobiologiques dans les Rivières du Congo Oriental. 11. Étude écologique." *Hydrobiologia*, Vol. VI, 1954.

[6] Carter, G. S. (1955) *The Papyrus Swamps of Uganda*. Heffer, Cambridge, 1955.

[7] Hickling, C. F. (1959). "The Fish Culture Research Station, Malacca." *Nature*, Vol. 183, 31 January, 1959.

[8] Marlier, G. (1951). "Recherches Hydrobiologiques dans les Rivières du Congo Oriental. La Conductivité Electrique." *Hydrobiologia*, Vol. III, 1951.

[9] Blanc, M., Daget, J., and d'Aubenton, F. (1955). "Recherches Hydrobiologiques dans le Bassin du Moyen Niger." *Bull. Inst. franç. Afr. noire*, Vol. XVII, Series A., No. 3, 1955.

[10] Braun R. (1952). "Limnologische Untersuchungen an einigen Seen im Amazonasgebiet." *Schweiz. Z. Hydrol.*, Vol. XIV, 1952.

[11] Beauchamp, R. S. A. (1956). *Nature*, Vol. 178, pp. 616-19, 1956.

[12] Clarke, F. W. (1920). "The Data of Geochemistry." U.S. Geological Survey, Bull. 695, Washington, 1920.

[13] Welch, P. (1952). *Limnology*. 2nd Edition. McGraw-Hill, 1952.

[14] Carter, G. S. (1934). "Results of the Cambridge Expedition to British Guiana, 1933. The Freshwaters of the Rain-Forest Areas of British Guiana." *J. Linn. Soc.*, (*Zool.*) London, Vol. XXIX (No. 264), October, 1934.

[15] Holden, M. J. and Green, J, 1960. "The Hydrology and Plankton of the River Sokoto." *J. Anim. Ecol.* 29 May, 1960.

[16] Ganapati, S. V., and Chacko, P. I. (1951). "An Investigation of the River Godavari, and the Effect of the Paper Mills", etc. *Proc. Indo-Pacif. Fish. Coun.*, 3rd Meeting, Madras, Sections II and III, Madras, 1952.

[17] Nair, K. K. (1944). "Calcutta Sewage Irrigation Fisheries." *Proc. nat. Inst. Sci. India*, Vol. 10, 1944.

[18] Vaas, K. F. (1948). "Notes on Freshwater Fish Culture in Domestic Sewage in the Tropics." *Landbouw*, Batavia, Vol. 20, 1948.

[19] Scheuring, D. L. (1939). "Die Reinigung und Verwertung der Abwässer von München." *Natur u. Volk*, Vol. 69, 1939.

[20] Buschkiel, A. L. (1937). "Lehren aus Tropischer Teichwirtschaft." *Z. Fisch.*, Vol, 35, 1937.

[21] Carter, G. S. (1931). Reports of an Expedition to Brazil and Paraguay. "The Fauna of the Swamps of the Paraguayan Chaco. I. Physico-Chemical Nature of the Environment." *J. Linn. Soc.* (*Zool.*) London, Vol. XXXVIII, 1930.

[22] Annual Report of the Northern Rhodesia Game and Tsetse Dept., 1956.

[23] Annual Report of the East African Fisheries Research Organisation, 1952.

[24] Brook, A. J. and Rzoska, J. (1954). "The Influence of the Gebel Aulia Dam on the Development of the Nile Plankton." *J. Anim. Ecol.*, Vol. 23, No. 1, May 1954.

[25] Clarke, G. L. (1939). "The Utilisation of Solar Energy by Aquatic Organisms." *Problems of Lake Biology*. Amer. Assoc. Adv. Sci., 1939.

[26] Beauchamp, R. S. A. (1940). "Chemistry and Hydrography of Lakes Tanganyika and Nyasa." *Nature*, Vol. 146, August, 1940.

[27] Kufferath, J. (1952). "Le Milieu Biochemique. Exploration Hydrobiologique du Lac Tanganika." *Res. Sci.*, Brussels, 1952.

[28] Beauchamp, R. S. A. (1953). "Hydrological Data for Lake Nyasa." *J. Ecol.*, 1953.

[29] Hulot, A. (1956). "Aperçu sur la Question de la Pêche industrielle aux Lacs Kivu, Edouard et Albert." *Bull. agric. Congo belge*, XLVII, No. 4, 1956.

[30] Damas, H. (1936). "Recherches Hydrologiques dans les Lacs Kivu, Édouard, et Ndagala." *Inst. des Parcs. nat. Congo belge, Mission H. Damas*, Fasc. 1, Brussels, 1935-6.

[31] Fish, G. R. (1957). "A Seiche Movement and its Effect on the Hydrology of Lake Victoria." Colonial Office Fish. Pubns. No. 10.

[32] van Meel, L. (1954). "Exploration Hydrobiologique du Lac Tanganika, Resultats Scientifiques." *Le Phytoplankton*. Vol. IV, Fasc. 1, Brussels, 1954.

[33] Fish, G. R. (1955). "The Oxygen Content of the Water in Dams in Ankole." *E. Afr. agric. J.* Vol. XX, No. 3, 1955.

[34] Kalle, K. (1948). "Zur Frage der Produktionsleistung des Meeres." *Dtsch. hydrogr. Z.* Bd. 1, Hft. 1, 1948.

[35] Holden, M. J. and Green, J., 1960 "The Hydrology and Plankton of the River Sokoto." *J. Anim. Ecol.* 29 May 1960.

[36] Smith, E. V., and Swingle, H. S. (1941). "The Use of Fertilizer for Controlling Several Submerged Aquatic Plants in Ponds." *Trans. Amer. Fish. Soc.*, Vol. 71, 1941.

[37] Reich, K., and Aschner, M. (1947). "Mass Development and Control of the Flagellate *Prymnesium parvuum* in Fishponds in Palestine." *Palest. J. Bot.* (*J.Ser.*), Vol. 4, 1947.

[38] Hummel, K. (1931). "Sedimente indonesischen Susswasserseen. Hydrographische und Hydrochemische Beobachtungen auf Java, Sumatra, und Bali." *Arch. für Hydrobiol. Suppt.*, Bd. VIII.

[39] Heinrici, A. T. (1939). "The Distribution of Bacteria in Lakes." *Problems of Lake Biology*. Amer. Ass. Adv. Sci., 1939.

[40] Debenham, F. (1952). *Study of an African Swamp*, H.M.S.O., London, 1952.

[41] Capart, A., and Kufferath, J. (1956). "Recherches Hydrobiologiques au Congo Belge et leurs Resultats pratiques." *Bull. agric. Congo belge*, Vol. XLVII, No. 4, 1956.

[42] Fish, G. R. (1955). "Digestion and Production of Sulphuric Acid by Mollusca." *Nature*, Vol. 175, 1955.

[43] Mortimer, C. H. (1941-2). "The Exchange of Dissolved Substances between Mud and Water in Lakes." *J. Ecol.* Cambridge, Vols. 29-30.

[44] Vaas, K. F. (1954). "Fisheries in the Lake District along the Kapuas River in West Borneo." *Indo-Pacif. Fish. Coun.* 4th Meeting, Quezon City, Sect. II and III, F.A.O., Bangkok.

[45] Hickling, C. F. (1959). "Observations on the Growth Rate of the Chinese Grass Carp." *Malay. agric. J.*, Vol. 43, No. 1, 1960.

[46] Blache, J. (1953-4). "Sur la Nutrition de quelques Poissons des Eaux douces de Cambodge." *Trav. Lab. Hydrobiol. Grenoble.* Ann, 1953-4.

[47] Gosse, J. P. (1955-6). "Dispositions speciales de l'appareil branchial des Tilapia et Citharinus." *Ann. Soc. Zool. Belg.* Fasc. 2, Tome LXXXVI, 1955-6.

⁴⁸ Hughes, G. M. and Shelton, G. (1957). "Pressure Changes during the Respiratory Movement of Teleostean Fishes." *Nature*, February, 1957.

⁴⁹ Fish, G. R. (1955). "The Food of Tilapia in East Africa." *Uganda J.*, Vol. 19, No. 1. March, 1955.

⁵⁰ Swynnerton, G. H. (1947). Report of an Investigation of the Fisheries of Lake Rukwa. Typescript; Dar-es-Salaam, 1947.

⁵¹ Schuster, W. H. "Fish Culture in Brackish Water Ponds of Java." *Indo-Pacif. Fish. Coun. Pubns. No.* 1, F.A.O.

⁵² Juday, C. (1940). "The Annual Energy Budget of an Inland Lake." *Ecology*, Vol. 21, 1940.

⁵³ Greenwood, P. H. (1953). "Feeding Mechanism of the Cichlid Fish *Tilapia esculenta* Graham." *Nature*, Vol. 172, 1953.

⁵⁴ Vaas, K. F., and Hofstede, A. E. (1952). "Studies on *Tilapia mossambica* Peters in Indonesia." *Contr. Inland Fish., Res, Sta.* No. 1 Bogor, Indonesia.

⁵⁵ Hofstede, A. E., and Botke, F. (1950). "*Tilapia mossambica* Peters as a Factor in Malarial Control." *Landbouw*, Vol. 22. 1950.

⁵⁶ Brown, J. M., and van Someren, V. D. (1953). "New Fish Culture Methods for Tilapia in East Africa." *Nature*, Vol. 172, 1953.

⁵⁷ Saanin, J. (1952). "Notes on the Fishery of the Cyprinid Fish *Thynnichthys vaillainti* in Indonesia." 4th Meeting, *Indo-Pacif. Fish. Coun. Proc.* Quezon City. F.A.O., Bangkok.

⁵⁸ Marlier, G. (1954). "Recherches Hydrobiologiques dans les Rivières du Congo Oriental. Pt. II. Le Milieu Biochimique." *Hydrobiologia*, Vol. VI, 1954.

⁵⁹ Fryer, G. (1959). "The Trophic Interrelationships and Ecology of some Littoral Communities of Lake Nyasa." *Proc. zool. Soc. Lond.* Vol. 132, Pt. 2, March, 1959.

⁶⁰ Vaas, K. F., and Sachlan, M. (1952). "Notes on Fisheries Exploitation of the artificial Lake Tjiburuj in West Java." *Contr. gen. agric. Res. Sta. Bogor*, No. 128, 1952.

⁶¹ Cott, H. B. (1952). "Fish Eating Birds." In *Report of East African Fisheries Organisation for 1952*. Nairobi.

⁶² Cott, H. B. (1954). "The Status of the Crocodile in Uganda." *Uganda J.*, Vol. 18, 1954.

⁶³ Carter, G. S., and Beadle, L. C. (1930). "The Fauna of the Swamps of the Paraguayan Chaco in Relation to its environment. II. Respiratory Adaptations in the Fish." *J. Linn. Soc. (Zool.)*, Vol. XXXVIII, No. 252, March, 1931.

⁶⁴ Fish, G. R. (1956). "Some Aspects of the Respiration of six species of fish from Uganda." *J. exp. Biol.*, Vol. 33, 1956.

⁶⁵ Depasse, P. (1956). "Monographie Piscicole de la Province Orientale." *Bull. agric. Congo belge.*, Vol. XLVII, No. 4, 1956.

⁶⁶ Welman, J. B. (1948). *Preliminary Survey of the Freshwater Fisheries of Nigeria.* Government Printer, Lagos, 1948.

⁶⁷ Johnels, A. G. (1954). "Notes on Fishes from the Gambia River." *Ark. Zool.*, Bd. 6, No. 1, 1954.

⁶⁸ Daget, J. (1956). "La Pêche à Diafarabé. Étude Monographique." *Bull. Inst. franç. Afr. noire*, Tome XVIII Ser. B, Nos. 1 et 2, 1956.

⁶⁹ Ibid. (1950). "La Passe à Poissons de Markkala." *Bull. Inst. Franç. Afr. Noire*, Tome, XII, No. 4, 1950.

⁷⁰ Chacko, P. I. (1952). Report on a Survey of the Dams and Migratory Fishes of Madras. *Contrib. Freshwater Fish., Biol., Sta, Madras*, No. 4, 1952.

⁷¹ Burdon, T. W. (1951). "A Consideration of the Classification of Fishing Gear and Methods." *Proc. Indo-Pacific Fish. Council (1951), Sect. II.*

[72] MacLaren, P. I. R. Unpublished duplicated paper.

[73] Lowe, R. H. (1952). Report on the Tilapia and other Fish and Fisheries of Lake Nyasa. *Colonial Office Fishery Pubns.* Vol. I, No. 2, 1952.

[74] Sao Leang, M., and Dom Saveun, M. (1952). "La Pêche au Day dans le Tonlé-Sap." *Indo-Pacif. Fish. Coun.* 4th Meeting, Quezon. F.A.O.

[76] Whitehead, P. J. P. (1955). *Review of Kenya Fisheries*, 1955, Nairobi.

[77] Burma (1886). *Report on the Fisheries in the Henzada District for the year 1886.* Rangoon, Government Press, 1886.

[78] Chevey, P., and le Poulain, F. (1940). "La Pêche dans les Eaux Douces du Cambodge." *Trav. Inst. Océan. de L'Indochine. 5me Memoire*, Saigon, 1940.

[79] Roth, V. (1943). *Fish Life in British Guiana. Daily Chronicle*, Ltd., Georgetown, British Guiana, 1943.

[80] Brown, H. H. "The Fisheries of British Guiana," *Bull. No. 3. Development and Welfare in the West Indies.*

[81] Mathieu, Y. (1957). "Une saison de Pêche au Ngola sur l'Uele à Sasi." *Bull. agric. Congo belge*, Vol. XLVIII, No. 3, 1957.

[82] Evans-Pritchard, E. (1940). *The Nuer.* Oxford, Clarendon Press, 1940.

[83] Jonglei Investigation Team, 1954. *The Equatorial Nile Project.* Sudan Government, 1954.

[84] Lemasson, J. (1949). *Aperçu Generale sur la Pêche de l'Indo-Chine.* Indo-Pacific Fish. Coun. F.A.O., 1949.

[85] Stubbs, J. M. (1949). "Fresh Water Fisheries in the Northern Bahr el Ghazal." *Sudan Notes and Records*, Vol. XXX, pt. 11, 1949.

[86] Gluckman, N. (1941). "The Economy of the Central Barotse Plain." *Rhodes-Livingstone Papers No. 7.* Rhodes-Livingstone Inst., 1941.

[87] Blanc, M., Daget, J., and d'Aubenton, F. (1955). "L'Exploitation des Eaux douces dans le Bassin du Moyen Niger." *Bull. Inst. franç. Afr. noire*, XVII, ser. A, No. 4, 1955.

[88] Bertram, C. K. R., Borley, H. J. H., and Trewavas, E. (1942). *Report on the Fish and Fisheries of Lake Nyasa.* Crown Agents, 1942.

[89] Nielsen, S. (1959). "Commercial Fishing on Lake Nyasa." *Proceedings of the First Fisheries Day*, S. Rhodesia. Govt. Printer, Salisbury.

[90] Poll, M. (1952). "Les Vertèbres." *Résultats Scientifiques Exploration Hydrobiologique du Lac Tanganika.* Brussels, 1952.

[91] Collart, A. (1956). "Note sur la Pêche au Ndagala au Lac Tanganika." *Bull. agric. Congo belge*, Vol. XLVII, No. 4, 1956.

[92] Chacko, P. I., Abraham, J. G., and Andal, K. R. (1953). Report on a Survey of the Flora, Fauna, and Fisheries of Pulicat Lake, Madras State. Contrib. Freshwater Biol. Sta., Madras, No. 8.

[93] Worthington, E. B. (1932). *A Report on the Fisheries of Uganda.* Crown Agents, 1932.

[94] Worthington, E. B. (1929). *A Report on the Fishing Survey of Lakes Albert and Kioga*, Crown Agents, 1929.

[95] Ricardo, C. K. (1936). *Report on the Fish and Fisheries of Lake Rukwa, and the Bangweulu*, Crown Agents, 1936.

[96] Graham, M. (1929). *Report on the Fishing Survey of Lake Victoria*, Crown Agents, 1929.

[97] Vaas, K. F., and Schuurman, J. J. (1949). "On the Ecology and Fisheries of some Javanese Freshwaters." *Communications of the General Agric. Res. Sta. Buitenzorg, Java*, No. 97, 1949.

[98] Macquarie, C. (1940). "Water-Gypsies of the Malagarasi." *Tanganyika Notes and Records*. No. 9, June, 1940.

[99] Livingstone, David (1874). *The Last Journals of David Livingstone.* John Murray, 1874.

[100] Brelsford, W. V. (1946). "Fishermen of the Bangweulu Swamps." *Rhodes-Livingstone Papers, No. 12,* N. Rhodesia.

[101] Pitman, C. R. S. (1933). In the Annual Report of the Game Dept., Uganda, 1933.

[102] Chacko, P. I., Krishnamurthi, B., and George, S. (1952). "Fisheries in the Kanigiri-Duvuur Reservoir in Nellore District, Madras." *Contr. Freshw. Fish. Biol. Sta. Madras,* No. 3, 1952.

[103] Mortimer, M. A. E. (1959). "Fishing in the Lunzadi Dam," *Rhod. agric. J.* Vol. 56, No. 2, 1959.

[104] Wallis, H. W. H. (1959). *Water Availability for Fish Production in Southern Rhodesia.* Proc. 1st Fisheries Day, Govt. Printer, Salisbury.

[105] Pillay, T. V. R. (1954). "The Ecology of a Brackish-Water Bheri." *Nat. Inst. Sci., India,* Vol. XX, No. 4, 1954.

[106] Hall, D. N. F. *Observations on the Taxonomy and Biology of some Indo-West Pacific Penaeidae.* Colonial Off. Fish. Pubns. H.M.S.O. (In press).

[107] Menon, M. K. (1955). "On the Paddy-Field Prawn Fishery of Travancore-Cochin." *Proc. Indo-Pacif. Fish. Coun.,* 5th Meeting, 1955.

[108] Hofstede, A. E., and Ardiwinata, R. (1950). "Compiling Statistical Data on Fish-Culture in Irrigated Ricefields in West Java." *Landbouw,* XXII, 1950.

[109] Soong, M. K. "The Fitness of Ecological Niches." *Proc. Indo-Pacif. Fish. Coun.,* 3rd Meeting, Sec. II and III.

[110] Morris, K. R. S. (1952). Report on the Dept. of Tsetse Control. January, 1950 to March 1951, Gold Coast, 1952.

[111] Soong, M. K. (1948). "Fishes of the Malayan Padi-Fields I." *Malay. Nat. J.,* Vol. III, No. 2, 1948.

[112] ibid. (1950). "Fishes of the Malayan Padi-Fields III." *Malay. Nat. J.,* Vol. V, No, 2, 1950.

[113] Thienemann, A. (1951). "Bilder aus der Binnenfischerei auf Java und Sumatra." *Arch. für Hydrobiol,* Supplement Bd. XLX, 1951.

[114] de Kimpe P. (1957). "Le contrôle de la jacinthe d'eau." *Bull. agric. Congo belge,* Vol. XLVIII, No. 1, 1957,[105].

[115] Report on Kenya Fisheries, 1958.

[116] Ann. Repts. Dept. of Game, Tsetse and Fisheries, Nyasaland.

[117] Ann. Rept. East African Fisheries Res. Organisation, 1958.

[118] Ann. Rept. Uganda Game and Fisheries, 1956.

[119] Marlier, G. (1957). "Le Ndakala: Poisson Pelagique du Lac Tanganika." *Bull. agric. Congo belge,* XLIX, No. 5, 1957.

[120] Collart A. "Pêche Artisanale et Pêche Industrielle au Lac Tanganika." *Bull. agric. Congo belge,* XLIX, No. 5, 1958.

[121] Service des Eaux et Forêts, Section Chasse et Pêche. "Aperçu sur la Pêche lacustre et fluviale au Congo Belge et au Ruanda-Urundi." *Bull. agric. Congo belge,* L, No. 6, 1959.

[122] Rept. of Game and Tsetse Dept., N. Rhodesia, 1957.

[123] Rept. of Game and Fisheries Dept., Uganda, 1958.

[124] ibid., 1947.

[125] ibid., 1948.

[126] Rept. Lake Victoria Fisheries Service, 1958-9.

[127] Rept. Dept. of Agriculture, Tanganyika, 1949.

[128] ibid., 1950.

[129] Rept. Game and Tsetse, N. Rhodesia, 1943 et seq.

[130] Rept. Game and Fisheries Dept., Uganda, 1951.

[131] ibid., 1953.

[132] Rept. Lake Victoria Fisheries Service. 1957-8.

[133] Rept. Dept. of Agriculture, Tanganyika, 1955.

[134] ibid., 1956.

[135] ibid., 1957.

[136] Simpson, J. R., and Butters, B. (1958). "A Pot Study of Lake Mud as a Fertiliser." Appendix D in Annual Rept. East African Fisheries Research Organisation, 1958.

[137] Ann. Rept. East African Fisheries Research Organisation, 1958.

[138] Ann. Rept. Fisheries Dept., Ghana, 1957.

[139] Ann. Repts., Fisheries Dept., Gold Coast, 1950-1.

[140] Ann. Rept. Game and Tsetse Dept., N. Rhodesia, 1954.

[141] Rept. of the Uganda Game and Fisheries Dept., 1943.

[142] Williams R. H. (1956). "*Salvinia auriculata* Aublet. The chemical eradication of a serious aquatic weed in Ceylon." *Trop. Agriculture, Trin.*, Vol. 33 (1956), p. 145.

[143] Chow C. Y., Thevasagayam, and Wambeek E.S. (1955). "Control of Salvinia," *W.H.O. Bull.* 12 (1955), p. 365.

[144] Capart A., and Kufferath J. (1957) "Considérations biologiques sur la Pisciculture au Congo Belge." *Bull. agric. Congo belge*, XLVIII, No. 5, October 1957, p. 1245.

[145] Bell-Cross G. (1960). "Observations on the movements of fish in a fish-ladder in Northern Rhodesia." *Symposium on Problems of Major Lakes*, Lusaka, 1960.

[146] Greenwood, P. H. (1956). "Two new Records of non-Cichlid fish from Lake Victoria and the Victoria Nile." *2nd Symposium on African Hydrobiology and Inland Fisheries, Brazzaville (C.C.T.A.)*, 1956.

[147] Davis, F. M. "An Account of the Fishing Gear of England and Wales." *Fish. Invest., Lond.*, Vol. V, No. 4, London, 1923.

[148] Soong, M. K., and Merican A. B. (1958). The use of Endrin as a Piscicide in Tin-mining Pools and Fishponds in Malaya. *Proc. Indo-Pacif. Fish. Coun.*, 8th Session, Colombo, 1958.

INDEX

Access roads in fishery development, 106, 159, 178, 193, 198, 210, 244; lack of, 209

Accessory air-breathing organs; in swamp fishes, 22, 53, 73, 76, 135, 216, 217, 236; ease marketing, 247, 272; structure of, 74, 75; in conservancies, 268, 269; pits to catch fish with, 94

Albert, Lake, 192 et seq.; colour of, 41; composition of, 42; fish mortalities in, 76; surveys of, 104, 192 et seq.

Alestes (Figure 2), migrations of, 85-87, 150-152, 207; suggested transplantation of, 181; in Lake Albert, 192, 198; in Lake Tanganyika, 168

Algae, 39, 48, 50, 262; filamentous, 12, 15, 40, 68, 265; blue-green, 62, 65, 192, 268; epiphytic, 65, 66; and mosquito-breeding, 257; see also "*Aufwuchs*"

Amazon, River, composition of, 8, 9, 43, 77; stratification in, 10, 32; fish of, 56, 65

Amerindians, 124, 127, 128

Amino acids, 45

Ammonium compounds, 42; in regeneration, 45; stored in hypolimnion, 46, 47, 51, 52

Anabantid fish (Figure 1), 22, 73, 216, 217, 240, 272

Ancistrus, 75

Antibiotic substances, 50, 51

Arab influence, 98, 103, 168

Arapaima (Figure 3), 65, 125

Arawhana (*Osteoglossum*) (Figure 3) 125

Arrows, 91, 125

Astatereochromis, 69, 258

Atmosphere, 1, 2

Attraction of fish by light, 97, 164, 165, 172, 174, 178, 184, 263, 272

Auchenoglanis, 85, 168, 234

"*Aufwuchs*", 66, 68, 69

Autolysis, 45, 53

Babati, Lake, 252

Bacteria, 45, 46, 48, 50, 53, 60; as food for fish, 57, 58; see also Fermentation

Bagrus (Figure 2), 163, 185, 192, 207, 209; migrations of, 85

Battues of fish, 117, 133, 146, 147, 185

Bahi Swamp (Plate 12), 218 et seq.

Bait, 128, 168, 193, 219, 234, 271; see also Lures

Baling out water, to catch fish (Colour Plate V), 91, 134, 141, 152, 273

Bangweulu Swamp, 17, 22, 226 et seq.; lack of oxygen in, 23, 76, 82; methane in, 46

Barbus (Figure 2), 70, 111, 112, 116, 120, 163, 179, 180, 207, 209, 253, 256, 273; migrations of, 86, 88, 89, 110, 270, 272

Barilius (Figure 2), 70, 112, 179

Barotseland, 146

Barrage, Markkala, 86, 87

Barriers to catch fish (Plates 12, 14), 80-84, 93-95, 109-110, 112-116, 123, 140-141, 143, 146, 151-153, 158, 219, 230

Beach seines, see Seines

"Beauchamp's Hypothesis", 49

Beating the water to catch fish (Plate 20), 100, 101, 120, 128, 170, 183, 184, 223, 224, 232

Bengs, 131, 135

Bheris, 259, 260

Birds, 49, 71

Bicycles in fish distribution, 106, 111, 150, 199, 233

Bilharzia, 69, 257, 258

Bonorowo, Rawa, 215-217

Boron, 42

Borneo, West, 55, 56, 66, 82, 122, 123, 136, 211-213

Bottom deposits, 49, 58, 60, 76, 77, 185, 192; see also Detritus and Muds

Boulengerochromis, 168, 169

Brazil, 31

British Guiana, 10, 75, 81, 91, 124 et seq., 135, 268, 272

Buffering capacity of humic acids, 78

Bunyoni, Lake, 257

Burma, 94, 115, 123, 145

Calcium, see Lime

Cambodia, 56, 95, 131, 154